**Teacher Edition**

# Eureka Math
# Grade 3
# Module 1

Special thanks go to the Gordon A. Cain Center and to the Department of Mathematics at Louisiana State University for their support in the development of *Eureka Math*.

For a free *Eureka Math* Teacher
Resource Pack, Parent Tip
Sheets,  and more please
visit www.Eureka.tools

**Published by the non-profit Great Minds**

Copyright © 2015 Great Minds. No part of this work may be reproduced, sold, or commercialized, in whole or in part, without written permission from Great Minds. Non-commercial use is licensed pursuant to a Creative Commons Attribution-NonCommercial-ShareAlike 4.0 license; for more information, go to http://greatminds.net/maps/math/copyright. "Great Minds" and "Eureka Math" are registered trademarks of Great Minds.

Printed in the U.S.A.

This book may be purchased from the publisher at eureka-math.org

10  9

ISBN 978-1-63255-363-8

***Eureka Math: A Story of Units*** **Contributors**

Katrina Abdussalaam, Curriculum Writer
Tiah Alphonso, Program Manager—Curriculum Production
Kelly Alsup, Lead Writer / Editor, Grade 4
Catriona Anderson, Program Manager—Implementation Support
Debbie Andorka-Aceves, Curriculum Writer
Eric Angel, Curriculum Writer
Leslie Arceneaux, Lead Writer / Editor, Grade 5
Kate McGill Austin, Lead Writer / Editor, Grades PreK–K
Adam Baker, Lead Writer / Editor, Grade 5
Scott Baldridge, Lead Mathematician and Lead Curriculum Writer
Beth Barnes, Curriculum Writer
Bonnie Bergstresser, Math Auditor
Bill Davidson, Fluency Specialist
Jill Diniz, Program Director
Nancy Diorio, Curriculum Writer
Nancy Doorey, Assessment Advisor
Lacy Endo-Peery, Lead Writer / Editor, Grades PreK–K
Ana Estela, Curriculum Writer
Lessa Faltermann, Math Auditor
Janice Fan, Curriculum Writer
Ellen Fort, Math Auditor
Peggy Golden, Curriculum Writer
Maria Gomes, Pre-Kindergarten Practitioner
Pam Goodner, Curriculum Writer
Greg Gorman, Curriculum Writer
Melanie Gutierrez, Curriculum Writer
Bob Hollister, Math Auditor
Kelley Isinger, Curriculum Writer
Nuhad Jamal, Curriculum Writer
Mary Jones, Lead Writer / Editor, Grade 4
Halle Kananak, Curriculum Writer
Susan Lee, Lead Writer / Editor, Grade 3
Jennifer Loftin, Program Manager—Professional Development
Soo Jin Lu, Curriculum Writer
Nell McAnelly, Project Director

# Mathematics Curriculum

**3**
GRADE

## Table of Contents

# GRADE 3 • MODULE 1

Properties of Multiplication and Division and Solving Problems with Units of 2–5 and 10

# Grade 3 • Module 1

# Properties of Multiplication and Division and Solving Problems with Units of 2–5 and 10

## OVERVIEW

This 25-day module begins the year by building on students' fluency with addition and their knowledge of arrays. In Topic A, students initially use repeated addition to find the total from a number of equal groups (**2.OA.4**). As students notice patterns, they let go of longer addition sentences in favor of more efficient multiplication facts (**3.OA.1**). Lessons in Topic A move students' Grade 2 work with arrays and repeated addition a step further by developing skip-counting rows as a strategy for multiplication. Arrays become a cornerstone of the module. Students use the language of multiplication as they understand what factors are and differentiate between the size of groups and the number of groups within a given context. In this module, the factors 2, 3, 4, 5, and 10 provide an entry point for moving into more difficult factors in later modules.

The study of factors links Topics A and B; Topic B extends the study to division. Students understand division as an unknown factor problem and relate the meaning of unknown factors to either the number or the size of groups (**3.OA.2, 3.OA.6**). By the end of Topic B, students are aware of a fundamental connection between multiplication and division that lays the foundation for the rest of the module.

In Topic C, students use the array model and familiar skip-counting strategies to solidify their understanding of multiplication and practice related facts of 2 and 3. They become fluent enough with arithmetic patterns to *add* or *subtract* groups from known products to solve more complex multiplication problems (**3.OA.1**). They apply their skills to word problems using drawings and equations with a symbol to find the unknown factor (**3.OA.3**). This culminates in students using arrays to model the distributive property as they decompose units to multiply (**3.OA.5**).

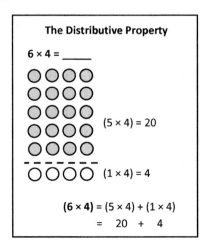

In Topic D, students model, write, and solve partitive and measurement division problems with 2 and 3 (**3.OA.2**). Consistent skip-counting strategies and the continued use of array models are pathways for students to naturally relate multiplication and division. Modeling advances as students use tape diagrams to represent multiplication and division. A final lesson in this topic solidifies a growing understanding of the relationship between operations (**3.OA.7**).

**EUREKA MATH™**

Topic E shifts students from simple understanding to analyzing the relationship between multiplication and division. Practice of both operations is combined—this time using units of 4—and a lesson is explicitly dedicated to modeling the connection between them (**3.OA.7**). Skip-counting, the distributive property, arrays, number bonds, and tape diagrams are tools for both operations (**3.OA.1**, **3.OA.2**). A final lesson invites students to explore their work with arrays and related facts through the lens of the commutative property as it relates to multiplication (**3.OA.5**).

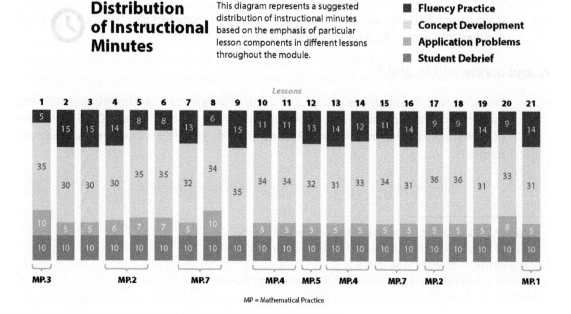

Topic F introduces the factors 5 and 10, familiar from skip-counting in Grade 2. Students apply the multiplication and division strategies they have used to mixed practice with all of the factors included in Module 1 (**3.OA.1**, **3.OA.2**, **3.OA.3**). Students model relationships between factors, analyzing the arithmetic patterns that emerge to compose and decompose numbers, as they further explore the relationship between multiplication and division (**3.OA.3**, **3.OA.5**, **3.OA.7**).

In the final lesson of the module, students apply the tools, representations, and concepts they have learned to problem solving with multi-step word problems using all four operations (**3.OA.3**, **3.OA.8**). They demonstrate the flexibility of their thinking as they assess the reasonableness of their answers for a variety of problem types.

The Mid-Module Assessment follows Topic C. The End-of-Module Assessment follows Topic F.

## Notes on Pacing for Differentiation

If pacing is a challenge, consider the following modifications and omissions.

Consolidate Lessons 12 and 13, both of which are division lessons sharing the same objective. Include units of 2 and units of 3 in the consolidated lesson.

Omit Lessons 15 and 19. Lesson 15 uses the tape diagram to provide a new perspective on the commutative property, a concept students have studied since Lesson 7. Lesson 19 introduces the significant complexity of the distributive property with division. The concepts from both lessons are reinforced within Module 3.

# Focus Grade Level Standards

## Represent and solve problems involving multiplication and division.[1]

**3.OA.1**   Interpret products of whole numbers, e.g., interpret 5 × 7 as the total number of objects in 5 groups of 7 objects each. *For example, describe a context in which a total number of objects can be expressed as 5 × 7.*

**3.OA.2**   Interpret whole-number quotients of whole numbers, e.g., interpret 56 ÷ 8 as the number of objects in each share when 56 objects are partitioned equally into 8 shares, or as a number of shares when 56 objects are partitioned into equal shares of 8 objects each. *For example, describe a context in which a number of shares or a number of groups can be expressed as 56 ÷ 8.*

**3.OA.3**   Use multiplication and division within 100 to solve word problems in situations involving equal groups, arrays, and measurement quantities, e.g., by using drawings and equations with a symbol for the unknown number to represent the problem. (See Glossary, Table 2.)

**3.OA.4**   Determine the unknown whole number in a multiplication or division equation relating three whole numbers. *For example, determine the unknown number that makes the equation true in each of the equations 8 × ? = 48, 5 = _ ÷ 3, 6 × 6 = ?*

## Understand properties of multiplication and the relationship between multiplication and division.[2]

**3.OA.5**   Apply properties of operations as strategies to multiply and divide. (Students need not use formal terms for these properties.) *Examples: If 6 × 4 = 24 is known, then 4 × 6 = 24 is also known. (Commutative property of multiplication.) 3 × 5 × 2 can be found by 3 × 5 = 15, then 15 × 2 = 30, or by 5 × 2 = 10, then 3 × 10 = 30. (Associative property of multiplication.) Knowing that 8 × 5 = 40 and 8 × 2 = 16, one can find 8 × 7 as 8 × (5 + 2) = (8 × 5) + (8 × 2) = 40 + 16 = 56. (Distributive property.)*[3]

**3.OA.6**   Understand division as an unknown-factor problem. *For example, find 32 ÷ 8 by finding the number that makes 32 when multiplied by 8.*

## Multiply and divide within 100.[4]

**3.OA.7**   Fluently multiply and divide within 100, using strategies such as the relationship between multiplication and division (e.g., knowing that 8 × 5 = 40, one knows 40 ÷ 5 = 8) or properties of operations. By the end of Grade 3, know from memory all products of two one-digit numbers.

---

[1]Limited to factors of 2–5 and 10 and the corresponding dividends in this module.
[2]Limited to factors of 2–5 and 10 and the corresponding dividends in this module.
[3]The associative property is addressed in Module 3.
[4]Limited to factors of 2–5 and 10 and the corresponding dividends in this module.

## Solve problems involving the four operations, and identify and explain patterns in arithmetic.[5]

**3.OA.8**     Solve two-step word problems using the four operations. Represent these problems using equations with a letter standing for the unknown quantity. Assess the reasonableness of answers using mental computation and estimation strategies including rounding. (This standard is limited to problems posed with whole numbers and having whole-number answers; students should know how to perform operations in the conventional order when there are no parentheses to specify a particular order, i.e., Order of Operations.)

## Foundational Standards

**2.OA.3**     Determine whether a group of objects (up to 20) has an odd or even number of members, e.g., by pairing objects or counting them by 2s; write an equation to express an even number as a sum of two equal addends.

**2.OA.4**     Use addition to find the total number of objects arranged in rectangular arrays with up to 5 rows and up to 5 columns; write an equation to express the total as a sum of equal addends.

**2.NBT.2**     Count within 1000; skip-count by 5s, 10s, and 100s.

## Focus Standards for Mathematical Practice

**MP.1**     **Make sense of problems and persevere in solving them.** Students model multiplication and division using the array model. They solve two-step mixed word problems and assess the reasonableness of their solutions.

**MP.2**     **Reason abstractly and quantitatively.** Students make sense of quantities and their relationships as they explore the properties of multiplication and division and the relationship between them. Students decontextualize when representing equal group situations as multiplication and when they represent division as partitioning objects into equal shares or as unknown factor problems. Students contextualize when they consider the value of units and understand the meaning of the quantities as they compute.

**MP.3**     **Construct viable arguments and critique the reasoning of others.** Students represent and solve multiplication and division problems using arrays and equations. As they compare methods, they construct arguments and critique the reasoning of others. This practice is particularly exemplified in daily Application Problems and in specific lessons dedicated to problem solving in which students solve and reason with others about their work.

**MP.4**     **Model with mathematics.** Students represent equal groups using arrays and equations to multiply, divide, add, and subtract.

**MP.7**     **Look for and make use of structure.** Students notice structure when they represent quantities by using drawings and equations to represent the commutative and distributive properties. The relationship between multiplication and division also highlights structure for students as they determine the unknown whole number in a multiplication or division equation.

---

[5]In this module, problem solving is limited to factors of 2–5 and 10 and the corresponding dividends. 3.OA.9 is addressed in Module 3.

# Overview of Module Topics and Lesson Objectives

| Standards | | Topics and Objectives | Days |
|---|---|---|---|
| **3.OA.1**<br>3.OA.3 | A | **Multiplication and the Meaning of the Factors**<br>Lesson 1:   Understand *equal groups of* as multiplication.<br>Lesson 2:   Relate multiplication to the array model.<br>Lesson 3:   Interpret the meaning of factors—the size of the group or the number of groups. | 3 |
| **3.OA.2**<br>**3.OA.6**<br>3.OA.3<br>3.OA.4 | B | **Division as an Unknown Factor Problem**<br>Lesson 4:   Understand the meaning of the unknown as the size of the group in division.<br>Lesson 5:   Understand the meaning of the unknown as the number of groups in division.<br>Lesson 6:   Interpret the unknown in division using the array model. | 3 |
| **3.OA.1**<br>**3.OA.5**<br>3.OA.3<br>3.OA.4 | C | **Multiplication Using Units of 2 and 3**<br>Lessons 7–8:   Demonstrate the commutativity of multiplication, and practice related facts by skip-counting objects in array models.<br>Lesson 9:   Find related multiplication facts by adding and subtracting equal groups in array models.<br>Lesson 10:   Model the distributive property with arrays to decompose units as a strategy to multiply. | 4 |
| | | Mid-Module Assessment:  Topics A–C (assessment ½ day, return ½ day, remediation or further applications 1 day) | 2 |
| **3.OA.2**<br>**3.OA.4**<br>**3.OA.6**<br>**3.OA.7**<br>3.OA.3<br>3.OA.8 | D | **Division Using Units of 2 and 3**<br>Lesson 11:   Model division as the unknown factor in multiplication using arrays and tape diagrams.<br>Lesson 12:   Interpret the quotient as the number of groups or the number of objects in each group using units of 2.<br>Lesson 13:   Interpret the quotient as the number of groups or the number of objects in each group using units of 3. | 3 |

      **Module 1:**   Properties of Multiplication and Division and Solving Problems with Units of 2–5 and 10

©2015 Great Minds. eureka-math.org<br>G3-M1-TE-B1-1.3.1-01.2016

| Standards | | Topics and Objectives | Days |
|---|---|---|---|
| **3.OA.5**<br>**3.OA.7**<br>3.OA.1<br>3.OA.2<br>3.OA.3<br>3.OA.4<br>3.OA.6 | E | **Multiplication and Division Using Units of 4** | 4 |
| | | Lesson 14:   Skip-count objects in models to build fluency with multiplication facts using units of 4. | |
| | | Lesson 15:   Relate arrays to tape diagrams to model the commutative property of multiplication. | |
| | | Lesson 16:   Use the distributive property as a strategy to find related multiplication facts. | |
| | | Lesson 17:   Model the relationship between multiplication and division. | |
| **3.OA.3**<br>**3.OA.5**<br>**3.OA.7**<br>**3.OA.8**<br>3.OA.1<br>3.OA.2<br>3.OA.4<br>3.OA.6 | F | **Distributive Property and Problem Solving Using Units of 2–5 and 10** | 4 |
| | | Lessons 18–19: Apply the distributive property to decompose units. | |
| | | Lesson 20:   Solve two-step word problems involving multiplication and division, and assess the reasonableness of answers. | |
| | | Lesson 21:   Solve two-step word problems involving all four operations, and assess the reasonableness of answers. | |
| | | End-of-Module Assessment: Topics A–F (assessment ½ day, return ½ day, remediation or further application 1 day) | 2 |
| **Total Number of Instructional Days** | | | **25** |

# Terminology

## New or Recently Introduced Terms

- Array[6] (arrangement of objects in rows and columns)
- Commutative property/commutative (e.g., rotate a rectangular array 90 degrees to demonstrate that factors in a multiplication sentence can switch places)
- Equal groups (with reference to multiplication and division; one factor is the number of objects in a group and the other is a multiplier that indicates the number of groups)
- Distribute (with reference to the distributive property, e.g., in $12 \times 3 = (10 \times 3) + (2 \times 3)$ the 3 is the multiplier for each part of the decomposition)
- Divide/division (partitioning a total into equal groups to show how many equal groups add up to a specific number, e.g., $15 \div 5 = 3$)

---

[6]Originally introduced in Grade 2, Module 6 but treated as new vocabulary in this module.

©2015 Great Minds. eureka-math.org<br>
G3-M1-TE-B1-1.3.1-01.2016

- Factors (numbers that are multiplied to obtain a product)
- Multiplication/multiply (an operation showing how many times a number is added to itself, e.g., 5 × 3 =15)
- Number of groups (factor in a multiplication problem that refers to the total equal groups)
- Parentheses (symbols ( ) used around an expression or numbers within an equation)
- Product (the answer when one number is multiplied by another)
- Quotient (the answer when one number is divided by another)
- Rotate (turn, used with reference to turning arrays 90 degrees)
- Row/column[7] (in reference to rectangular arrays)
- Size of groups (factor in a multiplication problem that refers to how many in a group)
- Unit (one segment of a partitioned tape diagram)
- Unknown (the missing factor or quantity in multiplication or division)

**NOTES ON**
*EXPRESSION, EQUATION,*
AND *NUMBER SENTENCE:*

Please note the descriptions for the following terms, which are frequently misused.

- **Expression:** A number, or any combination of sums, differences, products, or divisions of numbers that evaluates to a number (e.g., 3 + 4, 8 × 3, 15 ÷ 3 as distinct from an equation or number sentence).
- **Equation:** A statement that two expressions are equal (e.g., 3 × ___ = 12, 5 × $b$ = 20, 3 + 2 = 5).
- **Number sentence** (also addition, subtraction, multiplication, or division sentence): An equation or inequality for which both expressions are numerical and can be evaluated to a single number (e.g., 4 + 3 = 6 + 1, 2 = 2, 21 > 7 × 2, 5 ÷ 5 = 1). Number sentences are either true or false (e.g., 4 + 4 < 6 × 2 and 21 ÷ 7 = 4) and contain no unknowns.

## Familiar Terms and Symbols[8]

- Add 1 unit, subtract 1 unit (add or subtract a single unit of two, ten, etc.)
- Expression (see expanded description in box above)
- Number bond (illustrates part–part–whole relationship, shown at right)
- Ones, twos, threes, etc. (units of one, two, or three)
- Repeated addition (adding equal groups together, e.g., 2 + 2 + 2 + 2)
- Tape diagram (a method for modeling problems)
- Value (how much)

## Suggested Tools and Representations

- 18 counters per student
- Tape diagram (a method for modeling problems)
- Number bond (shown at right)
- Array (arrangement of objects in rows and columns)

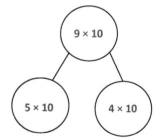

---

[7]Originally introduced in Grade 2, Module 6 but treated as new vocabulary in this module.
[8]These are terms and symbols students have used or seen previously.

# Suggested Methods of Instructional Delivery

## Directions for Administration of Sprints

Sprints are designed to develop fluency. They should be fun, adrenaline-rich activities that intentionally build energy and excitement. A fast pace is essential. During Sprint administration, teachers assume the role of athletic coaches. A rousing routine fuels students' motivation to do their personal best. Student recognition of increasing success is critical, and so every improvement is celebrated.

One Sprint has two parts with closely related problems on each. Students complete the two parts of the Sprint in quick succession with the goal of improving on the second part, even if only by one more.

With practice, the following routine takes about 9 minutes.

### Sprint A

Pass Sprint A out quickly, face down on student desks with instructions to not look at the problems until the signal is given. (Some Sprints include words. If necessary, prior to starting the Sprint, quickly review the words so that reading difficulty does not slow students down.)

T: You will have 60 seconds to do as many problems as you can. I do not expect you to finish all of them. Just do as many as you can, your personal best. (If some students are likely to finish before time is up, assign a number to count by on the back.)

T: Take your mark! Get set! THINK!

Students immediately turn papers over and work furiously to finish as many problems as they can in 60 seconds. Time precisely.

T: Stop! Circle the last problem you did. I will read just the answers. If you got it right, call out "Yes!" If you made a mistake, circle it. Ready?

T: (Energetically, rapid-fire call the first answer.)

S: Yes!

T: (Energetically, rapid-fire call the second answer.)

S: Yes!

Repeat to the end of Sprint A or until no student has a correct answer. If needed, read the count-by answers in the same way the Sprint answers were read. Each number counted-by on the back is considered a correct answer.

T: Fantastic! Now, write the number you got correct at the top of your page. This is your personal goal for Sprint B.

T: How many of you got one right? (All hands should go up.)

T: Keep your hand up until I say the number that is one more than the number you got correct. So, if you got 14 correct, when I say 15, your hand goes down. Ready?

T: (Continue quickly.) How many got two correct? Three? Four? Five? (Continue until all hands are down.)

If the class needs more practice with Sprint A, continue with the optional routine presented below.

T: I'll give you one minute to do more problems on this half of the Sprint. If you finish, stand behind your chair.

As students work, the student who scored highest on Sprint A might pass out Sprint B.

T: Stop! I will read just the answers. If you got it right, call out "Yes!" If you made a mistake, circle it. Ready? (Read the answers to the first half again as students stand.)

## Movement

To keep the energy and fun going, always do a stretch or a movement game in between Sprints A and B. For example, the class might do jumping jacks while skip-counting by 5 for about 1 minute. Feeling invigorated, students take their seats for Sprint B, ready to make every effort to complete more problems this time.

## Sprint B

Pass Sprint B out quickly, face down on student desks with instructions not to look at the problems until the signal is given. (Repeat the procedure for Sprint A up through the show of hands for how many right.)

T: Stand up if you got more correct on the second Sprint than on the first.

S: (Stand.)

T: Keep standing until I say the number that tells how many more you got right on Sprint B. If you got three more right on Sprint B than you did on Sprint A, when I say *three,* you sit down. Ready? (Call out numbers starting with one. Students sit as the number by which they improved is called. Celebrate the students who improved most with a cheer.)

T: Well done! Now, take a moment to go back and correct your mistakes. Think about what patterns you noticed in today's Sprint.

T: How did the patterns help you get better at solving the problems?

T: Rally Robin your thinking with your partner for 1 minute. Go!

Rally Robin is a style of sharing in which partners trade information back and forth, one statement at a time per person, for about 1 minute. This is an especially valuable part of the routine for students who benefit from their friends' support to identify patterns and try new strategies.

Students may take Sprints home.

**Module 1:** Properties of Multiplication and Division and Solving Problems with Units of 2–5 and 10

## RDW or Read, Draw, Write (an Equation and a Statement)

Mathematicians and teachers suggest a simple process applicable to all grades:

1. Read.
2. Draw and label.
3. Write an equation.
4. Write a word sentence (statement).

The more students participate in reasoning through problems with a systematic approach, the more they internalize those behaviors and thought processes.

- What do I see?
- Can I draw something?
- What conclusions can I make from my drawing?

| Modeling with Interactive Questioning | Guided Practice | Independent Practice |
| --- | --- | --- |
| The teacher models the whole process with interactive questioning, some choral response, and talk such as "What did Monique say, everyone?" After completing the problem, students might reflect with a partner on the steps they used to solve the problem. "Students, think back on what we did to solve this problem. What did we do first?" Students might then be given the same or a similar problem to solve for homework. | Each student has a copy of the question. Though guided by the teacher, they work independently at times and then come together again. Timing is important. Students might hear, "You have 2 minutes to do your drawing." Or, "Put your pencils down. Time to work together again." The Debrief might include selecting different student work to share. | Students are given a problem to solve and possibly a designated amount of time to solve it. The teacher circulates, supports, and thinks about which student work to show to support the mathematical objectives of the lesson. When sharing student work, students are encouraged to think about the work with questions such as, "What do you see that Jeremy did?" "What is the same about Jeremy's work and Sara's work?" "How did Jeremy show $\frac{3}{7}$ of the students?" "How did Sara show $\frac{3}{7}$ of the students?" |

## Personal White Boards

### Materials Needed for Personal White Boards

    1 heavy duty clear sheet protector
    1 piece of stiff red tag board 11" × 8 ¼"
    1 piece of stiff white tag board 11" × 8 ¼"
    1 3" × 3" piece of dark synthetic cloth for an eraser (e.g., felt)
    1 low odor blue dry erase marker, fine point

### Directions for Creating Personal White Boards

Cut the white and red tag to specifications. Slide into the sheet protector. Store the eraser on the red side. Store markers in a separate container to avoid stretching the sheet protector.

### Frequently Asked Questions About Personal White Boards

*Why is one side red and one white?*

- The white side of the board is the "paper." Students generally write on it, and if working individually, turn the board over to signal to the teacher they have completed their work. The teacher then says, "Show me your boards," when most of the class is ready.

*What are some of the benefits of a personal white board?*

- The teacher can respond quickly to gaps in student understandings and skills. "Let's do some of these on our personal white boards until we have more mastery."

- Students can erase quickly so that they do not have to suffer the evidence of their mistake.

- They are motivating. Students love both the drill and thrill capability and the chance to do story problems with an engaging medium.

- Checking work gives the teacher instant feedback about student understanding.

*What is the benefit of this personal white board over a commercially purchased dry erase board?*

- It is much less expensive.

- Templates such as place value charts, number bond mats, hundreds boards, and number lines can be stored between the two pieces of tag board for easy access and reuse.

- Worksheets, story problems, and other Problem Sets can be done without marking the paper so that students can work on the problems independently at another time.

- Strips with story problems, number lines, and arrays can be inserted and still have a full piece of paper on which to write.

- The red versus white side distinction clarifies expectations. When working collaboratively, there is no need to use the red side. When working independently, students know how to keep their work private.

- The tag board can be removed if necessary to project the work.

# Scaffolds[9]

The scaffolds integrated into *A Story of Units* give alternatives for how students access information as well as express and demonstrate their learning. Strategically placed margin notes are provided within each lesson elaborating on the use of specific scaffolds at applicable times. They address many needs presented by English language learners, students with disabilities, students performing above grade level, and students performing below grade level. Many of the suggestions are organized by Universal Design for Learning (UDL) principles and are applicable to more than one population. To read more about the approach to differentiated instruction in *A Story of Units,* please refer to "How to Implement *A Story of Units.*"

# Preparing to Teach a Module

Preparation of lessons will be more effective and efficient if there has been an adequate analysis of the module first. Each module in *A Story of Units* can be compared to a chapter in a book. How is the module moving the plot, the mathematics, forward? What new learning is taking place? How are the topics and objectives building on one another? The following is a suggested process for preparing to teach a module.

Step 1: Get a preview of the plot.

A: Read the Table of Contents. At a high level, what is the plot of the module? How does the story develop across the topics?

B: Preview the module's Exit Tickets[10] to see the trajectory of the module's mathematics and the nature of the work students are expected to be able to do.

Note: When studying a PDF file, enter "Exit Ticket" into the search feature to navigate from one Exit Ticket to the next.

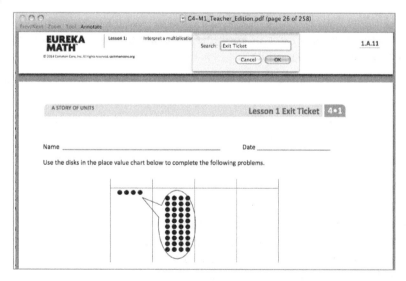

---

[9]Students with disabilities may require Braille, large print, audio, or special digital files. Please visit the website, www.p12.nysed.gov/specialed/aim, for specific information on how to obtain student materials that satisfy the National Instructional Materials Accessibility Standard (NIMAS) format.

[10] A more in-depth preview can be done by searching the Problem Sets rather than the Exit Tickets. Furthermore, this same process can be used to preview the coherence or flow of any component of the curriculum, such as Fluency Practice or Application Problems.

Step 2: Dig into the details.

A:  Dig into a careful reading of the Module Overview. While reading the narrative, *liberally* reference the lessons and Topic Overviews to clarify the meaning of the text—the lessons demonstrate the strategies, show how to use the models, clarify vocabulary, and build understanding of concepts. Consider searching the video gallery on *Eureka Math*'s website to watch demonstrations of the use of models and other teaching techniques.

B:  Having thoroughly investigated the Module Overview, read through the chart entitled Overview of Module Topics and Lesson Objectives to further discern the plot of the module. How do the topics flow and tell a coherent story? How do the objectives move from simple to complex?

Step 3: Summarize the story.

Complete the Mid- and End-of-Module Assessments. Use the strategies and models presented in the module to explain the thinking involved. Again, liberally reference the work done in the lessons to see how students who are learning with the curriculum might respond.

# Preparing to Teach a Lesson

A three-step process is suggested to prepare a lesson. It is understood that at times teachers may need to make adjustments (customizations) to lessons to fit the time constraints and unique needs of their students. The recommended planning process is outlined below. Note: The ladder of Step 2 is a metaphor for the teaching sequence. The sequence can be seen not only at the macro level in the role that this lesson plays in the overall story, but also at the lesson level, where each rung in the ladder represents the next step in understanding or the next skill needed to reach the objective. To reach the objective, or the top of the ladder, all students must be able to access the first rung and each successive rung.

Step 1: Discern the plot.

A:  Briefly review the module's Table of Contents, recalling the overall story of the module and analyzing the role of this lesson in the module.

B:  Read the Topic Overview related to the lesson, and then review the Problem Set and Exit Ticket of each lesson in the topic.

C:  Review the assessment following the topic, keeping in mind that assessments can be found midway through the module and at the end of the module.

Step 2: Find the ladder.

A:  Complete the lesson's Problem Set.

B:  Analyze and write notes on the new complexities of each problem as well as the sequences and progressions throughout problems (e.g., pictorial to abstract, smaller to larger numbers, single- to multi-step problems). The new complexities are the rungs of the ladder.

C:  Anticipate where students might struggle, and write a note about the potential cause of the struggle.

D:  Answer the Student Debrief questions, always anticipating how students will respond.

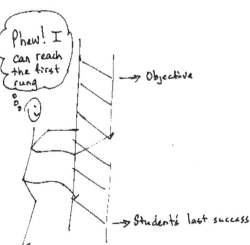

**Module 1:**  Properties of Multiplication and Division and Solving Problems with Units of 2–5 and 10

©2015 Great Minds. eureka-math.org
G3-M1-TE-B1-1.3.1-01.2016

**Step 3:  Hone the lesson.**

At times, the lesson and Problem Set are appropriate for all students and the day's schedule.  At others, they may need customizing.  If the decision is to customize based on either the needs of students or scheduling constraints, a suggestion is to decide upon and designate "Must Do" and "Could Do" problems.

A:  Select "Must Do" problems from the Problem Set that meet the objective and provide a coherent experience for students; reference the ladder.  The expectation is that the majority of the class will complete the "Must Do" problems within the allocated time.  While choosing the "Must Do" problems, keep in mind the need for a balance of calculations, various word problem types[11], and work at both the pictorial and abstract levels.

B:  "Must Do" problems might also include remedial work as necessary for the whole class, a small group, or individual students.  Depending on anticipated difficulties, those problems might take different forms as shown in the chart below.

| Anticipated Difficulty | "Must Do" Remedial Problem Suggestion |
|---|---|
| The first problem of the Problem Set is too challenging. | Write a short sequence of problems on the board that provides a ladder to Problem 1.  Direct the class or small group to complete those first problems to empower them to begin the Problem Set.  Consider labeling these problems "Zero Problems" since they are done prior to Problem 1. |
| There is too big of a jump in complexity between two problems. | Provide a problem or set of problems that creates a bridge between the two problems.  Label them with the number of the problem they follow.  For example, if the challenging jump is between Problems 2 and 3, consider labeling the bridging problems "Extra 2s." |
| Students lack fluency or foundational skills necessary for the lesson. | Before beginning the Problem Set, do a quick, engaging fluency exercise, such as a Rapid White Board Exchange, "Thrilling Drill," or Sprint.  Before beginning any fluency activity for the first time, assess that students are poised for success with the easiest problem in the set. |
| More work is needed at the concrete or pictorial level. | Provide manipulatives or the opportunity to draw solution strategies.  Especially in Kindergarten, at times the Problem Set or pencil and paper aspect might be completely excluded, allowing students to simply work with materials. |
| More work is needed at the abstract level. | Hone the Problem Set to reduce the amount of drawing as appropriate for certain students or the whole class. |

---

[11] See the Progression Documents "K, Counting and Cardinality" and "K–5, Operations and Algebraic Thinking" pp. 9 and 23, respectively.

C:  "Could Do" problems are for students who work with greater fluency and understanding and can, therefore, complete more work within a given time frame.  Adjust the Exit Ticket and Homework to reflect the "Must Do" problems or to address scheduling constraints.

D:  At times, a particularly tricky problem might be designated as a "Challenge!" problem.  This can be motivating, especially for advanced students.  Consider creating the opportunity for students to share their "Challenge!" solutions with the class at a weekly session or on video.

E:  Consider how to best use the vignettes of the Concept Development section of the lesson.  Read through the vignettes, and highlight selected parts to be included in the delivery of instruction so that students can be independently successful on the assigned task.

F:  Pay close attention to the questions chosen for the Student Debrief.  Regularly ask students, "What was the lesson's learning goal today?"  Help them articulate the goal.

## Assessment Summary

| Type | Administered | Format | Standards Addressed |
|------|--------------|--------|---------------------|
| Mid-Module Assessment Task | After Topic C | Constructed response with rubric | 3.OA.1 <br> 3.OA.2 <br> 3.OA.5 <br> 3.OA.6 |
| End-of-Module Assessment Task | After Topic F | Constructed response with rubric | 3.OA.1 <br> 3.OA.2 <br> 3.OA.3 <br> 3.OA.4 <br> 3.OA.5 <br> 3.OA.6 <br> 3.OA.7 <br> 3.OA.8 |

EUREKA MATH

# Mathematics Curriculum

GRADE
3

## Topic A

# Multiplication and the Meaning of the Factors

**3.OA.1,** 3.OA.3

| | | |
|---|---|---|
| **Focus Standard:** | 3.OA.1 | Interpret products of whole numbers, e.g., interpret 5 × 7 as the total number of objects in 5 groups of 7 objects each. *For example, describe a context in which a total number of objects can be expressed as 5 × 7.* |
| **Instructional Days:** | 3 | |
| **Coherence** -Links from: | G2–M6 | Foundations of Multiplication and Division |
| -Links to: | G4–M3 | Multi-Digit Multiplication and Division |

Lesson 1 introduces students to multiplication, starting with the concept of repeated addition, which is familiar from Grade 2. Students use repeated addition to find totals; for example, they use counters to make 6 equal groups of 2. They learn to recognize equal groups of counters as units and count units using the language of groups and unit form: "6 equal groups of 2 counters make 12 counters," or "6 twos make 12." By the end of Lesson 1, students use the multiplication symbol to represent these descriptions as more efficient multiplication equations.

In Lesson 2, students relate the equal groups of objects in scattered configurations from Lesson 1 to the array model, exploring the correspondence between 1 equal group and 1 row. They begin to distinguish between the number of groups and the size of groups as they count rows and *how many in 1 row* to write multiplication facts. Students recognize the efficiency of arrays as they skip-count to find totals. In Lesson 2, students use the following vocabulary: *row, array, number of groups,* and *size of groups.*

Lesson 3 solidifies students' ability to differentiate the meaning of factors. Students model dividing a whole into equal groups as well as analyze equal groups in scattered configurations and arrays to determine whether factors represent the number of groups or the size of groups. They create pictures, number bonds, and multiplication equations to model their understanding.

In this topic, students use a variety of factors since these lessons emphasize understanding the concept of multiplying rather than finding totals. Later topics limit facts to those involving one or two specific factors, allowing students to build fluency with simpler facts before moving on to more difficult ones.

| A Teaching Sequence Toward Mastery of Multiplication and the Meaning of the Factors |
| --- |

**Objective 1:**  Understand *equal groups of* as multiplication.
(Lesson 1)

**Objective 2:**  Relate multiplication to the array model.
(Lesson 2)

**Objective 3:**  Interpret the meaning of factors—the size of the group or the number of groups.
(Lesson 3)

EUREKA
MATH™

# Lesson 1

Objective: Understand *equal groups of* as multiplication.

## Suggested Lesson Structure

- ■ Fluency Practice          (5 minutes)
- ▨ Application Problem        (10 minutes)
- ▢ Concept Development        (35 minutes)
- ▦ Student Debrief           (10 minutes)

   **Total Time**            **(60 minutes)**

## Fluency Practice  (5 minutes)

- Group Counting **3.OA.1**        (5 minutes)

### Group Counting  (5 minutes)

Note: Basic skip-counting skills from Grade 2 shift focus in this Grade 3 activity. Group counting lays a foundation for interpreting multiplication as repeated addition. When students count groups in this activity, they add and subtract groups of 2 when counting up and down.

> **NOTES ON FLUENCY PRACTICE:**
>
> Think of fluency as having three goals:
>
> 1. Maintenance (staying sharp on previously learned skills).
> 2. Preparation (targeted practice for the current lesson).
> 3. Anticipation (skills that ensure that students will be ready for the in-depth work of upcoming lessons).

T:  Let's count to 20 forward and backward. Watch my fingers to know whether to count up or down. A closed hand means stop. (Show signals during the explanation.)

T:  (Rhythmically point up until a change is desired. Show a closed hand; then point down.)

S:  1, 2, 3, 4, 5, 6, 7, 8, 9, 10, 11, 12, 13, 14, 15, 16, 17, 18, 19, 20, 19, 18, 17, 16, 15, 14, 13, 12, 11, 10, 9, 8, 7, 6, 5, 4, 3, 2, 1, 0.

T:  Let's count to 20 forward and backward again. This time whisper every other number. Say the other numbers in a regular voice.

S:  (Whisper) 1, (speak) 2, (whisper) 3, (speak) 4, (whisper) 5, (speak) 6, etc.

T:  Let's count to 20 forward and backward again. This time, hum every other number instead of whispering. As you hum, think of the number.

S:  (Hum), 2, (hum), 4, (hum), 6, etc.

T:  Let's count to 20 forward and backward again. This time, think every other number instead of humming.

S:  (Think), 2, (think), 4, (think), 6, etc.

T:   What did we just count by?  Turn and talk to your partner.

S:   Twos.

T:   Let's count by twos.  (Direct students to count forward to and backward from 20, changing directions at times.)

## Application Problem  (10 minutes)

There are 83 girls and 76 boys in the third grade.  How many total students are in the third grade?

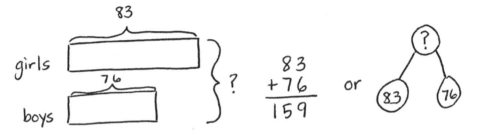

There are 159 students in third grade.

Note:  Students may choose to use a tape diagram or a number bond to model the problem.  They are also likely to solve today's Application Problem in less than 10 minutes.  Ten minutes have been allotted to allow for review of the RDW (Read, Draw, Write) process for problem solving.

Directions on the Read, Draw, Write (RDW) process:  Read the problem, draw and label, write an equation, and write a word sentence.  The more students participate in reasoning through problems with a systematic approach, the more they internalize those behaviors and thought processes.

(Excerpted from "How to Implement *A Story of Units*."  A more complete explanation can also be found in the Grade 3 Module 1 Overview.)

## Concept Development  (35 minutes)

Materials:   (S) 12 counters, personal white board

**Problem 1:  Skip-count to find the total number of objects.**

T:   (Select 10 students to come to the front.)  At the signal, say how many arms you each have.  (Signal.)

S:   2 arms!

T:   Since we each represent a group of 2 arms, let's skip-count our volunteers by twos to find how many arms they have altogether.  To keep track of our count, students will raise up their arms when we count them.

S:   (Count 2, 4, 6, … 20.)

**EUREKA MATH™**

T:  How many raised arms do we have in all?

S:  20.

T:  Arms down.  How many twos did we count to find the total?  Turn and whisper to your partner.

S:  10 twos.

T:  What did you count to find the number of twos?

S:  I counted the number of volunteers because each person has a group of two arms.

T:  Skip-count to find the total number of arms.

*Sample Teacher Board*

S:  (Say 2, 4, 6, …)

T:  (As they count, write 2 + 2 + 2 +…)

T:  Look at our addition sentence.  Show thumbs up if you see the correct number of twos.

$$2 + 2 + 2 + 2 + 2 + 2 + 2 + 2 + 2 + 2 = 20$$
$$10 \text{ twos}$$
$$10 \text{ groups of two is } 20.$$

S:  (Show thumbs up.)

T:  (Under the addition sentence, write *10 twos*.)  Clap 3 times if you agree that 10 groups of two is 20.

S:  (Clap 3 times.)

T:  (Write *10 groups of two is 20* under the other number sentences.)

**Problem 2: Understand the relationship between repeated addition, counting groups in unit form, and multiplication sentences.**

Seat students at tables with personal white boards and 12 counters each.

T:  You have 12 counters.  Use your counters to make **equal groups** of two.  How many counters will you put in each group?  Show with your fingers.

S:  (Hold up 2 fingers and make groups of two.)

T:  How many equal groups of two did you make?  Tell at the signal.  (Signal.)

S:  6 groups.

T:  6 equal groups of how many counters?

S:  6 equal groups of 2 counters.

T:  6 equal groups of 2 counters equal how many counters altogether?

S:  12 counters.

T:  Write an addition sentence to show your groups on your personal white board.

*Sample Teacher Board*

S:  (Write 2 + 2 + 2 + 2 + 2 + 2 = 12.)

T:  (Record the addition sentence on the board.)  In unit form, how many twos did we add to make 12?

$$2 + 2 + 2 + 2 + 2 + 2 = 12$$
$$6 \text{ twos} = 12$$
$$6 \times 2 = 12$$

S:  6 twos.

T:  (Record *6 twos = 12* under the addition sentence.)  6 × 2 is another way to write 2 + 2 + 2 + 2 + 2 + 2 or 6 twos.  (Record *6 × 2 = 12* under *6 twos = 12* on the board.)  These number sentences are all saying the same thing.

T:  Turn and talk to your partner. How do you think 6 × 2 = 12 relates to the other number sentences?

S:  They all have twos in them, and the answer is 12. →
I think the 6 shows how many twos there are. → You
have to count two 6 times because there are 6 groups
of them. That's how you get 6 times 2. → 6 × 2 might
be an easier way to write a long addition sentence.

T:  Ways that are easier and faster are efficient. When we
have equal groups, **multiplication** is a more efficient
way to find the total than repeated addition.

Repeat the process with 4 threes, 3 fours, and 2 sixes to get
students comfortable with the relationship between repeated
addition, counting groups in unit form, and multiplication
sentences.

**Problem 3:  Write multiplication sentences from equal groups.**

Draw or project the picture to the right.

T:  These are equal groups. Turn and tell your partner
why they are equal.

S:  There is the same number of grey circles in each group.
→ All of the grey circles are the same size and shape,
and there are 4 in each group.

T:  Work with your partner to write a repeated addition
and a multiplication sentence for this picture.

S:  (Write 4 + 4 = 8 and either 2 × 4 = 8 or 4 × 2 = 8.)

T:  (Project or draw the following.) Look at my new
drawing and the multiplication sentence I wrote to
represent it. Check my work by writing an addition
sentence and counting to find the total number of
objects.

   *3 × 4 = 12*

**MP.3**

S:  (Write 4 + 4 + 3 = 11.)

T:  Use your addition sentence as you talk to your partner about why you **agree** or **disagree** with my
work.

S:  I disagree because my addition sentence equals 11, not 12. → It's because that last group doesn't
have 4 circles. → You can do multiplication when the groups are equal. → Here, the groups aren't
equal, so the drawing doesn't show 3 × 4.

T:  I hear most students disagreeing because my groups are not equal. True, to **multiply** you must have
equal groups.

**NOTES ON
MULTIPLE MEANS
OF REPRESENTATION:**

It may be necessary to explicitly
connect *times* and the symbol ×. Have
students analyze the model. "How
many times do you see a group of
two?" Have them count the groups,
write the number sentence, and say
the words together.

- 6 groups of two equal 12.
- 6 times 2 equals 12.

**NOTES ON
MULTIPLE MEANS
OF ACTION AND
EXPRESSION:**

Some students may need more
scaffolding to realize that multiplication
cannot be used to find totals with
groups that are not equal. Use the
following questions to scaffold.

- Does the drawing show 3 fours?
- Does 3 times 4 represent this
drawing?
- How might we redraw the picture
to make it show 3 × 4?

**Lesson 1:**     Understand *equal groups of* as multiplication.

## Problem Set  (10 minutes)

Students should do their personal best to complete the Problem Set within the allotted 10 minutes.  Some problems do not specify a method for solving.  This is an intentional reduction of scaffolding that invokes MP.5, Use Appropriate Tools Strategically.  Students should solve these problems using the RDW approach used for Application Problems.

For some classes, it may be appropriate to modify the assignment by specifying which problems students should work on first.  With this option, let the purposeful sequencing of the Problem Set guide the selections so that problems continue to be scaffolded.  Balance word problems with other problem types to ensure a range of practice.  Consider assigning incomplete problems for homework or at another time during the day.

## Student Debrief  (10 minutes)

**Lesson Objective**:  Understand *equal groups of* as multiplication.

The Student Debrief is intended to invite reflection and active processing of the total lesson experience.

Invite students to review their solutions for the Problem Set.  They should check work by comparing answers with a partner before going over answers as a class.  Look for misconceptions or misunderstandings that can be addressed in the Debrief.  Guide students in a conversation to debrief the Problem Set and process the lesson.

Any combination of the questions below may be used to lead the discussion.

- On the first page, what did you notice about the answers to your problems?
- Discuss the relationship between repeated addition and the unit form *2 groups of three* or *3 groups of two,* depending on the drawing.
- Discuss the relationship between repeated addition, unit form, and the multiplication sentence 3 × 2 = 6.
- Review the new vocabulary presented in the lesson: **equal groups**, **multiplication**, and **multiply**.

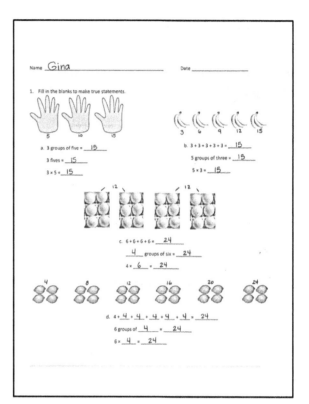

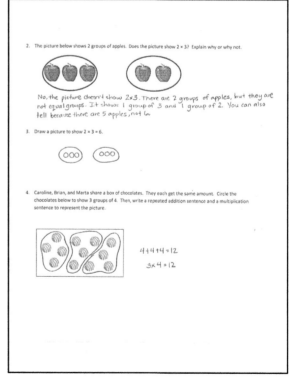

## Exit Ticket  (3 minutes)

After the Student Debrief, instruct students to complete the Exit Ticket.  A review of their work will help with assessing students' understanding of the concepts that were presented in today's lesson and planning more effectively for future lessons.  The questions may be read aloud to the students.

Name _____ Date _____

1. Fill in the blanks to make true statements.

a. 3 groups of five = _____

   3 fives = _____

   $3 \times 5$ = _____

b. $3 + 3 + 3 + 3 + 3$ = _____

   5 groups of three = _____

   $5 \times 3$ = _____

c. $6 + 6 + 6 + 6$ = _____

   _____ groups of six = _____

   $4 \times$ _____ = _____

d. $4 +$____ + ____ + ____ + ____ + ____ = _____

   6 groups of _____ = _____

   $6 \times$ _____ = _____

2.  The picture below shows 2 groups of apples.  Does the picture show 2 × 3?  Explain why or why not.

 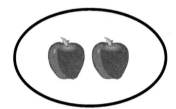

3.  Draw a picture to show 2 × 3 = 6.

4.  Caroline, Brian, and Marta share a box of chocolates.  They each get the same amount.  Circle the chocolates below to show 3 groups of 4.  Then, write a repeated addition sentence and a multiplication sentence to represent the picture.

EUREKA
MATH™

Name _____     Date _____

1.  The picture below shows 4 groups of 2 slices of watermelon.  Fill in the blanks to make true repeated addition and multiplication sentences that represent the picture.

2 + _____ + _____ + _____ = _____

4 × _____ = _____

2.  Draw a picture to show 3 + 3 + 3 = 9.  Then, write a multiplication sentence to represent the picture.

Name _____   Date _____

1.  Fill in the blanks to make true statements.

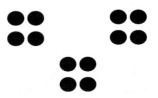

a.  4 groups of five = _____

   4 fives = _____

   4 × 5 = _____

b.  5 groups of four = _____

   5 fours = _____

   5 × 4 = _____

c.  6 + 6 + 6 = _____

   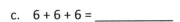 groups of six = _____

   3 × _____ = _____

d.  3 + ____ + ____ + ____ + ____ + ____ = _____

   6 groups of _____ = _____

   6 × _____ = _____

**Lesson 1:**   Understand *equal groups of* as multiplication.

EUREKA
MATH™

2.  The picture below shows 3 groups of hot dogs.  Does the picture show 3 × 3?  Explain why or why not.

3.  Draw a picture to show 4 × 2 = 8.

4.  Circle the pencils below to show 3 groups of 6.  Write a repeated addition and a multiplication sentence to represent the picture.

# Lesson 2

Objective: Relate multiplication to the array model.

## Suggested Lesson Structure

| | |
|---|---|
| ■ Fluency Practice | (15 minutes) |
| ▨ Application Problem | (5 minutes) |
| ▨ Concept Development | (30 minutes) |
| ■ Student Debrief | (10 minutes) |
| **Total Time** | **(60 minutes)** |

## Fluency Practice (15 minutes)

- Sprint:  Add or Subtract Using 2  **3.OA.1**        (9 minutes)
- Group Counting  **3.OA.1**                          (3 minutes)
- Add Equal Groups  **3.OA.1**                        (3 minutes)

### Sprint:  Add or Subtract Using 2  (9 minutes)

Materials:   (S)  Add or Subtract Using 2 Sprint

Note: This Sprint supports group counting skills that are foundational to interpreting multiplication as repeated addition.

### Directions for Administration of Sprints

A Sprint has two parts, A and B, with closely related problems on each.  Each part is organized into four quadrants that move from simple to complex.  This builds a challenge into each Sprint for every learner. Before the lesson, print Sprint A and Sprint B on two separate sheets of paper.  Students complete the two parts of the Sprint in quick succession with the goal of improving for the second part, even if only by one more.  With practice, the following routine takes about 9 minutes.

### Sprint A

Place Sprint A face down on student desks, and instruct students not to look at the problems until a signal is given.

T:   You will have 60 seconds to do as many problems as you can.  I do not expect you to finish all of them, just as many as you can, trying for your personal best.

T:   Take your mark!  Get set!  THINK!

Students turn papers over and work furiously to finish as many problems as they can in 60 seconds.  Time precisely.

T:   Stop!  Circle the last problem you completed.  I will read just the answers.  If you got the answer right, call out "Yes!"  If you made a mistake, circle it.  Ready?

Repeat to the end of Sprint A or until no student has a correct answer.

T:   Now, at the top of the page, write the number of problems you got correct.  This is your personal goal for Sprint B.

T:   How many of you got one right? (All hands should go up.)

T:   Keep your hand up until I say a number that is one more than the number you got right.  So, if you got 14 right, when I say 15, your hand goes down.  Ready?

T:   (Continue quickly.)  How many got two right?  Three?  Four?  Five?  (Continue until all hands are down.)

If the class needs more practice with Sprint A, continue with the optional routine presented below.

T:   Take one minute to do more problems on this half of the Sprint.

As students work, the student who scored highest on Sprint A might pass out Sprint B.

T:   Stop!  I will read just the answers.  If you got it right, call out "Yes!"  If you made a mistake, circle it.  Ready?

Read the answers to the first half again as students stand.

Movement:  To keep the energy and fun going, do a stretch or a movement game in between Sprints.

### Sprint B

Place Sprint B face down on student desks, and instruct students not to look at the problems until a signal is given.  Repeat the procedure for Sprint A up through the show of hands for how many correct answers.

T:   Stand up if you got more correct on the second Sprint than on the first.  *[handwritten: Type in the chat]*

S:   (Stand.)

T:   Keep standing until I say the number that tells how many more you got right on Sprint B.  If you got three more right on Sprint B than on Sprint A, when I say *three*, you sit down.  Ready?

Call out numbers, starting with one.  Students sit as the number by which they improved is called.  Students may take Sprints home.


### Group Counting  (3 minutes)

Note:  Basic skip-counting skills from Grade 2 shift focus in this Grade 3 activity.  Group counting lays a foundation for interpreting multiplication as repeated addition.  When students count groups in this activity, they add and subtract groups of three when counting up and down.

T:   Let's count to 18 forward and backward.  I want you to whisper, whisper, and then speak numbers.

T:   Watch my fingers to know whether to count up or down.  A closed hand means stop.  (Show signals while explaining.)

T:   (Rhythmically point up until a change is desired.  Show a closed hand then point down.)

S:   (Whisper) 1, (whisper) 2, (speak) 3, etc.

T:   Let's count to 18 forward and backward again.  This time, think every number instead of whispering.

S:   (Think), (think), 3, (think), (think), 6, (think), (think), 9, etc.

T:   What did we just count by?  Turn and talk to your partner.

S:   Threes.

T:   Let's count by threes.  (Direct students to count forward and backward to 18, periodically changing directions.  Emphasize the 9 to 12 transition.)

## Add Equal Groups  (3 minutes)

Materials:   (S) Personal white board

Note:  This activity reviews Lesson 1.  Students directly relate repeated addition to multiplication.  They interpret products as the number of equal groups times the number of objects in each group.

T:   (Project a picture array with 3 groups of 2 circled.)  How many groups are circled?

S:   3.

T:   How many are in each group?

S:   2.

T:   Write this as an addition sentence.

S:   (Write 2 + 2 + 2 = 6.)

T:   Write a multiplication sentence for 3 twos equals 6.

S:   (Write 3 × 2 = 6.)

Continue with this possible sequence:  3 groups of 5, 5 groups of 10, and 3 groups of 4.

## Application Problem  (5 minutes)

Jordan uses 3 lemons to make 1 pitcher of lemonade.  He makes 4 pitchers.  How many lemons does he use altogether? Use the RDW process to show your solution.

$$4 \times 3 = 12$$

Jordan uses 12 lemons altogether.

Note:  Present the image of 4 groups of 3 lemons with the word problem as a scaffold.  This problem reviews multiplying equal groups from Lesson 1.  It also leads into today's Concept Development in which students relate multiplication to the array model.

EUREKA
MATH™

## Concept Development  (30 minutes)

Materials:   (S) Personal white board with threes array
(Template) inserted (pictured below), lemons image
from Application Problem, 1 sheet of blank paper

**Problem 1:  Relate equal groups to arrays.**

Note:  Students' templates should be vertical rather
than horizontal, as shown below.

NOTES ON
MULTIPLE MEANS
OF REPRESENTATION:

The words *array* and *row* were
introduced in Grade 2, Module 6 but
are treated as new vocabulary in this
lesson.

When reviewing the concept, have
students trace a row on the array with
a finger while saying the word *row*.
Provide a real-world example by having
students count the rows on various
cupcake pans (miniature and regular
size) before using the template.

- T:   Look back at Jordan's lemons.  Compare the way his
lemons are organized with the groups of 3 circles on
your template.
- S:   The lemons are touching each other, but the circles
have space between them.  → Each line on the
template shows three, like each group of lemons.
→ The template is organized with everything in
straight lines.
- T:   Many students are noticing straight lines on the
template.  Let's call a straight line going across a **row**.
Use your blank paper to cover all but the top row.
- S:   (Cover all but the top row.)
- T:   Uncover 1 row at a time in the picture.  As you uncover
each row, write the new total number of circles to the
right of it.
- S:   (Skip-count by three using the threes array template.)
- T:   At the signal, say the total number of circles you
counted.  (Signal.)
- S:   30 circles!
- T:   Take 10 seconds to find how many rows of 3 you
counted.  At the signal say how many.  (Signal.)
- S:   10 rows!
- T:   True or false:  10 rows of 3 circles equals 30 circles?
- S:   True!
- T:   (Write $10 \times 3 = 30$ on the board.)  Use the picture on
your template to talk with your partner about why this
equation is true.
- S:   Yesterday, we learned that we can multiply equal
groups.  → We skip-counted 10 rows of 3 circles each
and the total is 30.  → It means 10 groups of 3.  When
you add 10 threes, you get 30.  → Yeah, but writing 10
× 3 is a lot easier than writing out 3 + 3 + 3 + 3 +…
- T:   We call this type of organized picture an **array**.

*Threes array template (with student work)*

| | |
|---|---|
| ⦿⦿⦿ | 3 |
| ⦿⦿⦿ | 6 |
| ⦿⦿⦿ | 9 |
| ⦿⦿⦿ | 12 |
| ⦿⦿⦿ | 15 |
| ⦿⦿⦿ | 18 |
| ⦿⦿⦿ | 21 |
| ⦿⦿⦿ | 24 |
| ⦿⦿⦿ | 27 |
| ⦿⦿⦿ | 30 |

NOTES ON
MULTIPLE MEANS
OF REPRESENTATION:

When presenting the concept of *array*,
it may be beneficial to ask students to
turn and talk, describing or defining an
array for their partner.

©2015 Great Minds. eureka-math.org
G3-M1-TE-B1-1.3.1-01.2016

T:   (Project or draw the image on the right.)  Take a look at this array.  At the signal, tell how many rectangles are in the top row.  (Signal.)

S:   4 rectangles.

T:   The size of 1 row is 4 rectangles.  Each row of 4 can also be called a group of 4.  At the signal, tell how many groups of four are in the array.  (Signal.)

S:   3 groups of four.

T:   To write this as an equation, we first write the **number of groups**.  How many groups?

S:   3 groups!

T:   (Write 3 × ____ = ____.)  Next, we write the **size of the group**.  How many rectangles are in each group?

S:   4 rectangles!

T:   (Fill in the equation to read 3 × 4 = ____.)  Skip-count to find the total number of rectangles in the array.

S:   4, 8, 12.

T:   (Fill in the equation to read 3 × 4 = 12.)  We just found the answer to the multiplication equation that represents the array.  In multiplication, the answer, or total, is called the **product**.

Show an array of 2 rows of 6 and repeat the process.

**Problem 2:  Redraw equal groups as arrays.**

T:   (Project or draw the image on the right.)  The drawing shows 3 equal groups of 5.  On your personal white board, re-draw the picture as an array with 3 rows of 5.

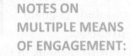

S:   (Draw 3 rows of 5.)

T:   Write a multiplication expression to describe your array.  Remember, an expression is different from an equation because it doesn't have an equal sign.

S:   (Write 3 × 5.)

T:   Skip-count to find the product.

S:   5, 10, 15.

T:   With your partner, compare my drawing with your array.  Which is easier to count?  Why?

S:   (Discuss.)

Show 6 groups of 2 and repeat the process.

NOTES ON
MULTIPLE MEANS
OF ENGAGEMENT:

Provide a challenge in this part of the lesson by giving an equation (e.g., 5 × 4 = _____) and no picture. Have students draw both the equal groups and the array to represent the equation. Then, they skip-count to find the total.

EUREKA
MATH

## Problem Set  (10 minutes)

Students should do their personal best to complete the
Problem Set within the allotted 10 minutes.  For some
classes, it may be appropriate to modify the assignment by
specifying which problems they work on first.  Some
problems do not specify a method for solving.  Students
should solve these problems using the RDW approach
used for Application Problems.

Directions on this Problem Set include the words
*expression* and *equation*.  Remind students that while an
answer is not required with an expression, it should be
included with an equation.

## Student Debrief  (10 minutes)

**Lesson Objective**:  Relate multiplication to the array
model.

The Student Debrief is intended to invite reflection and
active processing of the total lesson experience.

Invite students to review their solutions for the Problem
Set.  They should check work by comparing answers with a
partner before going over answers as a class.  Look for
misconceptions or misunderstandings that can be
addressed in the Debrief.  Guide students in a
conversation to debrief the Problem Set and process the
lesson.

Any combination of the questions below may be used to
lead the discussion.

- In Problems 5 and 6, how do the arrays represent
  equal groups?
- Compare Problems 6 and 7.  (Arrays have the
  same number in each group but a different
  number of groups.)
- Compare equal groups in scattered
  configurations and arrays.
- Review new vocabulary: **row**, **array**, **number of
  groups**, **size of groups**, and **product**.
- Prompt students to notice arrays around the
  room and possibly think of arrays in real-world
  situations.

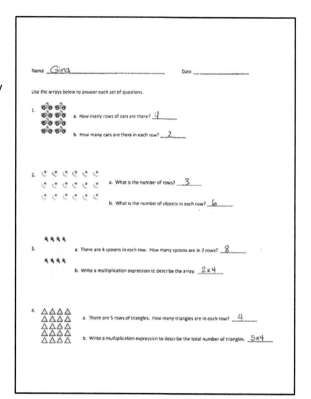

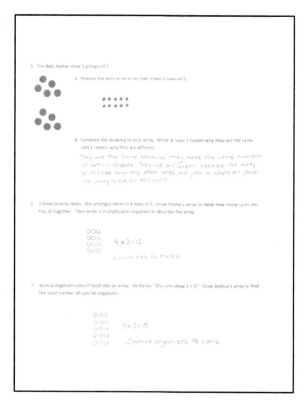

## Exit Ticket  (3 minutes)

After the Student Debrief, instruct students to complete the Exit Ticket.  A review of their work will help with assessing students' understanding of the concepts that were presented in today's lesson and planning more effectively for future lessons.  The questions may be read aloud to the students.

# A

Number Correct: _____

Add or Subtract Using 2

| | | | | | | |
|---|---|---|---|---|---|---|
| 1. | 0 + 2 = | | | 23. | 2 + 4 = | |
| 2. | 2 + 2 = | | | 24. | 2 + 6 = | |
| 3. | 4 + 2 = | | | 25. | 2 + 8 = | |
| 4. | 6 + 2 = | | | 26. | 2 + 10 = | |
| 5. | 8 + 2 = | | | 27. | 2 + 12 = | |
| 6. | 10 + 2 = | | | 28. | 2 + 14 = | |
| 7. | 12 + 2 = | | | 29. | 2 + 16 = | |
| 8. | 14 + 2 = | | | 30. | 2 + 18 = | |
| 9. | 16 + 2 = | | | 31. | 0 + 22 = | |
| 10. | 18 + 2 = | | | 32. | 22 + 22 = | |
| 11. | 20 − 2 = | | | 33. | 44 + 22 = | |
| 12. | 18 − 2 = | | | 34. | 66 + 22 = | |
| 13. | 16 − 2 = | | | 35. | 88 − 22 = | |
| 14. | 14 − 2 = | | | 36. | 66 − 22 = | |
| 15. | 12 − 2 = | | | 37. | 44 − 22 = | |
| 16. | 10 − 2 = | | | 38. | 22 − 22 = | |
| 17. | 8 − 2 = | | | 39. | 22 + 0 = | |
| 18. | 6 − 2 = | | | 40. | 22 + 22 = | |
| 19. | 4 − 2 = | | | 41. | 22 + 44 = | |
| 20. | 2 − 2 = | | | 42. | 66 + 22 = | |
| 21. | 2 + 0 = | | | 43. | 888 − 222 = | |
| 22. | 2 + 2 = | | | 44. | 666 − 222 = | |

# B

Number Correct: _____

Improvement: _____

Add or Subtract Using 2

| | | |
|---|---|---|
| 1. | 2 + 0 = | |
| 2. | 2 + 2 = | |
| 3. | 2 + 4 = | |
| 4. | 2 + 6 = | |
| 5. | 2 + 8 = | |
| 6. | 2 + 10 = | |
| 7. | 2 + 12 = | |
| 8. | 2 + 14 = | |
| 9. | 2 + 16 = | |
| 10. | 2 + 18 = | |
| 11. | 20 – 2 = | |
| 12. | 18 – 2 = | |
| 13. | 16 – 2 = | |
| 14. | 14 – 2 = | |
| 15. | 12 – 2 = | |
| 16. | 10 – 2 = | |
| 17. | 8 – 2 = | |
| 18. | 6 – 2 = | |
| 19. | 4 – 2 = | |
| 20. | 2 – 2 = | |
| 21. | 0 + 2 = | |
| 22. | 2 + 2 = | |

| | | |
|---|---|---|
| 23. | 4 + 2 = | |
| 24. | 6 + 2 = | |
| 25. | 8 + 2 = | |
| 26. | 10 + 2 = | |
| 27. | 12 + 2 = | |
| 28. | 14 + 2 = | |
| 29. | 16 + 2 = | |
| 30. | 18 + 2 = | |
| 31. | 0 + 22 = | |
| 32. | 22 + 22 = | |
| 33. | 22 + 44 = | |
| 34. | 66 + 22 = | |
| 35. | 88 – 22 = | |
| 36. | 66 – 22 = | |
| 37. | 44 – 22 = | |
| 38. | 22 – 22 = | |
| 39. | 22 + 0 = | |
| 40. | 22 + 22 = | |
| 41. | 22 + 44 = | |
| 42. | 66 + 22 = | |
| 43. | 666 – 222 = | |
| 44. | 888 – 222 = | |

**Lesson 2:**    Relate multiplication to the array model.

EUREKA
MATH™

©2015 Great Minds. eureka-math.org
G3-M1-TE-B1-1.3.1-01.2016

Name _____ Date _____

Use the arrays below to answer each set of questions.

1.    a. How many rows of cars are there? _____

      b. How many cars are there in each row? _____

2.    a. What is the number of rows? _____

      b. What is the number of objects in each row? _____

3.    a. There are 4 spoons in each row.  How many spoons are in 2 rows? _____

      b. Write a multiplication expression to describe the array. _____

4.    a. There are 5 rows of triangles.  How many triangles are in each row? _____

      b. Write a multiplication expression to describe the total number of triangles.

      _____

5. The dots below show 2 groups of 5.

   a. Redraw the dots as an array that shows 2 rows of 5.

   b. Compare the drawing to your array. Write at least 1 reason why they are the same and 1 reason why they are different.

6. Emma collects rocks. She arranges them in 4 rows of 3. Draw Emma's array to show how many rocks she has altogether. Then, write a multiplication equation to describe the array.

7. Joshua organizes cans of food into an array. He thinks, "My cans show 5 × 3!" Draw Joshua's array to find the total number of cans he organizes.

EUREKA
MATH™

©2015 Great Minds. eureka-math.org
G3-M1-TE-B1-1.3.1-01.2016

Name _____     Date _____

1.   ⭐ ⭐ ⭐
     ⭐ ⭐ ⭐
     ⭐ ⭐ ⭐
     ⭐ ⭐ ⭐

a.  There are 4 rows of stars.  How many stars are in each row? _____

b.  Write a multiplication equation to describe the array. _____

2.  Judy collects seashells.  She arranges them in 3 rows of 6.  Draw Judy's array to show how many seashells she has altogether.  Then, write a multiplication equation to describe the array.

Name _____  Date _____

Use the arrays below to answer each set of questions.

1. 

   a. How many rows of erasers are there? _____

   b. How many erasers are there in each row? _____

2. 

   a. What is the number of rows? _____

   b. What is the number of objects in each row? _____

3. 

   a. There are 3 squares in each row. How many squares are in 5 rows? _____

   b. Write a multiplication expression to describe the array. _____

4. 

   a. There are 6 rows of stars. How many stars are in each row? _____

   b. Write a multiplication expression to describe the array. _____

Lesson 2: Relate multiplication to the array model.

EUREKA
MATH

5.  The triangles below show 3 groups of four.

a.  Redraw the triangles as an array that shows 3 rows of four.

b.  Compare the drawing to your array.  How are they the same?  How are they different?

6.  Roger has a collection of stamps.  He arranges the stamps into 5 rows of four.  Draw an array to represent Roger's stamps.  Then, write a multiplication equation to describe the array.

7.  Kimberly arranges her 18 markers as an array.  Draw an array that Kimberly might make.  Then, write a multiplication equation to describe your array.

threes array

**Lesson 2:**   Relate multiplication to the array model.

EUREKA
MATH™

# Lesson 3

Objective: Interpret the meaning of factors—the size of the group or the number of groups.

## Suggested Lesson Structure

■ Fluency Practice        (15 minutes)
░ Application Problem      (5 minutes)
░ Concept Development      (30 minutes)
▓ Student Debrief         (10 minutes)

**Total Time**          **(60 minutes)**

## Fluency Practice  (15 minutes)

- Sprint: Add Equal Groups  **3.OA.1**        (9 minutes)
- Group Counting  **3.OA.1**                  (3 minutes)
- Add to Multiply  **3.OA.1**                 (3 minutes)

### Sprint:  Add Equal Groups  (9 minutes)

Materials:   (S) Add Equal Groups Sprint

Note:  This Sprint reviews Lesson 1.  See Lesson 2 for the directions for administering a Sprint.

### Group Counting  (3 minutes)

Note:  Basic skip-counting skills from Grade 2 shift focus in this Grade 3 activity.  Group counting reviews interpreting multiplication as repeated addition.  Counting by twos and threes in this activity anticipates work with those factors in Topic B.

- T:   Let's count by twos.  (Direct students to count forward and backward to 20, periodically changing directions.)
- T:   Let's count by threes.  (Direct students to count forward and backward to 21, periodically changing directions.  Emphasize the 9 to 12 and 18 to 21 transitions.)

Lesson 3:     Interpret the meaning of factors—the size of the group or the number
of groups.

©2015 Great Minds. eureka-math.org
G3-M1-TE-B1-1.3.1-01.2016

45

## Add to Multiply  (3 minutes)

Materials:   (S) Personal white board

Note:  This activity reviews Lesson 2.  Students directly relate repeated addition to multiplication.  They interpret products using the array.

- T:  (Project a picture with 3 groups of 5 circled.)  How many groups are circled?
- S:  3.
- T:  How many are in each group?
- S:  5.
- T:  Write it as an addition sentence.
- S:  (Write 5 + 5 + 5 = 15.)
- T:  Write a multiplication sentence representing *3 fives equals 15*.
- S:  3 × 5 = 15.

Continue with this possible sequence:  3 groups of 10, 3 groups of 4, and 7 groups of 2.

## Application Problem  (5 minutes)

Robbie sees that a carton of eggs shows an array with 2 rows of 6 eggs.  What is the total number of eggs in the carton?  Use the RDW process to show your solution.

Note:  This problem reviews writing multiplication sentences from arrays learned in Lesson 2.  The egg carton provides a natural array for students to see 2 rows of 6.

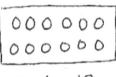

2 × 6 = 12

There are 12 eggs in Robbie's carton.

## Concept Development  (30 minutes)

Materials:   (S) Personal white board

The following opening activity should take about 5 minutes.

- T:  Here are the rules for our opening activity.
  1.  **Divide** yourselves into 4 equal groups.
  2.  Each group will stand in a corner of the room.
  3.  Divide silently.  You can use body movements to gesture, but no words.
- T:  Show thumbs up when your group is ready.  Be sure to look around the room to double check that all 4 groups are equal before showing you're ready.
- S:  (Move around the room silently until there are 4 equal groups, 1 in each corner.)

**NOTES ON OPENING ACTIVITY:**

Adjust the directions for the opening activity depending on the total number of students in the class.  Avoid having students make 4 groups of four.  Do this either by having students form groups near objects in the classroom rather than in corners to adjust the number of groups or by having an adult, teddy bear, etc., stand in to adjust the size of the groups.

Lesson 3:       Interpret the meaning of factors—the size of the group or the number of groups.

©2015 Great Minds. eureka-math.org
G3-M1-TE-B1-1.3.1-01.2016

T: At the signal, tell how many equal groups we've made.  (Signal.)

S: 4 equal groups.

T: (Write 4 × ___ = ___.)  At the signal, tell the size of each group.  (Signal.)

S: (Respond depending on class numbers.)

T: (Fill in the equation on the board.)
   These numbers—the number of groups and the number in each group—are called **factors**.

 Students transition back to their seats.

T: Use the multiplication equation on the board to draw an array.  Make sure that your board is vertical.

S: (Draw a 4 × ____ array.)

T: Let's draw a number bond for our equation.  Draw a circle with our class total.

S: (Draw.)

T: Draw parts coming from the total.  Make 1 part to represent each row in our array.

S: (Draw 4 circles coming from the total.)

T: Show the size of 1 row with your fingers.

S: (Show fingers.)

T: Write the factor representing the size of the group inside the circles.

S: (Write 6 inside each circle.)

T: Look back at the equation.  How is the factor 4 represented in the number bond?

S: It's in the number of parts.  → Groups are like parts. → In the number bond, the part circles actually represent equal groups, so there are 4.  The number inside is the size of the group.

T: Here is an analysis of our equation.

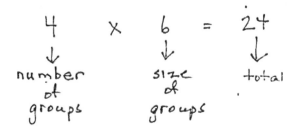

NOTES ON NUMBER BONDS:

The number bond is a pictorial representation of part–part–whole relationships and shows that within a part–whole relationship, smaller numbers (the parts) make up larger numbers (the whole).  (Excerpted from "How to Implement *A Story of Units*.")

*Sample Number Bond (Class of 24)*

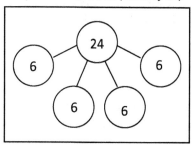

NOTES ON MULTIPLE MEANS OF ACTION AND EXPRESSION:

The number bond is another way for students to explore the relationship between factors in multiplication. Suggested explorations and questions:

- Let's count the groups to make sure the number bond matches our number sentence. (1 six, 2 sixes, etc.)
- What is the number of groups?
- What is the size of each group?
- What multiplication sentence represents the number bond?

Another option is to have students compare how the number bond can represent multiplication and addition to distinguish the importance of equal groups in multiplication.

Lesson 3:    Interpret the meaning of factors—the size of the group or the number of groups.

©2015 Great Minds. eureka-math.org
G3-M1-TE-B1-1.3.1-01.2016

47

As time allows, continue with the following possible suggestions:

- 2 groups of 8
- 3 rows of 5
- Number bond showing 6 groups of 3
- The equation 5 × 4 = 20

## Problem Set  (10 minutes)

Students should do their personal best to complete the Problem Set within the allotted 10 minutes.  For some classes, it may be appropriate to modify the assignment by specifying which problems they work on first.  Some problems do not specify a method for solving.  Students should solve these problems using the RDW approach used for Application Problems.

## Student Debrief  (10 minutes)

**Lesson Objective:**  Interpret the meaning of factors—the size of the group or the number of groups.

The Student Debrief is intended to invite reflection and active processing of the total lesson experience.  Invite students to review their solutions for the Problem Set. They should check work by comparing answers with a partner before going over answers as a class.  Look for misconceptions or misunderstandings that can be addressed in the Debrief.  Guide students in a conversation to debrief the Problem Set and process the lesson.

Any combination of the questions below may be used to lead the discussion.

- Why do you think I started the lesson by asking you to **divide** yourselves into equal groups in the corners of the room?
- Identify the **factors** and their meanings from each image in Problems 1–5.
- In Problem 6, discuss the two ways to draw the array and number bond with factors 2 and 3.

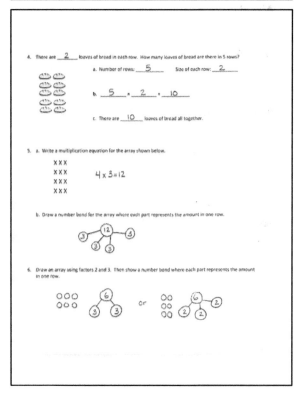

EUREKA
MATH™

- Module 1 introduces many new vocabulary words: *row, array, multiply, multiplication, number of groups, size of groups, divide, factor,* etc. Consider having students make a vocabulary page in their math journals.
- Relate factors to their meaning: the size of the group or the number of groups. Have students share the definition in pairs. Then, ask students to write the word and a definition or example next to it in their journals.

## Exit Ticket  (3 minutes)

After the Student Debrief, instruct students to complete the Exit Ticket. A review of their work will help with assessing students' understanding of the concepts that were presented in today's lesson and planning more effectively for future lessons. The questions may be read aloud to the students.

**EUREKA MATH™**

**Lesson 3:**    Interpret the meaning of factors—the size of the group or the number of groups.

©2015 Great Minds. eureka-math.org
G3-M1-TE-B1-1.3.1-01.2016

49

# A

Number Correct: _____

Add Equal Groups

| | | |
|---|---|---|
| 1. | 2 + 2 = | |
| 2. | 2 twos = | |
| 3. | 5 + 5 = | |
| 4. | 2 fives = | |
| 5. | 2 + 2 + 2 = | |
| 6. | 3 twos = | |
| 7. | 2 + 2 + 2 + 2 = | |
| 8. | 4 twos = | |
| 9. | 5 + 5 + 5 = | |
| 10. | 3 fives = | |
| 11. | 5 + 5 + 5 + 5 = | |
| 12. | 4 fives = | |
| 13. | 2 fours = | |
| 14. | 4 + 4 = | |
| 15. | 2 threes = | |
| 16. | 3 + 3 = | |
| 17. | 2 sixes = | |
| 18. | 6 + 6 = | |
| 19. | 5 twos = | |
| 20. | 2 + 2 + 2 + 2 + 2 = | |
| 21. | 5 fives = | |
| 22. | 5 + 5 + 5 + 5 + 5 = | |

| | | |
|---|---|---|
| 23. | 7 + 7 = | |
| 24. | 2 sevens = | |
| 25. | 9 + 9 = | |
| 26. | 2 nines = | |
| 27. | 8 + 8 = | |
| 28. | 2 eights = | |
| 29. | 3 + 3 + 3 = | |
| 30. | 3 threes = | |
| 31. | 4 + 4 + 4 = | |
| 32. | 3 fours = | |
| 33. | 3 + 3 + 3 + 3 = | |
| 34. | 4 threes = | |
| 35. | 4 fives = | |
| 36. | 5 + 5 + 5 + 5 = | |
| 37. | 3 sixes = | |
| 38. | 6 + 6 + 6 = | |
| 39. | 3 eights = | |
| 40. | 8 + 8 + 8 = | |
| 41. | 3 sevens = | |
| 42. | 7 + 7 + 7 = | |
| 43. | 3 nines = | |
| 44. | 9 + 9 + 9 = | |

**Lesson 3:** Interpret the meaning of factors—the size of the group or the number of groups.

EUREKA MATH™

# B

Number Correct: _____

Improvement: _____

Add Equal Groups

| | | |
|---|---|---|
| 1. | 5 + 5 = | |
| 2. | 2 fives = | |
| 3. | 2 + 2 = | |
| 4. | 2 twos = | |
| 5. | 5 + 5 + 5 = | |
| 6. | 3 fives = | |
| 7. | 5 + 5 + 5 + 5 = | |
| 8. | 4 fives = | |
| 9. | 2 + 2 + 2 = | |
| 10. | 3 twos = | |
| 11. | 2 + 2 + 2 + 2 = | |
| 12. | 4 twos = | |
| 13. | 2 threes = | |
| 14. | 3 + 3 = | |
| 15. | 2 sixes = | |
| 16. | 6 + 6 = | |
| 17. | 2 fours = | |
| 18. | 4 + 4 = | |
| 19. | 5 fives = | |
| 20. | 5 + 5 + 5 + 5 + 5 = | |
| 21. | 5 twos = | |
| 22. | 2 + 2 + 2 + 2 + 2 = | |

| | | |
|---|---|---|
| 23. | 8 + 8 = | |
| 24. | 2 eights = | |
| 25. | 7 + 7 = | |
| 26. | 2 sevens = | |
| 27. | 9 + 9 = | |
| 28. | 2 nines = | |
| 29. | 3 + 3 + 3 + 3 = | |
| 30. | 4 threes = | |
| 31. | 4 + 4 + 4 = | |
| 32. | 3 fours = | |
| 33. | 3 + 3 + 3 = | |
| 34. | 3 threes = | |
| 35. | 4 fives = | |
| 36. | 5 + 5 + 5 + 5 = | |
| 37. | 3 sevens = | |
| 38. | 7 + 7 + 7 = | |
| 39. | 3 nines = | |
| 40. | 9 + 9 + 9 = | |
| 41. | 3 sixes = | |
| 42. | 6 + 6 + 6 = | |
| 43. | 3 eights = | |
| 44. | 8 + 8 + 8 = | |

Lesson 3:     Interpret the meaning of factors—the size of the group or the number of groups.

51

©2015 Great Minds. eureka-math.org
G3-M1-TE-B1-1.3.1-01.2016

Name _____    Date _____

Solve Problems 1–4 using the pictures provided for each problem.

1.  There are 5 flowers in each bunch.  How many flowers are in 4 bunches?

   a.  Number of groups: _____    Size of each group: _____

   b.  4 × 5 = _____

   c.  There are _____ flowers altogether.

2.  There are _____ candies in each box.  How many candies are in 6 boxes?

   a.  Number of groups: _____    Size of each group: _____

   b.  6 × _____ = _____

   c.  There are _____ candies altogether.

3.  There are 4 oranges in each row.  How many oranges are there in _____ rows?

   a.  Number of rows: _____    Size of each row: _____

   b.  _____ × 4 = _____

   c.  There are _____ oranges altogether.

Lesson 3:   Interpret the meaning of factors—the size of the group or the number
                        of groups.

EUREKA
MATH

4.  There are _____ loaves of bread in each row.  How many loaves of bread are there in 5 rows?

a.  Number of rows: _____        Size of each row: _____

b.  _____ × _____ = _____

c.  There are _____ loaves of bread altogether.

5.  a.  Write a multiplication equation for the array shown below.

X X X

X X X

X X X

X X X

b.  Draw a number bond for the array where each part represents the amount in one row.

6.  Draw an array using factors 2 and 3.  Then, show a number bond where each part represents the amount in one row.

Name _____ Date _____

Draw an array that shows 5 rows of 3 squares.  Then, show a number bond where each part represents the amount in one row.

Interpret the meaning of factors—the size of the group or the number of groups.

©2015 Great Minds. eureka-math.org
G3-M1-TE-B1-1.3.1-01.2016

Name _____    Date _____

Solve Problems 1–4 using the pictures provided for each problem.

1.  There are 5 pineapples in each group.  How many pineapples are there in 5 groups?

    a.  Number of groups: _____    Size of each group: _____

    b.  $5 \times 5 =$ _____

    c.  There are _____ pineapples altogether.

---

2.  There are _____ apples in each basket.  How many apples are there in 6 baskets?

    a.  Number of groups: _____    Size of each group: _____

    b.  $6 \times$ _____ = _____

    c.  There are _____ apples altogether.

3.  There are 4 bananas in each row.  How many bananas are there in _____ rows?

a. Number of rows: _____  Size of each row: _____

b. _____ × 4 = _____

c. There are _____ bananas altogether.

4.  There are _____ peppers in each row.  How many peppers are there in 6 rows?

a. Number of rows: _____  Size of each row: _____

b. _____ × _____ = _____

c. There are _____ peppers altogether.

5.  Draw an array using factors 4 and 2.  Then, show a number bond where each part represents the amount in one row.

**Lesson 3:**  Interpret the meaning of factors—the size of the group or the number of groups.

©2015 Great Minds. eureka-math.org
G3-M1-TE-B1-1.3.1-01.2016

**EUREKA MATH**™

# Mathematics Curriculum

## Topic B
# Division as an Unknown Factor Problem

## 3.OA.2, 3.OA.6, 3.OA.3, 3.OA.4

| | | |
|---|---|---|
| **Focus Standard:** | 3.OA.2 | Interpret whole-number quotients of whole numbers, e.g., interpret 56 ÷ 8 as the number of objects in each share when 56 objects are partitioned equally into 8 shares, or as a number of shares when 56 objects are partitioned into equal shares of 8 objects each. *For example, describe a context in which a number of shares or a number of groups can be expressed as 56 ÷ 8.* |
| | 3.OA.6 | Understand division as an unknown-factor problem. *For example, find 32 ÷ 8 by finding the number that makes 32 when multiplied by 8.* |
| **Instructional Days:** | 3 | |
| **Coherence   -Links from:** | G2–M6 | Foundations of Multiplication and Division |
| **-Links to:** | G4–M3 | Multi-Digit Multiplication and Division |

The study of factors links Topics A and B.  Topic B extends the study to division.  Students continue to use a variety of factors in this topic as the emphasis in these lessons rests on conceptually understanding division and learning to interpret problems by writing division equations.  Students understand division as an unknown factor problem, and in Lessons 4 and 5, they relate the meaning of the unknown in division to the size of groups and the number of groups, respectively.  They work through word problems that help give meaning through context and then analyze more abstract drawings.

In Lesson 6, students explore division in the context of the array model, interpreting arrays by writing division equations.  Through the array, students relate the unknown factor in multiplication to the quotient in division.  They use arrays to write multiplication equations and find unknown factors, then write division equations where the quotient represents the same as the unknown factor.  By the end of this topic, students use the vocabulary terms *quotient* and *unknown factor,* and discussion moves toward solidifying understanding of the relationship between multiplication and division.

| A Teaching Sequence Toward Mastery of Division as an Unknown Factor Problem |
| --- |
| **Objective 1:** Understand the meaning of the unknown as the size of the group in division. (Lesson 4) |
| **Objective 2:** Understand the meaning of the unknown as the number of groups in division. (Lesson 5) |
| **Objective 3:** Interpret the unknown in division using the array model. (Lesson 6) |

# Lesson 4

Objective:  Understand the meaning of the unknown as the size of the group in division.

## Suggested Lesson Structure

■ Fluency Practice          (14 minutes)
▨ Application Problem        (6 minutes)
▧ Concept Development        (30 minutes)
■ Student Debrief           (10 minutes)

   **Total Time**           **(60 minutes)**

## Fluency Practice  (14 minutes)

- Sprint:  Repeated Addition as Multiplication  **3.OA.1**          (9 minutes)
- Group Counting  **3.OA.1**          (3 minutes)
- Array Multiplication  **3.OA.1**          (2 minutes)

### Sprint:  Repeated Addition as Multiplication  (9 minutes)

Materials:   (S) Repeated Addition as Multiplication Sprint

Note:  Students relate repeated addition to multiplication.  This reviews Topic A's objectives.  See Lesson 2 for the directions for administering a Sprint.

### Group Counting  (3 minutes)

Note:  Group counting reviews interpreting multiplication as repeated addition.  Counting by twos and threes in this activity anticipates work with those factors in this lesson.

- T:   Let's count by twos.  (Direct students to count forward and backward to 20, periodically changing directions, e.g., 2, 4, 6, 8, 10, 8, 10, 12, 10, 12, 14, 16, 18, 20, 18, 20, 18, 16, 14, 12, 10, 12, 10, 8, 10, 8, 6, 4, 2, 0.)
- T:   Let's count by threes.  (Direct students to count forward and backward to 24, periodically changing directions.  Emphasize the 9 to 12 and 18 to 21 transitions, e.g., 3, 6, 9, 12, 9, 12, 9, 12, 15, 18, 21, 18, 21, 18, 21, 24, 21, 18, 21, 18, 15, 12, 15, 12, 9, 12, 9, 6, 3, 0.)

EUREKA
MATH™

**Lesson 4:**   Understand the meaning of the unknown as the size of the group in division.

©2015 Great Minds. eureka-math.org
G3-M1-TE-B1-1.3.1-01.2016

59

## Array Multiplication  (2 minutes)

Materials:   (S) Personal white board

Note:  This activity reviews Topic A's objectives.  Students directly relate repeated addition to multiplication, interpreting products using the array.

  T:   (Project a picture with 3 groups of 2 circled.)  Say the repeated addition equation.
  S:   2 + 2 + 2 = 6.
  T:   (Write 3 × _____ = _____.)  On your personal white board, complete the multiplication equation.
  S:   (Write 3 × 2 = 6.)

Continue with the following possible sequence:  4 groups of 10, 3 groups of 4, 7 groups of 3, and 8 groups of 2.

## Application Problem  (6 minutes)

The student council holds a meeting in Mr. Chang's classroom.  They arrange the chairs in 3 rows of 5.  How many chairs are used in all?  Use the RDW process.

Note:  This problem reviews relating multiplication to the array model from Lesson 2.  Students might choose to solve by drawing an array (Lesson 2) or a number bond (Lesson 3) where each part represents the amount of chairs in each row.

## Concept Development  (30 minutes)

Materials:   (S) Personal white board, 18 counters

**Concrete to abstract:  Division as fair-share, relate the answer to the unknown factor.**

  **MP.2**

  T:   Yesterday, Mr. Ziegler bought a new pack of 18 markers.  He shared them with me by dividing them into 2 equal groups.  Now, I have a bunch of new markers for making our charts!  Do you want to know how many he gave me?
  S:   Yes.
  T:   What are we trying to find, the number of groups or the size of the group?
  S:   The size of the group.
  T:   Your 18 counters represent the markers.  Divide your 18 counters into 2 equal groups by giving one to Mr. Z, one to me, one to Mr. Z, one to me.  (Model partitioning.)

NOTES ON
MULTIPLE MEANS
OF ACTION AND
EXPRESSION:

This may be students' first time independently dividing in a formal context.  Life experience has likely taught them the fair-share strategy of going back and forth to give 1 and 1, 2 and 2, 3 and 3, etc., until there are no more to distribute.  Encourage those who are unsure what to do, or who are using a less efficient strategy, toward fair-share.

S:   (Divide using the fair-share strategy.)

T:   Using a complete sentence, tell how many counters are in each group.

S:   There are 9 counters in each group.

T:   Then, how many markers did Mr. Ziegler give me?

S:   9 markers!

T:   Let's write a number sentence to show our work, starting from the beginning. What is our total number of counters?

S:   18 counters.

T:   (Write 18 on the board.) We divided our 18 counters into how many equal groups?

S:   We divided into 2 equal groups.

T:   (Write ÷ 2 = _____ on the board next to the 18.)

T:   If 18 is our total and 2 represents our equal groups, then remind me, what does our **unknown** factor represent? (Point to where the answer will go.)

S:   The size of the groups.

T:   That is?

S:   9.

T:   18 divided by 2 equals 9. (Finish writing as you read 18 ÷ 2 = 9.)

T:   How many markers did Mr. Ziegler give me…?

S:   9 markers!

Repeat the process with 15 ÷ 3 = ___: Suppose Mr. Ziegler had 15 markers and shared fairly with 3 teachers. This time, also review that ÷ means to divide.

T:   In what ways does dividing remind you of our work with multiplication?

S:   It's also about the size of groups and the number of groups, but we used a different symbol. → It still uses factors and a total. → This time the total is not the answer. It's the beginning! → So, the answer has to do with groups, not the total.

T:   Right. We multiply when we want to find the total. Here, we divided when we knew the total and wanted to find the size of the groups.

**Pictorial to abstract: Analyze a picture to write a division sentence in which the solution tells the size of the group.**

T:   (Project or draw the following image.) This is how Diana arranges her star stickers.

T:   What does 12 represent in the picture?

S:   The total number of Diana's star stickers.

T:   What does 3 represent?

S:   The number of equal groups.

Lesson 4:     Understand the meaning of the unknown as the size of the group in division.

©2015 Great Minds. eureka-math.org
G3-M1-TE-B1-1.3.1-01.2016

T:   What does 4 represent?

S:   The size of each group.

T:   Write a number sentence to represent Diana's stickers where the answer represents the size of the group.

S:   (Write 12 ÷ 3 = 4.)

T:   (Write 12 ÷ 3 = 4 and 12 ÷ 4 = 3 on the board, even if students have written the correct number sentence.)  What is the difference between these **division** sentences?

S:   In the first one, the answer represents the size of each group.  In the second one, the answer represents the number of groups.

T:   If we're writing a division sentence where the answer represents the size of the group, then which number sentence should we use?

S:   12 ÷ 3 = 4.

**Abstract to pictorial:  Analyze equations for the meaning of the solution and represent the equation with a drawing.**

Write 8 ÷ 4 = ___.

T:   If 8 is the total and 4 is the number of groups, then what does the unknown factor represent?

S:   The size of the groups!

T:   Draw a picture on your personal white board to go with my division equation.  Use your picture to help you find the unknown factor, then write the complete equation.

S:   (Draw various pictures that show 8 ÷ 4, then write 8 ÷ 4 = 2.)

Repeat the process with 10 ÷ 2.  While designing examples, keep in mind that Lesson 5 introduces students to division where the unknown factor represents the number of groups.

## Problem Set  (10 minutes)

Students should do their personal best to complete the Problem Set within the allotted 10 minutes.  For some classes, it may be appropriate to modify the assignment by specifying which problems they work on first.  Some problems do not specify a method for solving.  Students should solve these problems using the RDW approach used for Application Problems.

## Student Debrief  (10 minutes)

**Lesson Objective:**  Understand the meaning of the unknown as the size of the group in division.

The Student Debrief is intended to invite reflection and active processing of the total lesson experience.  Invite students to review their solutions for the Problem Set.  They should check work by comparing answers with a partner before going over answers as a class.  Look for misconceptions or misunderstandings that can be addressed in the Debrief.  Guide students in a conversation to debrief the Problem Set and process the lesson.

©2015 Great Minds. eureka-math.org
G3-M1-TE-B1-1.3.1-01.2016

Any combination of the questions below may be used to lead the discussion.

- Ask students to share their division sentences for Problem 9. Because of the way the question is worded, answers will likely include 15 ÷ 5 = 3 (answer is the size of the group) and 15 ÷ 3 = 5 (answer is the number of groups). This presents an opportunity to begin a discussion in which students compare the division sentences by analyzing the meaning of the factors.

- Guide students to articulate the similarities and differences between multiplication and **division** so that they are clear that division is used to find the total number of groups or objects in a group. Students can think of division problems as having a known factor and an **unknown** factor.

- Review phrases that include new vocabulary such as *unknown factor* and *divided by*.

### Exit Ticket (3 minutes)

After the Student Debrief, instruct students to complete the Exit Ticket. A review of their work will help with assessing students' understanding of the concepts that were presented in today's lesson and planning more effectively for future lessons. The questions may be read aloud to the students.

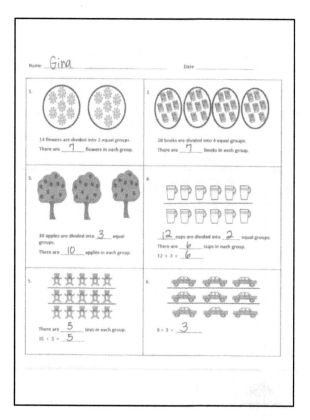

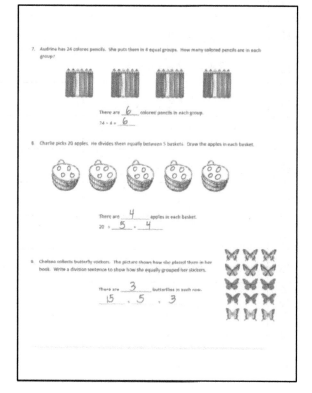

**Lesson 4:**  Understand the meaning of the unknown as the size of the group in division.

63

©2015 Great Minds. eureka-math.org
G3-M1-TE-B1-1.3.1-01.2016

# A

Number Correct: _____

Repeated Addition as Multiplication

| | | |
|---|---|---|
| 1. | 5 + 5 + 5 = | |
| 2. | 3 × 5 = | |
| 3. | 5 × 3 = | |
| 4. | 2 + 2 + 2 = | |
| 5. | 3 × 2 = | |
| 6. | 2 × 3 = | |
| 7. | 5 + 5 = | |
| 8. | 2 × 5 = | |
| 9. | 5 × 2 = | |
| 10. | 2 + 2 + 2 + 2 = | |
| 11. | 4 × 2 = | |
| 12. | 2 × 4 = | |
| 13. | 2 + 2 + 2 + 2 + 2 = | |
| 14. | 5 × 2 = | |
| 15. | 2 × 5 = | |
| 16. | 3 + 3 = | |
| 17. | 2 × 3 = | |
| 18. | 3 × 2 = | |
| 19. | 5 + 5 + 5 + 5 = | |
| 20. | 4 × 5 = | |
| 21. | 5 × 4 = | |
| 22. | 2 × 2 = | |

| | | |
|---|---|---|
| 23. | 3 + 3 + 3 + 3 = | |
| 24. | 4 × 3 = | |
| 25. | 3 × 4 = | |
| 26. | 3 + 3 + 3 = | |
| 27. | 3 × 3 = | |
| 28. | 3 + 3 + 3 + 3 + 3 = | |
| 29. | 5 × 3 = | |
| 30. | 3 × 5 = | |
| 31. | 7 + 7 = | |
| 32. | 2 × 7 = | |
| 33. | 7 × 2 = | |
| 34. | 9 + 9 = | |
| 35. | 2 × 9 = | |
| 36. | 9 × 2 = | |
| 37. | 6 + 6 = | |
| 38. | 6 × 2 = | |
| 39. | 2 × 6 = | |
| 40. | 8 + 8 = | |
| 41. | 2 × 8 = | |
| 42. | 8 × 2 = | |
| 43. | 7 + 7 + 7 + 7 = | |
| 44. | 4 × 7 = | |

**Lesson 4:** Understand the meaning of the unknown as the size of the group in division.

EUREKA MATH™

B

Number Correct: _____

Improvement: _____

Repeated Addition as Multiplication

| | | |
|---|---|---|
| 1. | 2 + 2 + 2 = | |
| 2. | 3 × 2 = | |
| 3. | 2 × 3 = | |
| 4. | 5 + 5 + 5 = | |
| 5. | 3 × 5 = | |
| 6. | 5 × 3 = | |
| 7. | 2 + 2 + 2 + 2 = | |
| 8. | 4 × 2 = | |
| 9. | 2 × 4 = | |
| 10. | 5 + 5 = | |
| 11. | 2 × 5 = | |
| 12. | 5 × 2 = | |
| 13. | 3 + 3 = | |
| 14. | 2 × 3 = | |
| 15. | 3 × 2 = | |
| 16. | 2 + 2 + 2 + 2 + 2 = | |
| 17. | 5 × 2 = | |
| 18. | 2 × 5 = | |
| 19. | 5 + 5 + 5 + 5 = | |
| 20. | 4 × 5 = | |
| 21. | 5 × 4 = | |
| 22. | 2 × 2 = | |

| | | |
|---|---|---|
| 23. | 4 + 4 + 4 = | |
| 24. | 3 × 4 = | |
| 25. | 4 × 3 = | |
| 26. | 4 + 4 + 4 + 4 = | |
| 27. | 4 × 4 = | |
| 28. | 4 + 4 + 4 + 4 + 4 = | |
| 29. | 4 × 5 = | |
| 30. | 5 × 4 = | |
| 31. | 6 + 6 = | |
| 32. | 6 × 2 = | |
| 33. | 2 × 6 = | |
| 34. | 8 + 8 = | |
| 35. | 2 × 8 = | |
| 36. | 8 × 2 = | |
| 37. | 7 + 7 = | |
| 38. | 2 × 7 = | |
| 39. | 7 × 2 = | |
| 40. | 9 + 9 = | |
| 41. | 2 × 9 = | |
| 42. | 9 × 2 = | |
| 43. | 6 + 6 + 6 + 6 = | |
| 44. | 4 × 6 = | |

**Lesson 4:** Understand the meaning of the unknown as the size of the group in division.

65

©2015 Great Minds. eureka-math.org
G3-M1-TE-B1-1.3.1-01.2016

Name _____ Date _____

1.

14 flowers are divided into 2 equal groups.

There are _____ flowers in each group.

2.

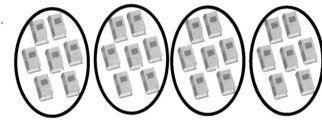

28 books are divided into 4 equal groups.

There are _____ books in each group.

3.

30 apples are divided into _____ equal groups.

There are _____ apples in each group.

4.

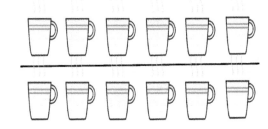

_____ cups are divided into _____ equal groups.

There are _____ cups in each group.

12 ÷ 2 = _____

5.

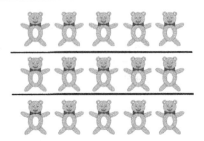

There are _____ toys in each group.

15 ÷ 3 = _____

6.

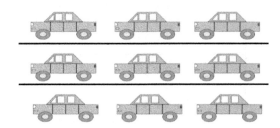

9 ÷ 3 = _____

Lesson 4:    Understand the meaning of the unknown as the size of the group in division.

EUREKA MATH

7. Audrina has 24 colored pencils. She puts them in 4 equal groups. How many colored pencils are in each group?

There are _____ colored pencils in each group.

24 ÷ 4 = _____

8. Charlie picks 20 apples. He divides them equally between 5 baskets. Draw the apples in each basket.

There are _____ apples in each basket.

20 ÷ _____ = _____

9. Chelsea collects butterfly stickers. The picture shows how she placed them in her book. Write a division sentence to show how she equally grouped her stickers.

There are _____ butterflies in each row.

_____ ÷ _____ = _____

Name _____   Date _____

1. There are 16 glue sticks for the class.  The teacher divides them into 4 equal groups.  Draw the number of glue sticks in each group.

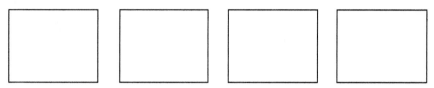

There are _____ glue sticks in each group.

16 ÷ _____ = _____

2. Draw a picture to show 15 ÷ 3.  Then, fill in the blank to make a true division sentence.

15 ÷ 3 = _____

Lesson 4:   Understand the meaning of the unknown as the size of the group in division.

EUREKA MATH™

Name _____   Date _____

1.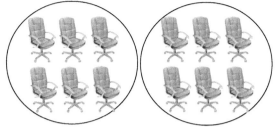

   12 chairs are divided into 2 equal groups.

   There are _____ chairs in each group.

2.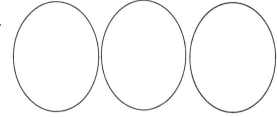

   21 triangles are divided into 3 equal groups.

   There are _____ triangles in each group.

3.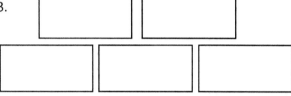

   25 erasers are divided into _____ equal groups.

   There are _____ erasers in each group.

4.

   _____ chickens are divided into _____ equal groups.

   There are _____ chickens in each group.

   9 ÷ 3 = _____

5.

   There are _____ buckets in each group.

   12 ÷ 4 = _____

6.

   16 ÷ 4 = _____

EUREKA
MATH™

Lesson 4:   Understand the meaning of the unknown as the size of the group in division.

69

7. Andrew has 21 keys. He puts them in 3 equal groups. How many keys are in each group?

There are _____ keys in each group.

21 ÷ 3 = _____

8. Mr. Doyle has 20 pencils. He divides them equally between 4 tables. Draw the pencils on each table.

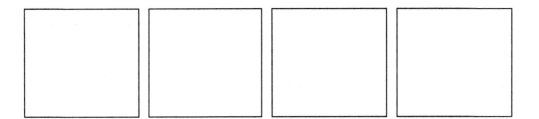

There are _____ pencils on each table.

20 ÷ _____ = _____

9. Jenna has markers. The picture shows how she placed them on her desk. Write a division sentence to represent how she equally grouped her markers.

There are _____ markers in each row.

_____ ÷ _____ = _____

**Lesson 4:**     Understand the meaning of the unknown as the size of the group in division.

**EUREKA MATH**™

# Lesson 5

Objective: Understand the meaning of the unknown as the number of groups in division.

## Suggested Lesson Structure

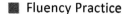

- ■ Fluency Practice        (8 minutes)
- ▨ Application Problem      (7 minutes)
- ▨ Concept Development      (35 minutes)
- ▨ Student Debrief         (10 minutes)

   **Total Time**          **(60 minutes)**

## Fluency Practice  (8 minutes)

- Group Counting **3.OA.1**        (3 minutes)
- Divide Equal Groups **3.OA.2**        (5 minutes)

### Group Counting  (3 minutes)

Note: Group counting reviews interpreting multiplication as repeated addition. Counting by twos and threes in this activity supports work with those factors in Topic B.

- T: Let's count by twos. (Direct students to count forward and backward to 20, emphasizing the 8 to 10, 10 to 12, and 18 to 20 transitions.)
- T: Let's count by threes. (Direct students to count forward and backward to 27, changing directions. Emphasize the 9 to 12 and 18 to 21 transitions.)

Record the count-by threes to use later in the lesson.

### Divide Equal Groups  (5 minutes)

Materials:   (S) Personal white board

Note: Students directly relate repeated addition to division. They interpret the number of groups as the unknown in division. This activity anticipates the lesson objective.

- T: (Project an array with 2 groups of 5.)  How many groups are there?
- S: 2.
- T: How many are in each group?
- S: 5.

Lesson 5:   Understand the meaning of the unknown as the number of groups in division.

©2015 Great Minds. eureka-math.org
G3-M1-TE-B1-1.3.1-01.2016

71

T:   Say the total as a repeated addition sentence.

S:   5 + 5 = 10.

T:   Write a division sentence for 10 divided into 2 equal groups.

S:   (Write 10 ÷ 2 = 5.)

Continue with the following possible sequence:  4 groups of 2, 3 groups of 4, and 2 groups of 6.


## Application Problem  (7 minutes)

Stacey has 18 bracelets.  After she organizes the bracelets by color, she has 3 equal groups.  How many bracelets are in each group?

Note:  This problem reviews the meaning of the unknown as the size of the group in division from Lesson 4.  It also provides a comparison to Problem 1 of the Concept Development where the unknown represents the number of groups in division.

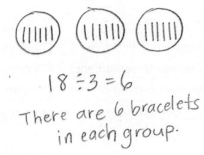

$18 \div 3 = 6$

There are 6 bracelets in each group.


## Concept Development  (35 minutes)

Materials:   (S) Personal white board, 18 counters, student work from Application Problem

**Problem 1:  Division as fair share with the unknown as the number of groups.**

T:   Next weekend, my friend Cynthia is having a party.  Eighteen people are coming.  I told her I'd help her set up tables.  We know that 6 people can sit at each table, but we're not sure how many tables we'll need.  Turn and talk with your partner.  What information do Cynthia and I already have?

S:   You know the total number of people.  It's 18.  → Yeah, and you know how many people are sitting together, 6.  That's the size of the group.

T:   What information don't we know?

S:   You don't know how many tables.  → Tables are like groups.  You don't know the number of groups.

**MP.2**

T:   Let's use counters to show the problem and check our thinking.  Each of you has 18 counters, 1 for each person coming to the party.   Put them into groups of 6.

S:   (Make groups of 6.)

T:   Do you still agree we know the total and the size of each group?

S:   Yes!

T:   Looking at our models, what else do we now know?

S:   We know there are 3 groups.  → So, that means Cynthia needs 3 tables to fit everyone.

T:   (Write 18 ÷ 6 = 3 on the board.)  How does this number sentence relate to the problem we just solved?

S:   It shows that we divided.  → We knew the total, 18 people.  We divided them into groups with 6 people.  Then, we figured out that meant 3 groups of people.  → We divided the total by the size of the group and found the number of groups.


Lesson 5:      Understand the meaning of the unknown as the number of groups in
                         division.

T:   Look back at your work from today's Application Problem.  With your partner, compare the steps you took to solve both the bracelet problem and the party problem.  Notice the number sentences too.

S:   For the bracelets, I drew circles to show 3 groups first.  Then, I shared the bracelets between the groups.  → In the party problem, we put the people in groups of 6 first.  Then, we found how many groups.  → The 6 and 3 switched places.  → That's because in the bracelet problem we had to find the size of the groups, but in the party problem we had to find the number of groups.

T:   I'm hearing you notice that the unknown was different in each problem.  We divide when we want to find the size of the groups *or* the number of groups.

*Sample Number Bond*

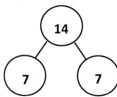

Repeat the process using $14 \div 7 =$ ____ without a story context.

Focus on 7 being the size of the groups.  Match the problem to a number bond like the one shown to the right.

**Problem 2:  Relate finding the number of groups to counting by the divisor.**

T:   Cynthia plans to buy 15 burgers.  Three burgers come in each pack.  How many packs should she buy?  Whisper to your partner what the numbers 15 and 3 represent in this problem.

S:   Fifteen is the total number of burgers.  Three is the number of burgers in a pack.

T:   Is the unknown the number of groups or the size of the group?

S:   The number of groups.

T:   On your personal white board, write the equation you would use to find how many packs to buy.

S:   (Write $15 \div 3 =$ ____.)

T:   Let's draw to find out how many packs Cynthia needs.

S:   (Draw.)

T:   How many packs does Cynthia need?

S:   5 packs.

T:   $15 \div 3$ is?

S:   5.

T:   Let's write the total number of burgers under each pack.  How many total burgers does Cynthia have in 1 pack?

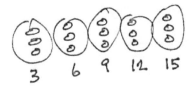

S:   3 burgers.

T:   In 2 packs?

S:   6 burgers (repeat the process up to 15).

NOTES ON
MULTIPLE MEANS
OF ACTION AND
EXPRESSION:

It may be tempting to skip the visual in this segment of the lesson, but for many students who are visual learners, it is an easy way to talk about what may be a common confusion.  There are not 6 burgers in the second pack, rather there are 6 burgers in 2 packs.  Even for advanced students, the visual helps make clear why the count-by works and also makes the connection to addition very evident.

Lesson 5:     Understand the meaning of the unknown as the number of groups in division.

73

©2015 Great Minds. eureka-math.org
G3-M1-TE-B1-1.3.1-01.2016

T: Let's read our numbers.

S: 3, 6, 9, 12, 15.

T: Why did we stop at 15?

S: Because Cynthia only needs 15 burgers.

T: What connection can you make between this problem and our fluency (indicate the count-by threes series from earlier)?

S: It's like counting by threes.

T: Yes. Each time we add a group, we add a three.

T: Count by threes with me, and track the number of threes on your fingers.

S: 3, 6, 9, 12, 15. (Track count using fingers.)

T: How many threes did we count?

S: 5 threes.

T: Skip-counting also shows us that Cynthia needs 5 packs.

Repeat the process with 21 ÷ 3 = ___ and 14 ÷ 2 = ___ without a story context.

T: A count-by can be a quick way to solve division problems when we need to find the **number of equal groups**, especially if we have a big total like 21.

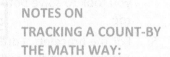

**NOTES ON TRACKING A COUNT-BY THE MATH WAY:**

Since Kindergarten, students have tracked counts on their fingers the Math Way, that is, by starting with the left pinky and moving across their fingers to the right. This mimics the number line and also facilitates easily recognizing groups of 5. Depending on the class, students may need to be reminded to utilize this familiar strategy as they track the count.

## Problem Set  (10 minutes)

Students should do their personal best to complete the Problem Set within the allotted 10 minutes. For some classes, it may be appropriate to modify the assignment by specifying which problems they work on first. Some problems do not specify a method for solving. Students should solve these problems using the RDW approach used for Application Problems.

## Student Debrief  (10 minutes)

**Lesson Objective:** Understand the meaning of the unknown as the number of groups in division.

The Student Debrief is intended to invite reflection and active processing of the total lesson experience.

Invite students to review their solutions for the Problem Set. They should check work by comparing answers with a partner before going over answers as a class.

Look for misconceptions or misunderstandings that can be addressed in the Debrief. Guide students in a conversation to debrief the Problem Set and process the lesson.

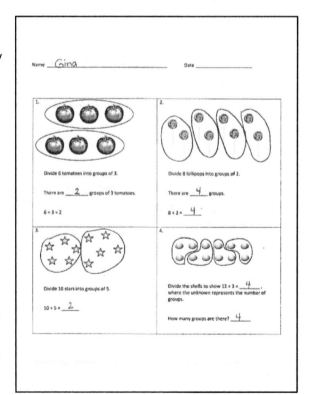

**Lesson 5:**   Understand the meaning of the unknown as the number of groups in division.

©2015 Great Minds. eureka-math.org
G3-M1-TE-B1-1.3.1-01.2016

Any combination of the questions below may be used to lead the discussion.

- Review the relationship between multiplication and division. Guide students to observe that division is used to find either factor—the unknown can be the size of groups (learned yesterday) or the number of groups (learned today).

- Practice using the count-by strategy to solve Problem 5 on the Problem Set. How is a number bond different from a drawing representing a count-by?

- In Problem 5, what would the division sentence be if we wanted to know the number of crackers in each bag? Why is it the same division sentence as when we found the number of bags?

## Exit Ticket (3 minutes)

After the Student Debrief, instruct students to complete the Exit Ticket. A review of their work will help with assessing students' understanding of the concepts that were presented in today's lesson and planning more effectively for future lessons. The questions may be read aloud to the students.

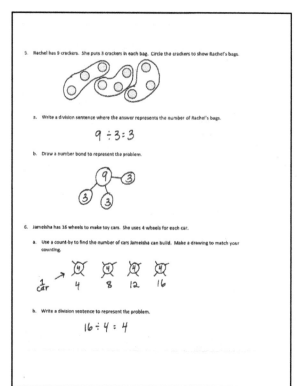

5. Rachel has 9 crackers. She puts 3 crackers in each bag. Circle the crackers to show Rachel's bags.

a. Write a division sentence where the answer represents the number of Rachel's bags.

$$9 \div 3 = 3$$

b. Draw a number bond to represent the problem.

6. Jameisha has 16 wheels to make toy cars. She uses 4 wheels for each car.

a. Use a count-by to find the number of cars Jameisha can build. Make a drawing to match your counting.

b. Write a division sentence to represent the problem.

$$16 \div 4 = 4$$

Lesson 5:    Understand the meaning of the unknown as the number of groups in division.

©2015 Great Minds. eureka-math.org
G3-M1-TE-B1-1.3.1-01.2016

EUREKA
MATH

75

Name _____ Date _____

1.

Divide 6 tomatoes into groups of 3.

There are _____ groups of 3 tomatoes.

6 ÷ 3 = 2

2.

Divide 8 lollipops into groups of 2.

There are _____ groups.

8 ÷ 2 = _____

3.

Divide 10 stars into groups of 5.

10 ÷ 5 = _____

4.

Divide the shells to show 12 ÷ 3 = _____, where the unknown represents the number of groups.

How many groups are there? _____

**Lesson 5:** Understand the meaning of the unknown as the number of groups in division.

EUREKA MATH™

5. Rachel has 9 crackers. She puts 3 crackers in each bag. Circle the crackers to show Rachel's bags.

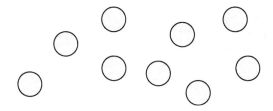

a. Write a division sentence where the answer represents the number of Rachel's bags.

b. Draw a number bond to represent the problem.

6. Jameisha has 16 wheels to make toy cars. She uses 4 wheels for each car.

a. Use a count-by to find the number of cars Jameisha can build. Make a drawing to match your counting.

b. Write a division sentence to represent the problem.

**Lesson 5:**    Understand the meaning of the unknown as the number of groups in
                 division.

©2015 Great Minds. eureka-math.org
G3-M1-TE-B1-1.3.1-01.2016

77

Name _____          Date _____

1. Divide 12 triangles into groups of 6.

     12 ÷ 6 = _____

2. Spencer buys 20 strawberries to make smoothies.  Each smoothie needs 5 strawberries.  Use a count-by to find the number of smoothies Spencer can make.  Make a drawing to match your counting.

**Lesson 5:**       Understand the meaning of the unknown as the number of groups in
                                division.

EUREKA
MATH™

Name _____    Date _____

**1.**

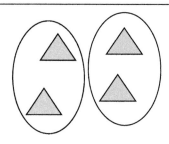

Divide 4 triangles into groups of 2.

There are _____ groups of 2 triangles.

4 ÷ 2 = 2

**2.**

Divide 9 eggs into groups of 3.

There are _____ groups.

9 ÷ 3 = _____

**3.**

Divide 12 buckets of paint into groups of 3.

12 ÷ 3 = _____

**4.**

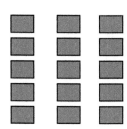

Group the squares to show 15 ÷ 5 = _____, where the unknown represents the number of groups.

How many groups are there? _____

EUREKA
MATH

Lesson 5:    Understand the meaning of the unknown as the number of groups in division.

79

©2015 Great Minds. eureka-math.org
G3-M1-TE-B1-1.3.1-01.2016

5.  Daniel has 12 apples.  He puts 6 apples in each bag.  Circle the apples to find the number of bags Daniel makes.

a.  Write a division sentence where the answer represents the number of Daniel's bags.

b.  Draw a number bond to represent the problem.

6.  Jacob draws cats.  He draws 4 legs on each cat for a total of 24 legs.

a.  Use a count-by to find the number of cats Jacob draws.  Make a drawing to match your counting.

b.  Write a division sentence to represent the problem.

EUREKA
MATH™

# Lesson 6

Objective:  Interpret the unknown in division using the array model.

## Suggested Lesson Structure

■ Fluency Practice          (8 minutes)
▨ Application Problem        (7 minutes)
□ Concept Development        (35 minutes)
■ Student Debrief           (10 minutes)

**Total Time**              **(60 minutes)**

## Fluency Practice  (8 minutes)

▪ Group Counting  **3.OA.1**          (3 minutes)
▪ Divide Equal Groups  **3.OA.2**     (5 minutes)

### Group Counting  (3 minutes)

Note:  Group counting reviews interpreting multiplication as repeated addition.  Counting by twos and threes in this activity supports work with those factors in Topic B.

T:  Let's count by twos.  (Direct students to count forward and backward to 20, emphasizing the 8 to 10, 10 to 12, and 18 to 20 transitions.)

T:  Let's count by threes.  (Direct students to count forward and backward to 30, periodically changing directions.  Emphasize the 9 to 12, 18 to 21, and 27 to 30 transitions.)

### Divide Equal Groups  (5 minutes)

Materials:  (S) Personal white board

Note:  Students directly relate repeated addition to division.  They interpret the unknown in division.  This activity bridges Lessons 5 and 6.

T:  (Project an array with 3 groups of 5.)  Say the total as a repeated addition sentence.

S:  5 + 5 + 5 = 15.

T:  Write a division sentence for 15 divided into 3 equal groups.

S:  (Write 15 ÷ 3 = 5.)

Continue with the following possible sequence:  5 groups of 3, 4 groups of 3, 3 groups of 4, 9 groups of 2, and 2 groups of 9.

Alternate between division sentences where the quotient represents either the number of objects in a group or the number of groups.

## Application Problem (7 minutes)

Twenty children play a game. There are 5 children on each team. How many teams play the game? Write a division sentence to represent the problem.

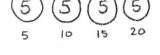

$$20 \div 5 = 4$$

4 teams play the game.

Note: This problem reviews division from Lesson 5 where the unknown represents the number of groups. It also leads into Problem 1 of the Concept Development, which relates division to the array model.

## Concept Development (35 minutes)

Materials: (S) Personal white board, Application Problem

**Problem 1: Relate division to an array model.**

Draw an array representing the Application Problem on the board.

Have students analyze the array and describe the following relationships:

- Total number of children and total number of dots
- Number of children on each team and number of dots in each row
- Number of teams and number of rows

Repeat the process with the following suggested examples. This time, guide students to draw the array from the division equations below. Alternate between having the quotient represent the size of the groups and the number of groups.

- $8 \div 2 = 4$
- $18 \div 6 = 3$

**NOTES ON ARRAYS:**

Problem 1 in this lesson introduces students to relating division to an array model. In Lesson 2, students related the rows in an array to the number of equal groups and the number of dots in each row to the size of the group. The same concept applies for division arrays, but now the problems begin with the total number.

**NOTES ON MULTIPLE MEANS OF REPRESENTATION:**

Some students may benefit from working with a partner. They may underline each row to literally show division and circle each row to show the size of each group. They should explain each step they take. This may be particularly helpful for students who prefer visual or kinesthetic practice along with auditory.

82     Lesson 6:    Interpret the unknown in division using the array model.

©2015 Great Minds. eureka-math.org
G3-M1-TE-B1-1.3.1-01.2016

EUREKA MATH

**Problem 2:  Use an array to relate the unknown factor in multiplication to the quotient in division.**

T:   Draw an array that shows the equation 15 ÷ 3 = 5 where the **quotient**—that means the answer—represents the size of the groups.

S:   (Draw array below.)

T:   Now, write both a division and a multiplication equation for the array.

S:   (Write 15 ÷ 3 = 5, 3 × 5 = 15.)

T:   Where do you find the quotient in our multiplication equation?

S:   It's the second number.  → It's the size of the groups.  → It's a factor.

T:   Circle the size of the groups in both problems.

S:   (Circle the 5 in both problems.)

Repeat the process with the following suggested examples.  Alternate between having the quotient represent the size of the groups and the number of groups.

- 4 rows of 2
- 7 rows of 3

T:   Use our equations to explain to your partner how the factors in a multiplication problem can help you find the quotient in division.

**Problem 3:  Relate multiplication and division.**

T:   (Write ___ × 3 = 24 on the board.)  Skip-count and track the number of threes to solve.

S:   3, 6, 9, 12, 15, 18, 21, 24.  (Write 8 to complete the equation.)

T:   How many threes make 24?  Answer in a complete sentence.

S:   Eight threes make 24.

T:   Write a related division equation where the quotient represents the unknown factor.

S:   (Write 24 ÷ 3 = 8.)

T:   Twenty-four divided in threes makes how many groups?  Answer in a complete sentence.

S:   Twenty-four divided in threes makes 8 groups.

T:   How are the unknown factor and the quotient related in these equations?

S:   The unknown factor is the same number as the quotient.

> **NOTES ON MULTIPLE MEANS OF ENGAGEMENT:**
>
> Some students may still benefit from the visual of an array in this problem.  If necessary, encourage students to draw an array.

EUREKA MATH™

Lesson 6:   Interpret the unknown in division using the array model.

83

©2015 Great Minds. eureka-math.org
G3-M1-TE-B1-1.3.1-01.2016

Repeat the process with the following suggested examples:

- 2 × ____ = 18 and 18 ÷ 2 = ____
- ____ × 9 = 27 and 27 ÷ 9 = ____

T: (Write __ × 3 = 24 and 24 ÷ 3 = __.) True or false: Both equations ask how many threes are in 24?

S: They look different, but they mean the same thing. In both, we're talking about 8 groups of 3 and a total of 24. So, it's true. → The quotient in a division equation is like finding the unknown factor in a multiplication equation.

## Problem Set (10 minutes)

Students should do their personal best to complete the Problem Set within the allotted 10 minutes. For some classes, it may be appropriate to modify the assignment by specifying which problems they work on first. Some problems do not specify a method for solving. Students should solve these problems using the RDW approach used for Application Problems.

## Student Debrief (10 minutes)

**Lesson Objective**: Interpret the unknown in division using the array model.

The Student Debrief is intended to invite reflection and active processing of the total lesson experience.

Invite students to review their solutions for the Problem Set. They should check work by comparing answers with a partner before going over answers as a class. Look for misconceptions or misunderstandings that can be addressed in the Debrief. Guide students in a conversation to debrief the Problem Set and process the lesson.

Any combination of the questions below may be used to lead the discussion.

- Analyze the four equations in Problem 3. Compare the multiplication and division equations, noticing differences in how the problem is represented by each one.

- How do arrays represent both multiplication and division?

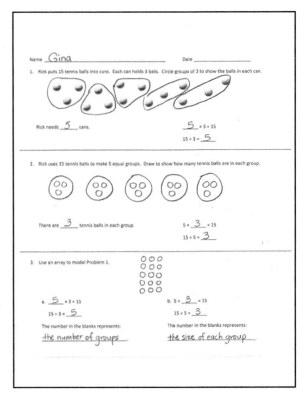

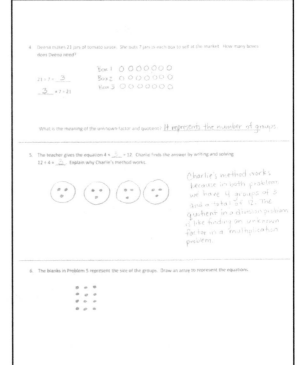

Lesson 6:    Interpret the unknown in division using the array model.

©2015 Great Minds. eureka-math.org
G3-M1-TE-B1-1.3.1-01.2016

- Based on your observation of arrays, what do multiplication and division have in common?
- What is the relationship between the **quotient** in division and the unknown factor in a related multiplication equation?

## Exit Ticket  (3 minutes)

After the Student Debrief, instruct students to complete the Exit Ticket. A review of their work will help with assessing students' understanding of the concepts that were presented in today's lesson and planning more effectively for future lessons. The questions may be read aloud to the students.

EUREKA
MATH™

Lesson 6:  Interpret the unknown in division using the array model.

85

©2015 Great Minds. eureka-math.org
G3-M1-TE-B1-1.3.1-01.2016

Name _____ Date _____

1. Rick puts 15 tennis balls into cans. Each can holds 3 balls. Circle groups of 3 to show the balls in each can.

Rick needs _____ cans.

_____ × 3 = 15

15 ÷ 3 = _____

---

2. Rick uses 15 tennis balls to make 5 equal groups. Draw to show how many tennis balls are in each group.

There are _____ tennis balls in each group.

5 × _____ = 15

15 ÷ 5 = _____

---

3. Use an array to model Problem 1.

a. _____ × 3 = 15

15 ÷ 3 = _____

The number in the blanks represents

_____.

b. 5 × _____ = 15

15 ÷ 5 = _____

The number in the blanks represents

_____.

**Lesson 6:** Interpret the unknown in division using the array model.

**EUREKA MATH**

4.  Deena makes 21 jars of tomato sauce.  She puts 7 jars in each box to sell at the market.  How many boxes does Deena need?

21 ÷ 7 = _____

_____ × 7 = 21

What is the meaning of the unknown factor and quotient? _____

5.  The teacher gives the equation 4 × _____ = 12.  Charlie finds the answer by writing and solving 12 ÷ 4 = _____.  Explain why Charlie's method works.

6.  The blanks in Problem 5 represent the size of the groups.  Draw an array to represent the equations.

**Lesson 6:**     Interpret the unknown in division using the array model.

©2015 Great Minds. eureka-math.org
G3-M1-TE-B1-1.3.1-01.2016

87

Name _____     Date _____

Cesar arranges 12 notecards into rows of 6 for his presentation.  Draw an array to represent the problem.

$12 \div 6 =$ _____

_____ $\times\ 6 = 12$

What do the unknown factor and quotient represent? _____

**Lesson 6:**        Interpret the unknown in division using the array model.

©2015 Great Minds. eureka-math.org
G3-M1-TE-B1-1.3.1-01.2016

EUREKA
MATH™

Name _____     Date _____

1. Mr. Hannigan puts 12 pencils into boxes. Each box holds 4 pencils. Circle groups of 4 to show the pencils in each box.

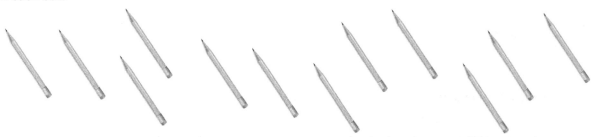

       Mr. Hannigan needs _____ boxes.                   _____ × 4 = 12

                                                        12 ÷ 4 = _____

2. Mr. Hannigan places 12 pencils into 3 equal groups. Draw to show how many pencils are in each group.

       There are _____ pencils in each group.             3 × _____ = 12

                                                       12 ÷ 3 = _____

3. Use an array to model Problem 1.

    a. _____ × 4 = 12                        b. 3 × _____ = 12

        12 ÷ 4 = _____                          12 ÷ 3 = _____

        The number in the blanks represents             The number in the blanks represents

        _____.             _____.

4. Judy washes 24 dishes. She then dries and stacks the dishes equally into 4 piles. How many dishes are in each pile?

$24 \div 4 =$ _____

$4 \times$ _____ $= 24$

What is the meaning of the unknown factor and quotient? _____

_____

5. Nate solves the equation _____ $\times 5 = 15$ by writing and solving $15 \div 5 =$ _____. Explain why Nate's method works.

_____

6. The blanks in Problem 5 represent the number of groups. Draw an array to represent the equations.

EUREKA
MATH™

©2015 Great Minds. eureka-math.org
G3-M1-TE-B1-1.3.1-01.2016

# Mathematics Curriculum

GRADE 3 • MODULE 1

## Topic C
# Multiplication Using Units of 2 and 3

**3.OA.1, 3.OA.5**, 3.OA.3, 3.OA.4

| Focus Standards: | 3.OA.1 | Interpret products of whole numbers, e.g., interpret 5 × 7 as the total number of objects in 5 groups of 7 objects each. *For example, describe a context in which a total number of objects can be expressed as 5 × 7.* |
| --- | --- | --- |
| | 3.OA.5 | Apply properties of operations as strategies to multiply and divide. *Examples: If 6 × 4 = 24 is known, then 4 × 6 = 24 is also known. (Commutative property of multiplication.) 3 × 5 × 2 can be found by 3 × 5 = 15, then 15 × 2 = 30, or by 5 × 2 = 10, then 3 × 10 = 30. (Associative property of multiplication.) Knowing that 8 × 5 = 40 and 8 × 2 = 16, one can find 8 × 7 as 8 × (5 + 2) = (8 × 5) + (8 × 2) = 40 + 16 = 56. (Distributive property.)* |
| Instructional Days: | 4 | |
| Coherence -Links from: | G2–M6 | Foundations of Multiplication and Division |
| -Links to: | G4–M3 | Multi-Digit Multiplication and Division |

In Topic C, students begin building fluency with facts of 2 and 3 using the array model and familiar skip-counting strategies.

Lessons 7 and 8 introduce the new complexity of manipulating arrays to study the commutative property. Students learn to distinguish rows from columns as they rotate arrays 90 degrees, noticing that the meaning of the factors changes depending on the orientation of the array. Students write two different multiplication sentences to interpret the same array. These lessons emphasize the equivalence of facts by demonstrating, for example, that 2 groups of 8 and 8 groups of 2 have the same product. Students observe the pattern and begin to recognize commutativity as a strategy for solving twice as many facts.

Lessons 9 and 10 introduce the distributive property as a strategy for multiplication. In Lesson 9, students use arrays to decompose unknown facts as the sum or difference of two known facts. For example, they analyze an array to see that 7 × 3 can be decomposed as 2 rows of 3 + 5 rows of 3. In Lesson 10, students learn to write the decomposition as (5 × 3) + (2 × 3) = 21. They explain each step of the solving process in anticipation of the work they are expected to complete independently on the Mid-Module Assessment.

**A Teaching Sequence Toward Mastery of Multiplication Using Units of 2 and 3**

**Objective 1:** Demonstrate the commutativity of multiplication, and practice related facts by skip-counting objects in array models.
(Lessons 7–8)

**Objective 2:** Find related multiplication facts by adding and subtracting equal groups in array models.
(Lesson 9)

**Objective 3:** Model the distributive property with arrays to decompose units as a strategy to multiply.
(Lesson 10)

©2015 Great Minds. eureka-math.org
G3-M1-TE-B1-1.3.1-01.2016

# Lesson 7

Objective: Demonstrate the commutativity of multiplication, and practice related facts by skip-counting objects in array models.

## Suggested Lesson Structure

■ Fluency Practice          (13 minutes)
▨ Application Problem        (5 minutes)
▢ Concept Development        (32 minutes)
▨ Student Debrief           (10 minutes)

   **Total Time**           **(60 minutes)**

## Fluency Practice (13 minutes)

- Group Counting **3.OA.1**          (3 minutes)
- Divide Equal Groups **3.OA.2**     (5 minutes)
- Multiply with Twos **3.OA.7**      (5 minutes)

### Group Counting (3 minutes)

Note: Group counting reviews interpreting multiplication as repeated addition. Counting by twos and threes in this activity anticipates work with those factors in Topic C.

- T: Let's count by twos. (Direct students to count forward and backward to 20, emphasizing the 8 to 10, 10 to 12, and 18 to 20 transitions.)
- T: Let's count by threes. (Direct students to count forward and backward to 30, periodically changing directions. Emphasize the 9 to 12, 18 to 21, and 27 to 30 transitions.)

### Divide Equal Groups (5 minutes)

Materials: (S) Personal white board

Note: Students directly relate repeated addition to division. They interpret the unknown in division. This activity reviews Lesson 6.

- T: (Project an array with 2 groups of 4.) Say the total as a repeated addition sentence.
- S: 4 + 4 = 8.
- T: Write a division sentence for 8 divided into 2 equal groups.
- S: (Write 8 ÷ 2 = 4.)

Lesson 7:    Demonstrate the commutativity of multiplication, and practice related          93
             facts by skip-counting objects in array models.

©2015 Great Minds. eureka-math.org
G3-M1-TE-B1-1.3.1-01.2016

T:   Below that division sentence write a division sentence dividing 8 into 4 equal groups.

S:   (Write 8 ÷ 4 = 2.)

Continue with this possible sequence:  5 groups of 3, 3 groups of 4, and 6 groups of 2.

## Multiply with Twos  (5 minutes)

Materials:   (S) Personal white board, twos array (Fluency Template), blank paper

Note:  Students unit count objects in an array and write multiplication sentences that match the count-by in anticipation of this lesson's objective.

*Twos Array Fluency Template*

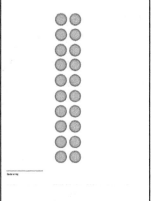

T:   Slip your template into your personal white board.

T:   Turn your board so that it's vertical.  Use your blank paper to cover all but the first row of dots.

T:   How many twos show?

S:   1 two.

T:   Say the multiplication sentence to represent the array that's shown and solve.

S:   $1 \times 2 = 2$.

T:   Uncover another row.

Continue this sequence having students uncover twos for $2 \times 2$, $3 \times 2$, $10 \times 2$, $4 \times 2$, $5 \times 2$, $6 \times 2$, $7 \times 2$, $9 \times 2$, and $8 \times 2$.

## Application Problem  (5 minutes)

Anna picks 24 flowers.  She makes equal bundles of flowers and gives 1 bundle to each of her 7 friends.  She keeps a bundle for herself too.  How many flowers does Anna put in each bundle?

$$24 \div 8 = 3$$

Anna puts 3 flowers in each bundle.

Note:  This problem reviews division from Lesson 5 where the unknown represents the size of the group.  The problem's complexity is in understanding that the flowers are divided equally into 8 bundles, not 7, in order to include a bundle for Anna.  Students might choose to solve by drawing a division array learned in Lesson 6 or a number bond learned in Lesson 3.

EUREKA
MATH

## Concept Development (32 minutes)

**Materials:** (S) Personal white board

*Personal White Board*

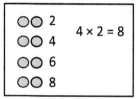

**Problem 1: Rotate arrays 90 degrees.**

T: Position your board so that the long side is horizontal. Draw an array that shows 4 rows of 2.

S: (Draw the array, as shown to the right.)

T: Write a skip-count by twos to find the total. Then write a multiplication sentence where the first factor represents the number of rows.

S: (Write 2, 4, 6, 8 and 4 × 2 = 8 as shown to the right.)

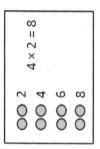

T: **Rotate** your board 90 degrees so that the long side is vertical.

S: (Rotate, as shown to the right.)

T: What happened to the array?

S: It has 2 rows of 4. → It has 4 groups of 2, but they're up and down instead of in rows.

T: Now the twos are **columns**, vertical groups in an array.

T: I'll rotate my board. You tell me if the twos are columns or rows.

T: (Show the twos as rows.)

S: Rows!

T: (Rotate your board and show the twos as columns.)

S: Columns!

T: Skip-count the rows by four!

S: (Point to the rows as students count.) 4, 8.

T: Add that skip-count to your board. (Allow time.) What multiplication sentence can represent this array?

S: 2 × 4 = 8.

T: (Write 4 × 2 = 8 and 2 × 4 = 8 on the board with their corresponding arrays drawn as shown.) What do you notice about the multiplication sentences?

S: The 4 and the 2 switched places.

T: What do the 4 and 2 represent in each? Talk to your partner.

S: In A, the 4 represents the number of rows, but in B, it represents the size of the row. → The twos are rows in A but columns in B.

T: Did the meaning of the 8 change?

S: No.

T: So factors can switch places and trade meanings, but the total stays the same. We call that the **commutative property**. Talk to your partner about why the total stays the same.

S: (Discuss.)

Continue with 2 × 5 and 3 × 4 arrays.

> **NOTES ON VOCABULARY:**
>
> The word *column* was originally introduced in Grade 2, Module 6 but is treated as new vocabulary in this lesson.

**Lesson 7:** Demonstrate the commutativity of multiplication, and practice related facts by skip-counting objects in array models.

©2015 Great Minds. eureka-math.org
G3-M1-TE-B1-1.3.1-01.2016

**Problem 2:  Interpreting rows and columns in rotated arrays.**

Ask students to draw an array that shows 8 rows of 2.  They should write a skip-count to find the total and a number sentence to represent the array.  (See the example to the right.)

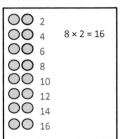

*Personal White Board*

T:   What does the first factor—the 8—in your equation represent?

S:   The number of equal groups in the array.  → The number of rows.

T:   Can the 8 also represent the size of the group? Talk to your partner.

S:   It can be the vertical group.  → It can mean the size of the column!

T:   If we think of 8 as the size of the groups, then how many groups does the array show?

S:   2 groups.

T:   Are those 2 groups shown by columns or by rows?

S:   By columns.

T:   Does the total change if we think of 8 as the size of the groups and 2 as the number of groups?

S:   No, the total is still 16 because you still have to multiply 8 and 2.

T:   Talk with a partner.  Does $8 \times 2 = 16$ represent this array even if we think of 8 as the size of the groups and 2 columns as the number of groups?

S:   No, it should be written as $2 \times 8 = 16$.  → We just learned that factors can trade meanings.  → They can trade meanings, but they also switch places.  → The total stays the same, so I think it works.

T:   Factors can trade meanings without always having to switch places in the equation.  It's okay to write $8 \times 2 = 16$ and think of 8 as the size of the groups and 2 columns as the number of groups.  In third grade we'll usually write multiplication sentences so that the first factor represents the number of groups.  That makes them a little easier to read.  But either factor can mean the size of the groups or the number of groups.

## Problem Set  (10 minutes)

Students should do their personal best to complete the Problem Set within the allotted 10 minutes.  For some classes, it may be appropriate to modify the assignment by specifying which problems they work on first.  Some problems do not specify a method for solving.  Students should solve these problems using the RDW approach used for Application Problems.

**Lesson 7:**     Demonstrate the commutativity of multiplication, and practice related
                  facts by skip-counting objects in array models.

EUREKA
MATH™

## Student Debrief (10 minutes)

**Lesson Objective:** Demonstrate the commutativity of multiplication, and practice related facts by skip-counting objects in array models.

The Student Debrief is intended to invite reflection and active processing of the total lesson experience. Invite students to review their solutions for the Problem Set. They should check work by comparing answers with a partner before going over answers as a class. Look for misconceptions or misunderstandings that can be addressed in the Debrief. Guide students in a conversation to debrief the Problem Set and process the lesson.

Any combination of the questions below may be used to lead the discussion.

- How did **rotating** our boards help us see rows as **columns** and columns as rows?

- What did you learn today about changing the order of the factors?

- Can you think of different number sentences Ms. Nenadal could have written to get at the same idea in Problem 6?

- Factors can change their order without changing the total. We call that the **commutative property**. Let's test addition, subtraction, and division and see if the commutative property applies to them too.

**NOTES ON
MULTIPLE MEANS
OF REPRESENTATION:**

Students need not master the term *commutative property* (**3.OA.5**). However, they will need to be familiar with the vocabulary moving forward in this module.

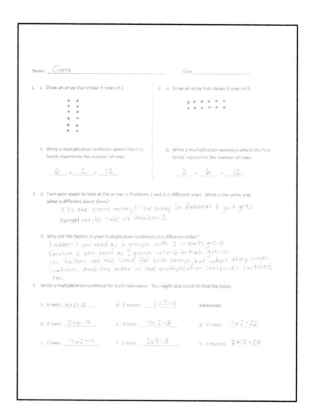

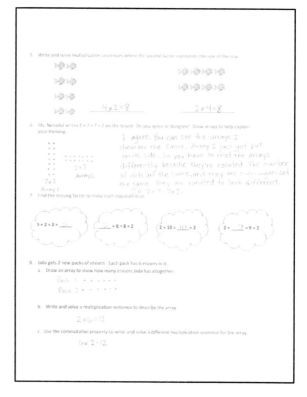

**Lesson 7:** Demonstrate the commutativity of multiplication, and practice related facts by skip-counting objects in array models.

97

©2015 Great Minds. eureka-math.org
G3-M1-TE-B1-1.3.1-01.2016

## Exit Ticket  (3 minutes)

After the Student Debrief, instruct students to complete the Exit Ticket.  A review of their work will help with assessing students' understanding of the concepts that were presented in today's lesson and planning more effectively for future lessons.  The questions may be read aloud to the students.

Lesson 7:     Demonstrate the commutativity of multiplication, and practice related facts by skip-counting objects in array models.

©2015 Great Minds. eureka-math.org
G3-M1-TE-B1-1.3.1-01.2016

Name _____     Date _____

1.  a. Draw an array that shows 6 rows of 2.

    b. Write a multiplication sentence where the first factor represents the number of rows.

    _____ × _____ = _____

2.  a. Draw an array that shows 2 rows of 6.

    b. Write a multiplication sentence where the first factor represents the number of rows.

    _____ × _____ = _____

3.  a. Turn your paper to look at the arrays in Problems 1 and 2 in different ways.  What is the same and what is different about them?

    b. Why are the factors in your multiplication sentences in a different order?

4.  Write a multiplication sentence for each expression.  You might skip-count to find the totals.

    a. 6 twos:  6 × 2 = 12          d. 2 sevens: _____       **Extension:**

    b. 2 sixes: _____     e. 9 twos: _____          g. 11 twos: _____

    c. 7 twos: _____      f. 2 nines: _____         h. 2 twelves: _____

     **Lesson 7:**     Demonstrate the commutativity of multiplication, and practice related       **99**
facts by skip-counting objects in array models.

©2015 Great Minds. eureka-math.org
G3-M1-TE-B1-1.3.1-01.2016

5.  Write and solve multiplication sentences where the second factor represents the size of the row.

_____              _____

6.  Ms. Nenadal writes 2 × 7 = 7 × 2 on the board.  Do you agree or disagree?  Draw arrays to help explain your thinking.

7.  Find the missing factor to make each equation true.

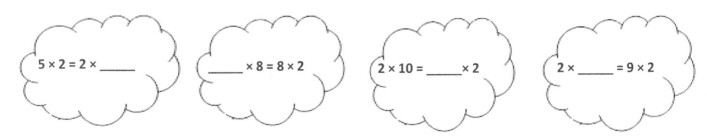

5 × 2 = 2 × _____

_____ × 8 = 8 × 2

2 × 10 = _____ × 2

2 × _____ = 9 × 2

8.  Jada gets 2 new packs of erasers.  Each pack has 6 erasers in it.
    a.  Draw an array to show how many erasers Jada has altogether.

    b.  Write and solve a multiplication sentence to describe the array.

    c.  Use the commutative property to write and solve a different multiplication sentence for the array.

Demonstrate the commutativity of multiplication, and practice related facts by skip-counting objects in array models.

EUREKA
MATH™

Name _____   Date _____

$$2 \times 5 = 5 \times 2$$

Do you agree or disagree with the statement in the box?  Draw arrays and use skip-counting to explain your thinking.

Lesson 7:    Demonstrate the commutativity of multiplication, and practice related
            facts by skip-counting objects in array models.

101

©2015 Great Minds. eureka-math.org
G3-M1-TE-B1-1.3.1-01.2016

Name _____     Date _____

1.  a.  Draw an array that shows 7 rows of 2.

    b.  Write a multiplication sentence where the first factor represents the number of rows.

    _____ × _____ = _____

2.  a.  Draw an array that shows 2 rows of 7.

    b.  Write a multiplication sentence where the first factor represents the number of rows.

    _____ × _____ = _____

3.  a.  Turn your paper to look at the arrays in Problems 1 and 2 in different ways.  What is the same and what is different about them?

    b.  Why are the factors in your multiplication sentences in a different order?

4.  Write a multiplication sentence to match the number of groups.  Skip-count to find the totals.  The first one is done for you.

    a.  2 twos:  _2 × 2 = 4____        d.  2 fours: _____        g.  2 fives: _____

    b.  3 twos:  _____          e.  4 twos: _____         h.  6 twos: _____

    c.  2 threes:  _____        f.  5 twos: _____         i.  2 sixes: _____

Lesson 7:    Demonstrate the commutativity of multiplication, and practice related facts by skip-counting objects in array models.

©2015 Great Minds. eureka-math.org
G3-M1-TE-B1-1.3.1-01.2016

EUREKA
MATH

5.  Write and solve multiplication sentences where the second factor represents the size of the row.

_____  _____

6.  Angel writes 2 × 8 = 8 × 2 in his notebook.  Do you agree or disagree?  Draw arrays to help explain your thinking.

7.  Find the missing factor to make each equation true.

| 2 × 6 = 6 × \_\_\_\_\_ | \_\_\_\_\_ × 2 = 2 × 7 | 9 × 2 = \_\_\_\_\_ × 9 | 2 × \_\_\_\_\_ = 10 × 2 |

8.  Tamia buys 2 bags of candy.  Each bag has 7 pieces of candy in it.
    a.  Draw an array to show how many pieces of candy Tamia has altogether.

    b.  Write and solve a multiplication sentence to describe the array.

    c.  Use the commutative property to write and solve a different multiplication sentence for the array.

EUREKA MATH

Lesson 7:   Demonstrate the commutativity of multiplication, and practice related facts by skip-counting objects in array models.

©2015 Great Minds. eureka-math.org
G3-M1-TE-B1-1.3.1-01.2016

103

twos array

**Lesson 7:** Demonstrate the commutativity of multiplication, and practice related facts by skip-counting objects in array models.

©2015 Great Minds. eureka-math.org
G3-M1-TE-B1-1.3.1-01.2016

**EUREKA MATH**™

# Lesson 8

Objective: Demonstrate the commutativity of multiplication, and practice related facts by skip-counting objects in array models.

## Suggested Lesson Structure

■ Fluency Practice          (6 minutes)
▨ Application Problem        (10 minutes)
▢ Concept Development        (34 minutes)
▨ Student Debrief           (10 minutes)

   **Total Time**           **(60 minutes)**

## Fluency Practice  (6 minutes)

- Group Counting  **3.OA.1**                  (3 minutes)
- Commutative Multiplying  **3.OA.5**         (3 minutes)

## Group Counting  (3 minutes)

Note:  Group counting reviews interpreting multiplication as repeated addition.  Counting by twos, threes, and fours in this activity supports work with units of 2 and 3 in this topic and anticipates work using units of 4 in Topic E.

- T:  Let's count by twos to 20.  Whisper the numbers, and then speak them.
- T:  Let's count by twos to 20 again.  This time, hum the first number, and then speak it.  As you hum, think of the number.
- T:  Let's count by twos to 20.  This time, instead of humming, think every other number.
- T:  What did we just count by?
- S:  Twos.
- T:  Let's count by fours.  (Direct students to count forward and backward to 20, periodically changing directions.)
- T:  Let's count by threes.  (Direct students to count forward and backward to 30, periodically changing directions.  Emphasize the 9 to 12, 18 to 21, and 27 to 30 transitions.)

Lesson 8:   Demonstrate the commutativity of multiplication, and practice related facts by skip-counting objects in array models.

©2015 Great Minds. eureka-math.org
G3-M1-TE-B1-1.3.1-01.2016

105

## Commutative Multiplying  (3 minutes)

Materials:   (S) Personal white board

Note:  Practicing this concept, which was taught in Lesson 7, helps students build confidence and automaticity.

   T:   (Project a 3 × 2 array.)  How many groups of 2 do you see?
   S:   3 groups of 2.
   T:   Write two different multiplication sentences for the array.
   S:   (Write 3 × 2 = 6 and 2 × 3 = 6.)

Continue with the following possible sequence:  3 by 5 and 4 by 3.

   T:   (Write 4 × 2 = 2 × ___.)  On your board, fill in the blank.
   S:   (Write 4 × 2 = 2 × 4.)

Repeat the process for 9 × 5 = 5 × ___ and 3 × 6 = 6 × ___.

## Application Problem  (10 minutes)

Children sit in 2 rows of 9 on the carpet for math time.  Erin says, "We make 2 equal groups."  Vittesh says, "We make 9 equal groups."  Who is correct?  Explain how you know using models, numbers, and words.

Note:  This problem reviews the commutativity of multiplication introduced in Lesson 7 and prepares students for Day 2 of the same concept in today's lesson.

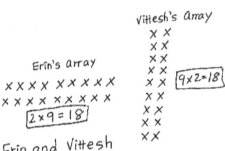

## Concept Development  (34 minutes)

Materials:   (S) Personal white board

**Problem 1:  Rotate arrays 90 degrees.**

   T:   Turn your personal white board so that the long side is vertical.  Skip-count by threes 4 times and write each number.
   S:   3, 6, 9, 12.
   T:   Draw an array to match your count where the number of rows represents the number of groups.
   T:   Discuss how many rows and columns you see.
   S:   (Students discuss that there are 4 rows and 3 columns.)
   T:   Turn your board so that the long side is horizontal.  How many rows and columns does it show now?

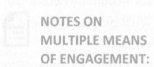

NOTES ON
MULTIPLE MEANS
OF ENGAGEMENT:

If students are very comfortable with the way an array changes depending on how it is turned, add a bit of complexity by having them imagine turning it horizontal rather than actually doing it.

©2015 Great Minds. eureka-math.org
G3-M1-TE-B1-1.3.1-01.2016

S:   (Turn boards 90 degrees.)  3 rows and 4 columns.

T:   Tell your partner a different skip-count that also represents the array.

S:   4, 8, 12.

T:   What is the difference between the vertical and horizontal arrays?

S:   In the vertical array the 4 threes were rows, and in the horizontal array they were columns.  → It's
the same with the 3 fours.  They were columns, then rows.

**MP.7**

T:   Did the total number of dots change?

S:   No.

T:   So, the total and the factors stay the same, but the factors switch places.  Yesterday, we learned a
special name for that.  It's called…

S:   Commutative!  → The commutative property!

T:   Use the commutative property to write two multiplication sentences for the array.

S:   (Write $4 \times 3 = 12$ and $3 \times 4 = 12$.)

Students practice with partners using the following examples.  Partner A gives skip-counting directions.
Partner B writes the count, draws an array, and writes multiplication sentences.  Then, partners switch roles.

- Skip-count by twos 3 times
- Skip-count by threes 6 times

**Problem 2:  Interpreting rows and columns in rotated arrays.**

T:   Work with your partner to draw an array that shows 5
rows and 3 columns.

S:   (Demonstrate one possible process.)  Let's draw 5
circles going down to show the start of each row.  →
Then we can draw 3 circles to show the columns across
the top.  → Wait, we already drew 1 column when we
made the rows, so we can just draw 2 more columns.

T:   Write an equation to match your array where the first
factor represents the number of rows.  Don't solve it
yet.

S:   (Write $5 \times 3 = \underline{\quad}$.)

T:   I'm going to change the problem slightly.  Listen
carefully and rotate your array to match:  3 rows and 5
columns.

S:   (Turn boards 90 degrees.)

T:   Write the equation for the new array.  Let the first factor
represent the number of rows.  Don't solve it yet.

S:   (Write $3 \times 5 = \underline{\quad}$.)

T:   Explain the difference between these problems to your
partner.

S:   The array turned and the factors switched places.

**NOTES ON
DRAWING ROWS
AND COLUMNS:**

Students may not immediately
recognize that they do not need to
redraw the corner circle to make 3
columns.  After drawing rows, they
already have 1 column and, for this
problem, only need to add 2 more
columns.  If they make a mistake, help
them recognize it by encouraging them
to recount their total columns.

**NOTES ON
MULTIPLE MEANS
OF ENGAGEMENT:**

If appropriate, provide a challenge for
students by having them cover the
array as they skip-count to solve.

Lesson 8:     Demonstrate the commutativity of multiplication, and practice related
facts by skip-counting objects in array models.                        107

©2015 Great Minds. eureka-math.org
G3-M1-TE-B1-1.3.1-01.2016

T:   When we rotated the array, we agreed the first factor would tell us the number of rows.  What did that do to the order of the factors?

S:   They switched!

T:   Did the total change?

S:   No.

T:   When we change the order of the factors, we are using the commutative property.

T:   Solve each of your equations by skip-counting.  Write each number as you say it.

S:   (Write 3, 6, 9, 12, 15 and 5, 10, 15.)

Continue with the following possible examples:

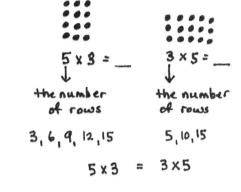

- 7 rows and 2 columns
- 3 rows and 9 columns

T:   (Once students have worked through the problem, write the final example in groups language:  3 groups of 9 and 9 groups of 3.)  Are these statements equal?  Use your array to discuss with your partner how you know.

## Problem Set  (10 minutes)

Students should do their personal best to complete the Problem Set within the allotted 10 minutes.  For some classes, it may be appropriate to modify the assignment by specifying which problems they work on first.  Some problems do not specify a method for solving.  Students should solve these problems using the RDW approach used for Application Problems.

## Student Debrief  (10 minutes)

**Lesson Objective:**  Demonstrate the commutativity of multiplication, and practice related facts by skip-counting objects in array models.

The Student Debrief is intended to invite reflection and active processing of the total lesson experience.

Invite students to review their solutions for the Problem Set.  They should check work by comparing answers with a partner before going over answers as a class.  Look for misconceptions or misunderstandings that can be addressed in the Debrief.  Guide students in a conversation to debrief the Problem Set and process the lesson.

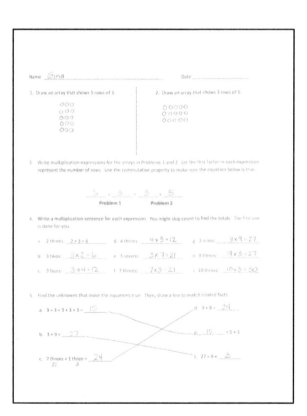

Lesson 8:   Demonstrate the commutativity of multiplication, and practice related facts by skip-counting objects in array models.

EUREKA MATH™

Any combination of the questions below may be used to lead the discussion.

- Share your answers to Problem 7 with a partner. Do your multiplication sentences look the same, or are they different? Why?

- Discuss the meaning of the commutative property and how it relates to equal groups, columns, rows, and arrays.

- Discuss the usefulness of skip-counting to solve multiplication problems.

- Build fluency by having students skip-count to find answers to the following expressions without the help of an array. They can keep track of their count using fingers.

  - 3 sixes, 6 threes
  - 3 eights, 8 threes
  - 5 threes, 3 fives

### Exit Ticket  (3 minutes)

After the Student Debrief, instruct students to complete the Exit Ticket. A review of their work will help with assessing students' understanding of the concepts that were presented in today's lesson and planning more effectively for future lessons. The questions may be read aloud to the students.

---

6. Isaac picks 3 tangerines from his tree every day for 7 days.

   a. Use circles to draw an array that represents the tangerines Isaac picks.

      OOO
      OOO
      OOO
      OOO
      OOO
      OOO
      XXX
      XXX
      XXX

   b. How many tangerines does Isaac pick in 7 days? Write and solve a multiplication sentence to find the total.

      7 x 3 = 21
      Isaac picks 21 tangerines in 7 days.

   c. Isaac decides to pick 3 tangerines every day for 3 more days. Draw x's to show the new tangerines on the array in Part (a).

   d. Write and solve a multiplication sentence to find the total number of tangerines Isaac picks.

      10 x 3 = 30
      Isaac picks 30 tangerines in total.

7. Sarah buys bottles of soap. Each bottle costs $2.

   a. How much money does Sarah spend if she buys 3 bottles of soap?

      __3__ x $2 __ = $ 6

   b. How much money does Sarah spend if she buys 6 bottles of soap?

      __6__ x $2 __ = $ 12

**Lesson 8:**  Demonstrate the commutativity of multiplication, and practice related facts by skip-counting objects in array models.                                                109

©2015 Great Minds. eureka-math.org
G3-M1-TE-B1-1.3.1-01.2016

Name _____  Date _____

1.  Draw an array that shows 5 rows of 3.

2.  Draw an array that shows 3 rows of 5.

3.  Write multiplication expressions for the arrays in Problems 1 and 2.  Let the first factor in each expression represent the number of rows.  Use the commutative property to make sure the equation below is true.

_____ × _____ = _____ × _____

**Problem 1**          **Problem 2**

4.  Write a multiplication sentence for each expression.  You might skip-count to find the totals.  The first one is done for you.

a.  2 threes:  __2 × 3 = 6__

b.  3 twos: _____

c.  3 fours: _____

d.  4 threes: _____

e.  3 sevens: _____

f.  7 threes: _____

g.  3 nines: _____

h.  9 threes: _____

i.  10 threes: _____

5.  Find the unknowns that make the equations true.  Then, draw a line to match related facts.

a.  3 + 3 + 3 + 3 + 3 = _____

b.  3 × 9 = _____

c.  7 threes + 1 three = _____

d.  3 × 8 = _____

e.  _____ = 5 × 3

f.  27 = 9 × _____

Lesson 8:    Demonstrate the commutativity of multiplication, and practice related facts by skip-counting objects in array models.

©2015 Great Minds. eureka-math.org
G3-M1-TE-B1-1.3.1-01.2016

**EUREKA MATH**™

6.  Isaac picks 3 tangerines from his tree every day for 7 days.

    a.  Use circles to draw an array that represents the tangerines Isaac picks.

    b.  How many tangerines does Isaac pick in 7 days?  Write and solve a multiplication sentence to find the total.

    c.  Isaac decides to pick 3 tangerines every day for 3 more days.  Draw x's to show the new tangerines on the array in Part (a).

    d.  Write and solve a multiplication sentence to find the total number of tangerines Isaac picks.

7.  Sarah buys bottles of soap.  Each bottle costs $2.

    a.  How much money does Sarah spend if she buys 3 bottles of soap?

        _____ × _____ = $_____

    b.  How much money does Sarah spend if she buys 6 bottles of soap?

        _____ × _____ = $_____

**Lesson 8:**   Demonstrate the commutativity of multiplication, and practice related facts by skip-counting objects in array models.

©2015 Great Minds. eureka-math.org
G3-M1-TE-B1-1.3.1-01.2016

111

Name _____     Date _____

Mary Beth organizes stickers on a page in her sticker book.  She arranges them in 3 rows and 4 columns.

   a.   Draw an array to show Mary Beth's stickers.

   b.   Use your array to write a multiplication sentence to find Mary Beth's total number of stickers.

   c.   Label your array to show how you skip-count to solve your multiplication sentence.

   d.   Use what you know about the commutative property to write a different multiplication sentence for your array.

EUREKA
MATH™

Name _____  Date _____

1. Draw an array that shows 6 rows of 3.

2. Draw an array that shows 3 rows of 6.

3. Write multiplication expressions for the arrays in Problems 1 and 2.  Let the first factor in each expression represent the number of rows.  Use the commutative property to make sure the equation below is true.

_____ × _____ = _____ × _____

**Problem 1**          **Problem 2**

4. Write a multiplication sentence for each expression.  You might skip-count to find the totals.  The first one is done for you.

   a.  5 threes:  _5 × 3 = 15_          d. 3 sixes: _____          g. 8 threes: _____

   b.  3 fives: _____          e. 7 threes: _____          h. 3 nines: _____

   c.  6 threes: _____          f. 3 sevens: _____          i. 10 threes: _____

5. Find the unknowns that make the equations true.  Then, draw a line to match related facts.

   a.  3 + 3 + 3 + 3 + 3 + 3 = _____          d.  3 × 9 = _____

   b.  3 × 5 = _____          e.  _____ = 6 × 3

   c.  8 threes + 1 three = _____          f.  15 = 5 × _____

**EUREKA MATH**

**Lesson 8:**  Demonstrate the commutativity of multiplication, and practice related facts by skip-counting objects in array models.

©2015 Great Minds. eureka-math.org
G3-M1-TE-B1-1.3.1-01.2016

**113**

6. Fernando puts 3 pictures on each page of his photo album. He puts pictures on 8 pages.

   a. Use circles to draw an array that represents the total number of pictures in Fernando's photo album.

   b. Use your array to write and solve a multiplication sentence to find Fernando's total number of pictures.

   c. Fernando adds 2 more pages to his book. He puts 3 pictures on each new page. Draw x's to show the new pictures on the array in Part (a).

   d. Write and solve a multiplication sentence to find the new total number of pictures in Fernando's album.

7. Ivania recycles. She gets 3 cents for every can she recycles.

   a. How much money does Ivania make if she recycles 4 cans?

   _____ × _____ = _____ cents

   b. How much money does Ivania make if she recycles 7 cans?

   _____ × _____ = _____ cents

Lesson 8:   Demonstrate the commutativity of multiplication, and practice related facts by skip-counting objects in array models.

EUREKA MATH

# Lesson 9

Objective: Find related multiplication facts by adding and subtracting equal groups in array models.

## Suggested Lesson Structure

■ Fluency Practice     (15 minutes)
▢ Concept Development   (35 minutes)
▣ Student Debrief      (10 minutes)
  **Total Time**       **(60 minutes)**

## Fluency Practice  (15 minutes)

- Multiply by 2 Pattern Sheet **3.OA.7**   (8 minutes)
- Group Counting **3.OA.1**                (3 minutes)
- Forms of Multiplication **3.OA.1**       (4 minutes)

### Multiply by 2 Pattern Sheet  (8 minutes)

Materials:   (S) Multiply by 2 (1–5) (Pattern Sheet)

Note: This activity builds fluency with multiplication facts using units of 2. It works toward students knowing from memory all products of two one-digit numbers.

T:  (Write $5 \times 2 =$ _____.) Let's skip-count by twos to find the answer. (Count with fingers to 5 as students count. Record skip-count on the board.)

S:  2, 4, 6, 8, 10.

T:  (Circle 10 and write $5 \times 2 = 10$ above it. Write $3 \times 2 =$ _____.) Let's skip-count up by twos again. (Count with fingers to 3 as students count.)

S:  2, 4, 6.

T:  Let's see how we can skip-count down to find the answer, too. Start at 10 with 5 fingers, 1 for each two. (Count down with your fingers as students say numbers.)

S:  10 (5 fingers), 8 (4 fingers), 6 (3 fingers).

Repeat the process for $4 \times 2$.

T:  Let's practice multiplying by 2.

**Lesson 9:**   Find related multiplication facts by adding and subtracting equal groups in array models.

115

**Directions for Administration of Multiply-By Pattern Sheet**

- Distribute Multiply-By Pattern Sheet.
- Allow a maximum of 2 minutes for students to complete as many problems as possible.
- Direct students to work left to right across the page.
- Encourage skip-counting strategies to solve unknown facts.

## Group Counting  (3 minutes)

Note:  Group counting reviews interpreting multiplication as repeated addition.  Counting by threes and fours in this activity supports work with units of 3 in this topic and anticipates work using units of 4 in Topic E.

T:   Let's count by threes. (Direct students to count forward and backward to 30, emphasizing the transition from 18 to 21.)

T:   Let's count by fours. (Direct students to count forward and backward to 24, emphasizing the 16 to 20 transition.)

## Forms of Multiplication  (4 minutes)

Materials:   (S) Personal white board

Note:  Students directly relate repeated addition to multiplication in preparation for using the distributive property in this lesson.

T:   (Project a $3 \times 5$ array.)  Represent this array as a repeated addition sentence using 5 as the size of the groups.

S:   (Write $5 + 5 + 5 = 15$.)

T:   (Project a $3 \times 4$ array.  Write _____ fours = _____.)  Complete the equation on your personal white board.

S:   (Write 3 fours = 12.)

T:   (Project a $7 \times 2$ array.)  Write two multiplication sentences for 7 groups of 2.

S:   (Write $7 \times 2 = 14$ and $2 \times 7 = 14$.)

T:   (Project a $6 \times 3$ array.  Write $18 = 6 \times$ _____.)  Complete the equation on your personal white board.

S:   (Write $18 = 6 \times 3$.)

T:   (Project a $5 \times 3$ array.  Write 5 threes = ___.)  Complete the equation on your personal white board.

S:   (Write 5 threes = 15.)

T:   (Add one more group of 3 to the array.  Write 5 threes + 1 three = _____ threes = _____ ones.)  Complete the equation on your personal white board.

S:   (Write 5 threes + 1 three = 6 threes = 18 ones.)

**Lesson 9:**   Find related multiplication facts by adding and subtracting equal groups in array models.

**EUREKA MATH™**

## Concept Development (35 minutes)

**Materials:** (S) Personal white board, threes array no fill (Template) (pictured on the right), blank paper

*Threes Array No Fill Template*

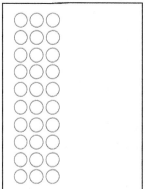

**Problem 1: Add two known smaller facts to solve an unknown larger fact.**

T: Slip the template into your board. Cover part of the array with blank paper to show 5 rows of 3. Draw a box around the uncovered array. Write and solve a multiplication sentence to describe it.

S: (Cover, then box array, and write 5 × 3 = 15.)

T: Move the paper so the array shows 7 × 3. Shade the rows you added.

S: (Shade 2 rows.)

T: Write and solve a multiplication sentence to describe the shaded part of your array.

S: (Write 2 × 3 = 6.)

T: How many threes are in 5 × 3?

S: 5 threes.

T: How many threes did you add to 5 × 3 to make the array show 7 × 3?

S: 2 threes.

T: (Write 7 threes = 5 threes + 2 threes.) So, 7 threes equals 5 threes plus 2 threes.

T: (Write 7 × 3 = 5 × 3 + 2 × 3 as shown to the right.) Do you agree or disagree?

S: I agree. That's just adding the two parts of the array together. → 7 rows of three is the same as 5 rows of three plus 2 rows of three.

T: We already wrote totals for the two parts of our array. Let's add those to find the total for the whole array. What is the total of 5 × 3?

S: 15.

T: (Write 15 + on the board.) What is the total of 2 × 3?

S: 6.

T: (Add to the board so the equation reads _____ = 15 + 6.) Say the total at the signal. (Signal.)

S: 21.

**NOTES ON
MULTIPLE MEANS
OF REPRESENTATION:**

Decomposing this way naturally relates to the part–whole relationship that students studied in Grades K–2. The vignette implies the relationship, but a more formal connection to prior knowledge may be appropriate for some classes.

*Sample Teacher Board*

7 threes = 5 threes + 2 threes

7 × 3 = 5 × 3 + 2 × 3

21 = 15 + 6

**Lesson 9:** Find related multiplication facts by adding and subtracting equal groups in array models.

117

©2015 Great Minds. eureka-math.org
G3-M1-TE-B1-1.3.1-01.2016

Provide students with another example. Have them use the template to add the totals of 4 × 3 and 4 × 3 to find the answer to 8 × 3. Teach them to double the total for 4 × 3.

T: Explain how we added to find 7 × 3 = 21 and 8 × 3 = 24.

S: We added the totals of smaller facts together to find the whole. → We used two facts we already knew to find one we didn't know.

**Problem 2: Subtract two known smaller facts to solve an unknown larger fact.**

T: Draw a box around an array that shows 9 × 3. Notice that 9 × 3 is very close to 10 × 3. 10 × 3 is easier to solve because we can count by tens to get the total. Let's do that now.

S: 10, 20, 30.

T: Let's use 10 × 3 = 30 to help us solve 9 × 3.

T: Use your finger to trace 10 threes.

T: What should we subtract to show 9 threes instead?

S: 1 three!

T: (Write 10 threes – 1 three = _____ on the board.) 10 threes equals?

S: 30.

T: 30 – 3 equals?

S: 27.

Provide another example. Have students subtract to find the answer to 8 × 3. 10 × 3 is the basic fact, so the subtraction to find 8 × 3 is 30 – 6.

T: Tell your partner how we used 10 × 3 to help us find the answer to 9 × 3 and 8 × 3.

S: (Discuss.)

## Problem Set (10 minutes)

Students should do their personal best to complete the Problem Set within the allotted 10 minutes. For some classes, it may be appropriate to modify the assignment by specifying which problems they work on first. Some problems do not specify a method for solving. Students should solve these problems using the RDW approach used for Application Problems.

NOTES ON
MULTIPLE MEANS
OF ENGAGEMENT:

The second example for subtraction (8 × 3) is intentionally the same as the second example for addition. Solving the same problem in two ways provides an opportunity for students to compare the strategies. Ask students who benefit from a challenge to analyze the strategies independently or in pairs, and then present their thinking to others during the Debrief.

NOTES ON
VOCABULARY:

Introduce the word *distribute* into everyday classroom language. This will help with students' understanding of the distributive property, which is formally introduced in Lesson 16.

For example, "Paper monitors, please distribute the papers to the class."

EUREKA
MATH™

## Student Debrief  (10 minutes)

**Lesson Objective:**  Find related multiplication facts by adding and subtracting equal groups in array models.

The Student Debrief is intended to invite reflection and active processing of the total lesson experience.

Invite students to review their solutions for the Problem Set.  They should check work by comparing answers with a partner before going over answers as a class.  Look for misconceptions or misunderstandings that can be addressed in the Debrief.  Guide students in a conversation to debrief the Problem Set and process the lesson.

Any combination of the questions below may be used to lead the discussion.

- Review the strategy of adding and subtracting the totals of known "easy" facts for solving unknown facts.
- Differentiate between when to apply addition or subtraction through analysis of the example 8 × 3 from the Concept Development.  (Students solved 8 × 3 using both addition and subtraction.)  Ask students to apply the strategy to solve 8 × 4.

## Exit Ticket  (3 minutes)

After the Student Debrief, instruct students to complete the Exit Ticket.  A review of their work will help with assessing students' understanding of the concepts that were presented in today's lesson and planning more effectively for future lessons.  The questions may be read aloud to the students.

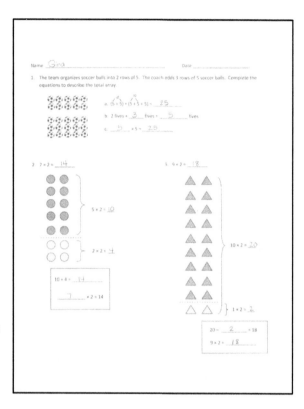

**Lesson 9:**    Find related multiplication facts by adding and subtracting equal groups in array models.

©2015 Great Minds. eureka-math.org
G3-M1-TE-B1-1.3.1-01.2016

119

Multiply.

2 x 1 = _____     2 x 2 = _____     2 x 3 = _____     2 x 4 = _____

2 x 5 = _____     2 x 1 = _____     2 x 2 = _____     2 x 1 = _____

2 x 3 = _____     2 x 1 = _____     2 x 4 = _____     2 x 1 = _____

2 x 5 = _____     2 x 1 = _____     2 x 2 = _____     2 x 3 = _____

2 x 2 = _____     2 x 4 = _____     2 x 2 = _____     2 x 5 = _____

2 x 2 = _____     2 x 1 = _____     2 x 2 = _____     2 x 3 = _____

2 x 1 = _____     2 x 3 = _____     2 x 2 = _____     2 x 3 = _____

2 x 4 = _____     2 x 3 = _____     2 x 5 = _____     2 x 3 = _____

2 x 4 = _____     2 x 1 = _____     2 x 4 = _____     2 x 2 = _____

2 x 4 = _____     2 x 3 = _____     2 x 4 = _____     2 x 5 = _____

2 x 4 = _____     2 x 5 = _____     2 x 1 = _____     2 x 5 = _____

2 x 2 = _____     2 x 5 = _____     2 x 3 = _____     2 x 5 = _____

2 x 4 = _____     2 x 2 = _____     2 x 4 = _____     2 x 3 = _____

2 x 5 = _____     2 x 3 = _____     2 x 2 = _____     2 x 4 = _____

2 x 3 = _____     2 x 5 = _____     2 x 2 = _____     2 x 4 = _____

multiply by 2 (1–5)

**Lesson 9:**    Find related multiplication facts by adding and subtracting equal groups in array models.

EUREKA MATH™

Name _____    Date _____

1. The team organizes soccer balls into 2 rows of 5. The coach adds 3 rows of 5 soccer balls. Complete the equations to describe the total array.

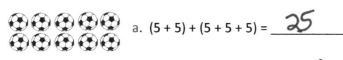

a. $(5 + 5) + (5 + 5 + 5) =$ __25__

b. 2 fives + __3__ fives = __5__ fives

c. __5__ $\times 5 =$ __25__

2. $7 \times 2 =$ __14__

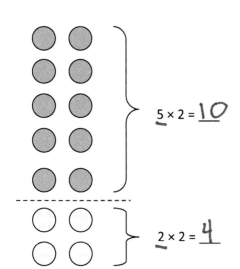

$5 \times 2 = 10$

$2 \times 2 = 4$

$10 + 4 =$ __14__

__7__ $\times 2 = 14$

3. $9 \times 2 =$ _____

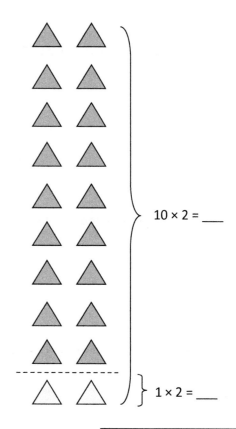

$10 \times 2 =$ ___

$1 \times 2 =$ ___

$20 -$ _____ $= 18$

$9 \times 2 =$ _____

**EUREKA MATH**    **Lesson 9:**    Find related multiplication facts by adding and subtracting equal groups in array models.    **121**

©2015 Great Minds. eureka-math.org
G3-M1-TE-B1-1.3.1-01.2016

4. Matthew organizes his baseball cards in 4 rows of 3.

   a. Draw an array that represents Matthew's cards using an x to show each card.

   b. Solve the equation to find Matthew's total number of cards.   4 × 3 = _____

5. Matthew adds 2 more rows. Use circles to show his new cards on the array in Problem 4(a).

   a. Write and solve a multiplication equation to represent the circles you added to the array.

   _____ × 3 = _____

   b. Add the totals from the equations in Problems 4(b) and 5(a) to find Matthew's total cards.

   _____ + _____ = 18

   c. Write the multiplication equation that shows Matthew's total number of cards.

   _____ × _____ = 18

**Lesson 9:**    Find related multiplication facts by adding and subtracting equal groups in array models.

**EUREKA MATH**

Name _____     Date _____

1. Mrs. Stern roasts cloves of garlic.  She places 10 rows of two cloves on a baking sheet.

   Write an equation to describe the number of cloves Mrs. Stern bakes.

   _____ × _____ = _____

2. When the garlic is roasted, Mrs. Stern uses some for a recipe.  There are 2 rows of two garlic cloves left on the pan.

   a. Complete the equation below to show how many garlic cloves Mrs. Stern uses.

      _____ twos − _____ twos = _____twos

   b. 20 − _____ = 16

   c. Write an equation to describe the number of garlic cloves Mrs. Stern uses.

      _____ × 2 = _____

Name _____     Date _____

1. Dan organizes his stickers into 3 rows of four. Irene adds 2 more rows of stickers. Complete the equations to describe the total number of stickers in the array.

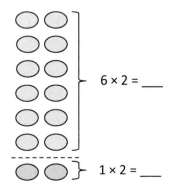

a. $(4 + 4 + 4) + (4 + 4) =$ _____

b. 3 fours + _____ fours = _____ fours

c. _____ $\times 4 =$ _____

2. $7 \times 2 =$ _____

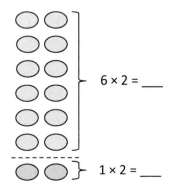

$6 \times 2 =$ ___

$1 \times 2 =$ ___

$12 + 2 =$ _____

_____ $\times 2 = 14$

3. $9 \times 3 =$ _____

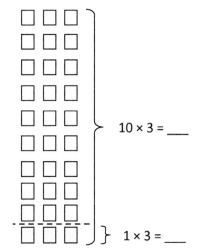

$10 \times 3 =$ ___

$1 \times 3 =$ ___

$30 -$ _____ $= 27$

_____ $\times 3 = 27$

   **Lesson 9:**    Find related multiplication facts by adding and subtracting equal groups in array models.

EUREKA MATH™

4. Franklin collects stickers. He organizes his stickers in 5 rows of four.

   a. Draw an array to represent Franklin's stickers. Use an x to show each sticker.

   b. Solve the equation to find Franklin's total number of stickers. $5 \times 4 =$ _____

5. Franklin adds 2 more rows. Use circles to show his new stickers on the array in Problem 4(a).

   a. Write and solve an equation to represent the circles you added to the array.

   _____ $\times 4 =$ _____

   b. Complete the equation to show how you add the totals of 2 multiplication facts to find Franklin's total number of stickers.

   _____ $+$ _____ $= 28$

   c. Complete the unknown to show Franklin's total number of stickers.

   _____ $\times 4 = 28$

EUREKA
MATH™

**Lesson 9:** Find related multiplication facts by adding and subtracting equal groups in array models.

©2015 Great Minds. eureka-math.org
G3-M1-TE-B1-1.3.1-01.2016

125

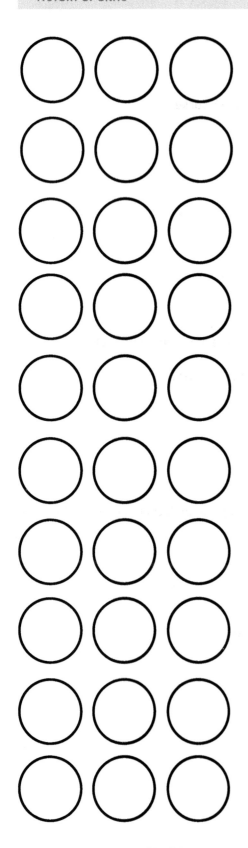

threes array no fill

Lesson 9: Find related multiplication facts by adding and subtracting equal groups in array models.

©2015 Great Minds. eureka-math.org
G3-M1-TE-B1-1.3.1-01.2016

EUREKA
MATH™

# Lesson 10

Objective: Model the distributive property with arrays to decompose units as a strategy to multiply.

## Suggested Lesson Structure

■ Fluency Practice       (11 minutes)
■ Application Problem      (5 minutes)
■ Concept Development    (34 minutes)
■ Student Debrief       (10 minutes)
   **Total Time**       **(60 minutes)**

## Fluency Practice  (11 minutes)

▪ Multiply by 2 Pattern Sheet  **3.OA.7**       (8 minutes)
▪ Group Counting  **3.OA.1**       (3 minutes)

### Multiply by 2 Pattern Sheet  (8 minutes)

Materials:  (S) Multiply by 2 (6–10) (Pattern Sheet)

Note: This activity builds fluency with multiplication facts using units of 2. It works toward students knowing from memory all products of two one-digit numbers. See Lesson 9 for the directions for administering a Multiply-By Pattern Sheet.

T:  (Write 7 × 2 = _____.) Let's skip-count up by twos. (Count with fingers to 7 as students count.)
S:  2, 4, 6, 8, 10, 12, 14.
T:  This time, let's start from 10 to find our answer more quickly. Show 5 fingers all at once to show 10.
S:  (Show 5 fingers.)
T:  Now, count by twos from 10. Raise another finger for each two you count. (Model as students count.)
S:  10, 12, 14. (Raise a sixth finger at 12, and a seventh finger at 14.)
T:  Let's see how we can skip-count down to find the answer, too. Start at 20. (Show 10 fingers to represent 20. Hide one finger at a time as students say numbers.)
S:  20, 18, 16, 14.

Repeat the process for 9 × 2 and 8 × 2.

T:  (Distribute Multiply by 2 Pattern Sheet.) Let's get some practice multiplying by 2. Be sure to work left to right across the page.

Lesson 10:   Model the distributive property with arrays to decompose units as a
          strategy to multiply.

©2015 Great Minds. eureka-math.org
G3-M1-TE-B1-1.3.1-01.2016

127

### Group Counting  (3 minutes)

Note:  Group counting reviews interpreting multiplication as repeated addition.  Counting by threes and fours in this activity supports work with units of 3 in this topic and anticipates work using units of 4 in Topic E.

- T:   Let's count by threes.  (Direct students to count forward and backward to 30, emphasizing the transition from 18 to 21.)
- T:   Let's count by fours.  (Direct students to count forward and backward to 24, emphasizing the 16 to 20 transition.)

### Application Problem  (5 minutes)

A guitar has 6 strings.  How many strings are there on 3 guitars?  Write a multiplication equation to solve.

Note:  This problem leads into today's Concept Development.  Students will compare their multiplication equation with the new equations presented in the lesson.

$3 \times 6 = 18$

There are 18 strings on 3 guitars.

### Concept Development  (34 minutes)

Materials:   (S) Personal white board, 1 sheet of blank paper

- T:   On your personal white board, draw an array to represent the total number of guitar strings.  Let the number of strings on one guitar be 1 row.
- S:   (Draw a 3 × 6 array, as shown below.)

- T:   Make a dotted line below the first row to show just **one** guitar.
- S:   (Draw line, as shown below.)

- T:   Write and solve a multiplication sentence to describe each part of your array.
- S:   (Write 1 × 6 = 6 and 2 × 6 = 12, as shown **below**.)

$1 \times 6 = 6$

$2 \times 6 = 12$

Lesson 10:    Model the distributive property with arrays to decompose units as a strategy to multiply.

EUREKA
MATH™

T:  (Write 6 + 12 = 3 sixes.)  Why is this true?

S:  1 six is 6, 2 sixes are 12. → When I add 6 and 12, I get 18, which is 3 sixes.

T:  (Write (1 × 6) + (2 × 6) = 3 sixes on the board as shown to the right.)  How do you know this equation is true?

S:  1 × 6 is the same as 1 six.  2 × 6 is the same as 2 sixes. 1 six plus 2 sixes is the same as 3 sixes. → 1 × 6 = 6 and 2 × 6 = 12.  12 + 6 = 18.  3 sixes = 18, so the equation is true.

*Sample Teacher Board*

6  +  12  = 3 sixes

(1 × 6) + (2 × 6) = 3 sixes

(1 × 6) + (2 × 6) = 6 + __12__

T:  (Write (1 × 6) + (2 × 6) = 6 + ____.)  With your partner, discuss what number completes the equation.

S:  1 × 6 equals 6.  That's how the teacher got 6. → To get the other number, we do 2 × 6.  That's 12. → I know it's 12 because you need the same amount on each side of the equal sign.  On the left, the value is 6 + 12 if you solve the multiplication.  That's what it should be on the right too.

T:  (Write 12 to fill in the equation.)

T:  Notice the symbols around my multiplication expressions.  They are called **parentheses**. Let's say that word together.

S:  Parentheses.

T:  (Write (1 × 6) + (2 × 6) = ___ and (1 + 2) × 6 = ___ below it, as shown to the right.)  My parentheses show how I make groups.  How did I rearrange the groups?

S:  You added the number of rows.  Then, you multiplied by 6.

T:  Look back at the array you drew.  Do the 1 and 2 represent the number of groups or the size of groups?

S:  The number of groups.

T:  What does the 6 represent?

S:  The size of the groups.

*Sample Teacher Board*

(1 × 6) + (2 × 6) = __18__

(1 + 2) × 6 = __18__

3 × 6 = __18__

(1 × 6) + (2 × 6) = 3 × 6

**MP.4**

T:  Use that language—the number of groups and the size of groups—to tell your partner about my second equation.

S:  The teacher added the number of groups first.  That's 1 + 2.  Then, she multiplied the number of groups times the size of the groups, which is 6.

T:  1 + 2 equals …?

S:  3.

T:  (Write 3 × 6 = _____ under the second equation.)  Look back at the work you did on today's Application Problem.  How does this equation compare with what you did?

S:  It's the same! → It's the number of groups times the size of groups, just like we did.

NOTES ON
MULTIPLE MEANS
OF ENGAGEMENT:

Support students to work at their individual levels of comfort by inviting them to choose to work independently or with a partner to solve the equations.

Lesson 10:  Model the distributive property with arrays to decompose units as a strategy to multiply.

©2015 Great Minds. eureka-math.org
G3-M1-TE-B1-1.3.1-01.2016

129

T: Rewrite each equation on your personal white board, and solve. What is the answer to all three

**MP.4** equations?

S: 18.

T: (Fill in the equations on the board.) Think back to the problem we're solving. 18 what?

S: 18 strings.

T: (Write $(1 \times 6) + (2 \times 6) = 3 \times 6$ on the board.) True or false?

S: True.

T: In your own words, tell your partner how we got $3 \times 6$ and why it's equal to $(1 \times 6) + (2 \times 6)$. Use the three equations you just solved to help you explain.

S: (Retell the steps using the three equations and solutions to guide them.)

## Problem Set (10 minutes)

Students should do their personal best to complete the Problem Set within the allotted 10 minutes. For some classes, it may be appropriate to modify the assignment by specifying which problems they work on first. Some problems do not specify a method for solving. Students should solve these problems using the RDW approach used for Application Problems.

## Student Debrief (10 minutes)

**Lesson Objective:** Model the distributive property with arrays to decompose units as a strategy to multiply.

The Student Debrief is intended to invite reflection and active processing of the total lesson experience.

Invite students to review their solutions for the Problem Set. They should check work by comparing answers with a partner before going over answers as a class. Look for misconceptions or misunderstandings that can be addressed in the Debrief. Guide students in a conversation to debrief the Problem Set and process the lesson.

Any combination of the questions below may be used to lead the discussion.

- In Problems 1 and 2, why might breaking an array into two parts to multiply, add, and then solve be easier than just multiplying the total number of groups times their size?

- Check Problem 3(a) by drawing and writing on the board as students give you verbal directions for how to create the page in Ruby's photo album.

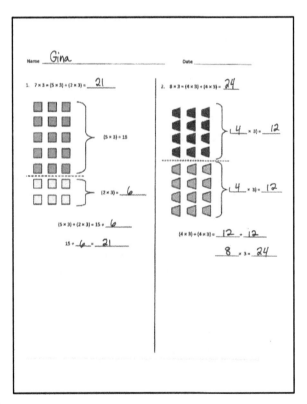

Lesson 10: Model the distributive property with arrays to decompose units as a strategy to multiply.

EUREKA
MATH™

- Invite several students to share their work on Problem 3(b), and guide the class to understand the following points.
  - 5 × 3 is the result of the number of groups added together and then multiplied by the size of groups in (2 × 3) + (3 × 3).
  - 6 and 9 are the products of each multiplication expression.
  - The factors in 5 × 3 relate to the number of groups and size of groups in the array.
  - Both sides of the equation 5 × 3 = 6 + 9 have a value of 15.
- Review the vocabulary term **parentheses**.

## Exit Ticket (3 minutes)

After the Student Debrief, instruct students to complete the Exit Ticket. A review of their work will help with assessing students' understanding of the concepts that were presented in today's lesson and planning more effectively for future lessons. The questions may be read aloud to the students.

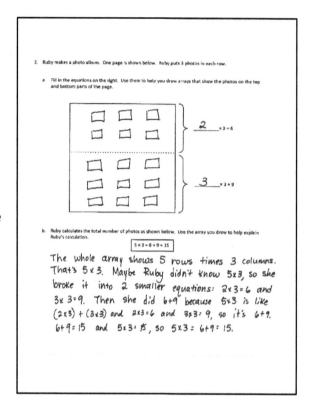

**Lesson 10:** Model the distributive property with arrays to decompose units as a strategy to multiply.

131

©2015 Great Minds. eureka-math.org
G3-M1-TE-B1-1.3.1-01.2016

Multiply.

2 x 1 = __2__    2 x 2 = __4__    2 x 3 = __6__    2 x 4 = __8__

2 x 5 = __10__    2 x 6 = __12__    2 x 7 = __14__    2 x 8 = __16__

2 x 9 = __18__    2 x 10 = __20__    2 x 5 = __10__    2 x 6 = __12__

2 x 5 = _____    2 x 7 = _____    2 x 5 = _____    2 x 8 = _____

2 x 5 = _____    2 x 9 = _____    2 x 5 = _____    2 x 10 = _____

2 x 6 = _____    2 x 5 = _____    2 x 6 = _____    2 x 7 = _____

2 x 6 = _____    2 x 8 = _____    2 x 6 = _____    2 x 9 = _____

2 x 6 = _____    2 x 7 = _____    2 x 6 = _____    2 x 7 = _____

2 x 8 = _____    2 x 7 = _____    2 x 9 = _____    2 x 7 = _____

2 x 8 = _____    2 x 6 = _____    2 x 8 = _____    2 x 7 = _____

2 x 8 = _____    2 x 9 = _____    2 x 9 = _____    2 x 6 = _____

2 x 9 = _____    2 x 7 = _____    2 x 9 = _____    2 x 8 = _____

2 x 9 = _____    2 x 8 = _____    2 x 6 = _____    2 x 9 = _____

2 x 7 = _____    2 x 9 = _____    2 x 6 = _____    2 x 8 = _____

2 x 9 = _____    2 x 7 = _____    2 x 6 = _____    2 x 8 = _____

multiply by 2 (6–10)

**Lesson 10:** Model the distributive property with arrays to decompose units as a strategy to multiply.

EUREKA MATH™

Name _____    Date _____

**1.** 7 × 3 = (5 × 3) + (2 × 3) = _____

        (5 × 3) = 15

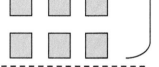        (2 × 3) = _6_

(5 × 3) + (2 × 3) = 15 + _6_

15 + _6_ = _21_

**2.** 8 × 3 = (4 × 3) + (4 × 3) = _____

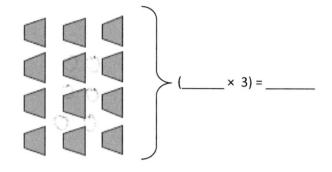   (_____ × 3) = _____

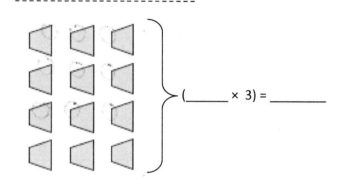   (_____ × 3) = _____

(4 × 3) + (4 × 3) = _____ + _____

_____ × 3 = _____

EUREKA
MATH™

**Lesson 10:**   Model the distributive property with arrays to decompose units as a
strategy to multiply.

©2015 Great Minds. eureka-math.org
G3-M1-TE-B1-1.3.1-01.2016

133

3. Ruby makes a photo album. One page is shown below. Ruby puts 3 photos in each row.

   a. Fill in the equations on the right. Use them to help you draw arrays that show the photos on the top and bottom parts of the page.

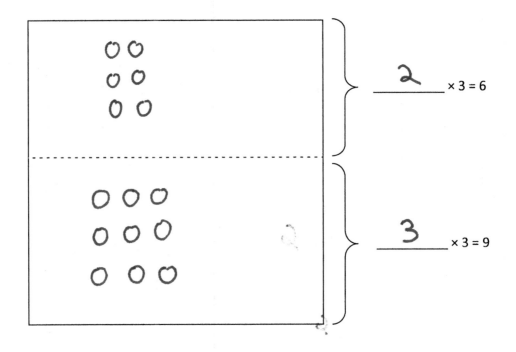

   b. Ruby calculates the total number of photos as shown below. Use the array you drew to help explain Ruby's calculation.

   $$5 \times 3 = 6 + 9 = 15$$

EUREKA
MATH

Name _____    Date _____

1.  6 × 3 = _____

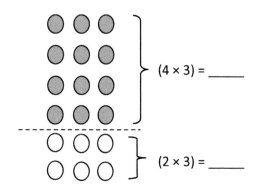

(4 × 3) = _____

(2 × 3) = _____

(4 × 3) + (2 × 3) = _____ + _____

6 × 3 = _____ + _____

_____ × 3 = _____

2.  7 × 3 = _____

(_____ × 3) = _____

(_____ × 3) = _____

(5 × 3) + (2 × 3) = _____ + _____

7 × 3 = _____ + _____

_____ × 3 = _____

EUREKA
MATH™

**Lesson 10:**    Model the distributive property with arrays to decompose units as a
strategy to multiply.

135

©2015 Great Minds. eureka-math.org
G3-M1-TE-B1-1.3.1-01.2016

Name _____ Date _____

1. 6 × 3 = _____

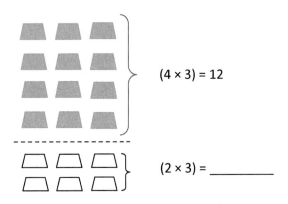

(4 × 3) = 12

(2 × 3) = _____

12 + _____ = _____

6 × 3 = _____

2. 8 × 2 = _____

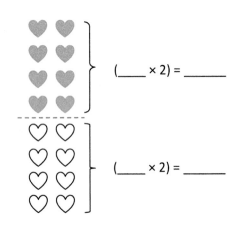

(____ × 2) = _____

(____ × 2) = _____

(4 × 2) + (4 × 2) = _____ + _____

____ × 2 = _____

Lesson 10: Model the distributive property with arrays to decompose units as a strategy to multiply.

EUREKA MATH

3.  Adriana organizes her books on shelves.  She puts 3 books in each row.

   a.  Fill in the equations on the right.  Use them to draw arrays that show the books on Adriana's top and bottom shelves.

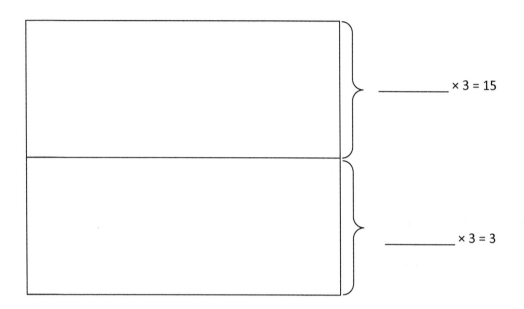

   _____ × 3 = 15

   _____ × 3 = 3

   b.  Adriana calculates the total number of books as shown below.  Use the array you drew to help explain Adriana's calculation.

   6 × 3 = 15 + 3 = 18

EUREKA
MATH™

Lesson 10:   Model the distributive property with arrays to decompose units as a
            strategy to multiply.

©2015 Great Minds. eureka-math.org
G3-M1-TE-B1-1.3.1-01.2016

137

Name _____    Date _____

1.  Mrs. Tran plants 2 rows of 5 carrots in her garden.

    a.  Draw an array that represents Mrs. Tran's carrots.  Use an X to show each carrot.

    b.  Mrs. Tran adds 3 more rows of 5 carrots to her garden.

        ▪  Use circles to show her new carrots on the array in Part (a).
        ▪  Fill in the blanks below to show how she added the five rows.

            _____ fives + _____ fives = _____ fives

        ▪  Write a sentence to explain your thinking.

    c.  Find the total number of carrots Mrs. Tran planted.

    d.  Write a multiplication sentence to describe the array representing the total number of carrots Mrs. Tran planted.

EUREKA
MATH

2. Mrs. Tran picks 15 tomatoes from her garden.  She puts 5 tomatoes in each bag.

   a. Draw Mrs. Tran's bags of tomatoes.

   b. Write a multiplication sentence that describes your drawing in Part (a).

3. Mrs. Tran plants 12 sunflowers in her garden.  She plants them in 3 rows.

   a. Fill in the blanks below to make a true division sentence.  What does the answer represent?

   _____ ÷ _____ = _____

   b. Mrs. Tran adds 2 more identical rows of sunflowers to her 3 original rows.  Draw an array to show how many flowers she has now.

   c. Mrs. Tran figured out how many flowers she planted.  Her work is shown in the box below.  Would Mrs. Tran get the same result if she multiplied 5 × 4?  Explain why or why not.

   $$(3 \times 4) + (2 \times 4) = 12 + 8$$
   $$= 20$$

**Represent and solve problems involving multiplication and division.**

**3.OA.1**     Interpret products of whole numbers, e.g., interpret 5 × 7 as the total number of objects in 5 groups of 7 objects each. *For example, describe a context in which a total number of objects can be expressed as 5 × 7.*

**3.OA.2**     Interpret whole-number quotients of whole numbers, e.g., interpret 56 ÷ 8 as the number of objects in each share when 56 objects are partitioned equally into 8 shares, or as a number of shares when 56 objects are partitioned into equal shares of 8 objects each. *For example, describe a context in which a number of shares or a number of groups can be expressed as 56 ÷ 8.*

**Understand properties of multiplication and the relationship between multiplication and division.**

**3.OA.5**     Apply properties of operations as strategies to multiply and divide. (Students need not use formal terms for these properties.) *Examples: If 6 × 4 = 24 is known, then 4 × 6 = 24 is also known. (Commutative property of multiplication.) 3 × 5 × 2 can be found by 3 × 5 = 15, then 15 × 2 = 30, or by 5 × 2 = 10, then 3 × 10 = 30. (Associative property of multiplication.) Knowing that 8 × 5 = 40 and 8 × 2 = 16, one can find 8 × 7 as 8 × (5 + 2) = (8 × 5) + (8 × 2) = 40 + 16 = 56. (Distributive property.)*

**3.OA.6**     Understand division as an unknown-factor problem. *For example, find 32 ÷ 8 by finding the number that makes 32 when multiplied by 8.*

## Evaluating Student Learning Outcomes

A Progression Toward Mastery is provided to describe steps that illuminate the gradually increasing understandings that students develop *on their way to proficiency.* In this chart, this progress is presented from left (Step 1) to right (Step 4). The learning goal for students is to achieve Step 4 mastery. These steps are meant to help teachers and students identify and celebrate what the students CAN do now and what they need to work on next.

©2015 Great Minds. eureka-math.org
G3-M1-TE-B1-1.3.1-01.2016

## A Progression Toward Mastery

| Assessment Task Item and Standards Addressed | STEP 1 Little evidence of reasoning without a correct answer. (1 Point) | STEP 2 Evidence of some reasoning without a correct answer. (2 Points) | STEP 3 Evidence of some reasoning with a correct answer or evidence of solid reasoning with an incorrect answer. (3 Points) | STEP 4 Evidence of solid reasoning with a correct answer. (4 Points) |
|---|---|---|---|---|
| **1** <br><br> 3.OA.1 <br> 3.OA.2 <br> 3.OA.6 | Student answers at least one question correctly. | Student answers at least two questions correctly. | Student answers at least three questions correctly. Mistakes may include the following: <br> ▪ Completes the equation in Part (b) incorrectly. <br> ▪ Provides inaccurate explanation in Part (b). <br> ▪ Writes a number sentence for Part (d) that describes the original array in Part (a) ($2 \times 5 = 10$ or $5 \times 2 = 10$). | Student answers every question: <br> ▪ Draws accurate arrays. <br> ▪ Accurately completes the equation in Part (b). <br> ▪ Provides accurate explanation of the equation in Part (b). <br> ▪ Accurately finds the total number of carrots. <br> ▪ Writes $5 \times 5 = 25$ in Part (d). |
| **2** <br><br> 3.OA.1 | Student is unable to answer either question correctly. The attempt shows the student may not understand the meaning of the questions. | Student may or may not answer one question correctly. Mistakes may include those listed in the box to the right, and/or: <br> ▪ Draws unequal groups. <br> ▪ Writes an equation using 5, 3, and 15 but a symbol or operation other than multiplication. | Student answers at least one question correctly. Mistakes may include one of the following: <br> ▪ Draws 5 equal groups. <br> ▪ Writes 15 as a factor. | Student correctly: <br> ▪ Represents 3 groups, each with a value of 5. <br> ▪ Writes $5 \times 3 = 15$ or $3 \times 5 = 15$. |

## A Progression Toward Mastery

| 3<br><br>3.OA.1<br>3.OA.5 | Student is unable to answer any question correctly. The attempt shows the student may not understand the meaning of the questions. | Student answers at least one question correctly. Mistakes may include those listed in the box to the right, and/or:<br>• Mixes up the order of numbers in the division sentence (e.g., $3 \div 12 = 4$).<br>• Incorrectly identifies what the answer represents in Part (a).<br>• Inaccurately draws the array. | Student answers at least two questions correctly. Mistakes may include:<br>• Not identifying the distributive property in Part (c).<br>• Explanation may only recognize that $5 \times 4$ also equals 20. | Student correctly:<br>• Writes $12 \div 3 = 4$.<br>• Identifies that the answer represents the number of flowers in each row.<br>• Draws an array.<br>• Writes an explanation that includes the distributive property (may or may not use the words *distributive property*). |
|---|---|---|---|---|

EUREKA MATH™

Name ___Gina_____    Date _____

1. Mrs. Tran plants 2 rows of 5 carrots in her garden.

   a. Draw an array that represents Mrs. Tran's carrots. Use an X to show each carrot.

   X X X X X
   X X X X X
   O O O O O
   O O O O O
   O O O O O

   b. Mrs. Tran adds 3 more rows of 5 carrots to her garden.

   ▪ Use circles to show her new carrots on the array in Part (a).
   ▪ Fill in the blanks below to show how she added the five rows.

   ___2___ fives + ___3___ fives = ___5___ fives

   ▪ Write a sentence to explain your thinking.

   Mrs. Tran planted 2 rows of five first. Then she
   planted 3 more rows of five. Now she has 5
   rows of five.

   c. Find the total number of carrots Mrs. Tran planted.

   R1   R2   R3   R4   R5
   5,  10,  15,  20, 25

   d. Write a multiplication sentence to describe the array representing the total number of carrots Mrs. Tran planted.

   5 x 5 = 25

   Mrs. Tran planted 25 carrots.

**Module 1:**   Properties of Multiplication and Division and Solving Problems with
Units of 2–5 and 10

2.  Mrs. Tran picks 15 tomatoes from her garden.  She puts 5 tomatoes in each bag.

    a.  Draw Mrs. Tran's bags of tomatoes.

    b.  Write a multiplication sentence that describes your drawing in Part (a).

    $3 \times 5 = 15$

3.  Mrs. Tran plants 12 sunflowers in her garden.  She plants them in 3 rows.

    a.  Fill in the blanks below to make a true division sentence.  What does the answer represent?

    $\underline{12} \div \underline{3} = \underline{4}$    The answer, 4, is how many flowers are in each row.

    b.  Mrs. Tran adds 2 more identical rows of sunflowers to her 3 original rows.  Draw an array to show how many flowers she has now.

    X X X X 4
    X X X X 8
    X X X X 12
    O O O O 16
    O O O O 20

    She has 20 flowers now.

    c.  Mrs. Tran figured out how many flowers she planted.  Her work is shown in the box below.  Would Mrs. Tran get the same result if she multiplied 5 × 4?  Explain why or why not.

    $$(3 \times 4) + (2 \times 4) = 12 + 8$$
    $$= 20$$

    Yes, she would get the same answer!  $5 \times 4 = 20$
    If you look at her work, $(3 \times 4) + (2 \times 4)$ is the
    same as $(3 + 2) \times 4$, which is $5 \times 4$. Her work shows
    the new rows of flowers and the old rows of
    flowers added together.

**Module 1:**    Properties of Multiplication and Division and Solving Problems with
Units of 2–5 and 10

EUREKA
MATH

3
GRADE

# Mathematics Curriculum

## Topic D
# Division Using Units of 2 and 3

**3.OA.2, 3.OA.4, 3.OA.6, 3.OA.7,** 3.OA.3, 3.OA.8

| | | | |
|---|---|---|---|
| **Focus Standard:** | 3.OA.2 | | Interpret whole-number quotients of whole numbers, e.g., interpret 56 ÷ 8 as the number of objects in each share when 56 objects are partitioned equally into 8 shares, or as a number of shares when 56 objects are partitioned into equal shares of 8 objects each. *For example, describe a context in which a number of shares or a number of groups can be expressed as 56 ÷ 8.* |
| | 3.OA.4 | | Determine the unknown whole number in a multiplication or division equation relating three whole numbers. *For example, determine the unknown number that makes the equation true in each of the equations 8 × ? = 48, 5 = _ ÷ 3, 6 × 6 = ?* |
| | 3.OA.6 | | Understand division as an unknown-factor problem. *For example, find 32 ÷ 8 by finding the number that makes 32 when multiplied by 8.* |
| | 3.OA.7 | | Fluently multiply and divide within 100, using strategies such as the relationship between multiplication and division (e.g., knowing that 8 × 5 = 40, one knows 40 ÷ 5 = 8) or properties of operations. By the end of Grade 3, know from memory all products of two one-digit numbers. |
| **Instructional Days:** | 3 | | |
| **Coherence   -Links from:** | G2–M6 | | Foundations of Multiplication and Division |
| **-Links to:** | G4–M3 | | Multi-Digit Multiplication and Division |

In Topic D, students solve two types of division situations—partitive (group size unknown) and measurement (number of groups unknown)—using factors of 2 and 3. Students build on their background knowledge of tape diagrams and apply it to represent division. In Lesson 11, the tape diagram is used as a tool to help students recognize and distinguish between types of division. By the end of Lessons 11 and 12, students independently draw and label tape diagrams that help them to compare and analyze problems that may use the same division sentence but have quotients representing different things.

Lesson 13 solidifies growing understanding that the unknown can also be found from the related multiplication sentence. Students initially work through word problems using arrays and tape diagrams to practice solving the two types of division and then transition to problem solving using abstract division and multiplication equations.

| A Teaching Sequence Toward Mastery of Division Using Units of 2 and 3 |
| --- |

**Objective 1:** Model division as the unknown factor in multiplication using arrays and tape diagrams.
(Lesson 11)

**Objective 2:** Interpret the quotient as the number of groups or the number of objects in each group using units of 2.
(Lesson 12)

**Objective 3:** Interpret the quotient as the number of groups or the number of objects in each group using units of 3.
(Lesson 13)

©2015 Great Minds. eureka-math.org
G3-M1-TE-B1-1.3.1-01.2016

# Lesson 11

Objective: Model division as the unknown factor in multiplication using arrays and tape diagrams.

## Suggested Lesson Structure

- ■ Fluency Practice          (11 minutes)
- ▨ Application Problem        (5 minutes)
- ▨ Concept Development        (34 minutes)
- ■ Student Debrief           (10 minutes)
- **Total Time**             **(60 minutes)**

## Fluency Practice (11 minutes)

- Multiply by 3 Pattern Sheet **3.OA.7**      (8 minutes)
- Group Counting **3.OA.1**              (3 minutes)

### Multiply by 3 (8 minutes)

Materials:  (S) Multiply by 3 (1–5) (Pattern Sheet)

Note: This activity builds fluency with multiplication facts using units of 3. It works toward students knowing from memory all products of two one-digit numbers. See Lesson 9 for the directions for administering a Multiply-By Pattern Sheet.

T:  (Write $5 \times 3 =$ _____.) Let's skip-count up by threes to solve. (Raise a finger for each number to track the count. Record the skip-count answers on the board.)

S:  3, 6, 9, 12, 15.

T:  (Circle 15 and write $5 \times 3 = 15$ above it. Write $4 \times 3 =$ _____.) Skip-count up by threes to find the answer. (Track with fingers as students count.)

S:  3, 6, 9, 12.

T:  Let's count down to find the answer to $4 \times 3$, too. Start at 15. (Count down with fingers as students say numbers.)

S:  15, 12.

T:  Let's practice multiplying by 3. Be sure to work left to right across the page. (Distribute Multiply by 3 Pattern Sheet.)

**NOTES ON
MULTIPLE MEANS
OF REPRESENTATION:**

Use this activity to teach skip-counting as a strategy for building automaticity with multiplication facts. Once students know that $3 \times 5 = 15$, they can flash 5 fingers to show 15 and then count on the other hand. How solving $3 \times 8$ looks and sounds is illustrated below.

**EUREKA
MATH™**

Lesson 11:  Model division as the unknown factor in multiplication using arrays and tape diagrams.

147

©2015 Great Minds. eureka-math.org
G3-M1-TE-B1-1.3.1-01.2016

## Group Counting  (3 minutes)

Note:  Group counting reviews interpreting multiplication as repeated addition.  Counting by twos and fours in this activity reviews multiplication with units of 2 from Topic C and anticipates using units of 4 in Topic E.

  T:    Let's count by twos.  (Direct students to count forward and backward to 20.)
  T:    Let's count by fours.  (Direct students to count forward and backward to 36, emphasizing the 20 to 24 and 28 to 32 transitions.)

## Application Problem  (5 minutes)

Rosie puts 2 lemon slices in each cup of iced tea.  She uses a total of 8 slices.  How many cups of iced tea does Rosie make?

Note:  Students may have solved the problem as shown or by using division ($8 \div 2 = 4$).  This problem leads into modeling with tape diagrams, which is introduced in the Concept Development.

$$\underline{\quad} \times 2 = 8$$

Rosie makes 4 cups of iced tea.

> **NOTES ON MULTIPLE MEANS OF ENGAGEMENT:**
>
> The numbers in the Application Problem may be too simple.  They were chosen to compliment the introduction of the tape diagram in the Concept Development.  If needed, change the numbers in the Application Problem to meet the needs of the class, and adjust the opening language of the Concept Development accordingly.

## Concept Development  (34 minutes)

Materials:   (S) Personal white board, Application Problem

**Problem 1:  Relate arrays to tape diagrams, modeling division where the quotient represents the number of groups.**

  T:    (Draw or project a 2 × 4 array.)  The columns in this array show the number of lemon slices in 1 cup of Rosie's iced tea.  Reread the Application Problem, and tell your partner what the unknown represents.
  S:    The unknown is the number of cups, or groups.
  **MP.4** T:    How might this array help us solve $8 \div 2 = \underline{\quad}$?
  S:    We can count the number of columns to find how many cups.
        → 2 times 4 equals 8, so $8 \div 2 = 4$.

8 lemon slices
? cups

2 slices

8 lemon slices
? cups

$8 \div 2 = \underline{\quad}$
$\underline{\quad} \times 2 = 8$

**Lesson 11:**    Model division as the unknown factor in multiplication using arrays and tape diagrams.

**EUREKA MATH**

T:  (Draw a rectangle around the array.)  What is the total number of lemon slices?

S:  8 lemon slices.

T:  (Bracket the rectangle and label the whole *8 lemon slices*.)  The question asks how many cups of iced tea Rosie makes.  Do the cups represent the number of groups or the number of lemon slices in each group?

**MP.4**

S:  The number of groups.

T:  (Under *8 lemon slices*, label the unknown as *? cups*.)

T:  Watch how I show the number of slices in one cup.  (Draw lines to divide columns and label 1 unit as *2 slices*.)  Where do we see the cups in our diagram?

S:  You made 4 cups with the dividing lines.

T:  By adding lines and labels to our array, we made a tape diagram.  Each boxed column shows 1 **unit**.  One unit represents 1 cup and has a value of 2 slices.  Notice that I labeled the diagram with all of the known and unknown information from the problem as we solved.  That made it a helpful tool for understanding the problem.

T:  (Write 8 ÷ 2 = ___ and ___ × 2 = 8.)  Talk to your partner about how the tape diagram helps you see the unknown in both equations.

S:  (Discuss.)

> **NOTES ON TAPE DIAGRAMS:**
>
> Students are familiar with tape diagrams from Grade 2.  They use tape diagrams to represent the information given in a problem, and then analyze the model to help determine the unknown and solve.  As tape diagrams are reviewed, ask why the diagram might have that name.  Guide students to make connections that help them remember the name.

In Problem 1, the quotient represents the number of groups.  Repeat the process using the following examples, reminding students to label known and unknown information from the problem on every tape diagram.

- 10 ÷ 2 = 5
- 18 ÷ 3 = 6

**Problem 2:  Use arrays to draw tape diagrams, modeling division where the quotient represents the number of objects in each group.**

Write or project the following problem:  Ms. Alves puts 21 papers in 7 piles.  How many papers are in each pile?

T:  Read the problem.  What is unknown?

S:  The number of objects in each group.

T:  Model the problem on your personal white board as an array where each column represents 1 pile.

S:  (Draw array, shown at right.)

T:  Count to find how many papers are in each of Ms. Alves's piles.

S:  (Count to find 3 papers.)

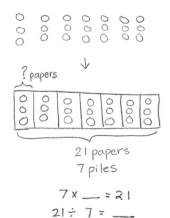

T:  Work with a partner to model the problem as a tape diagram.  Be sure to label the diagram with known and unknown information.  Use your array to help.

S:  (Draw tape diagram shown on previous page.)

T:  Use the tape diagram to write multiplication and division equations that show the unknown.

S:  (Write 7 × ___ = 21 and 21 ÷ 7 = ___.)

In Problem 2, the quotient represents the number of objects in each group.  Repeat the process using the following examples:

- 16 ÷ 2 = 8
- 24 ÷ 3 = 8

T:  Compare models.  What are the similarities and differences between arrays and tape diagrams?

S:  The tape diagram is like a labeled and boxed array.  → They both show the 7 piles, 3 papers in each pile, and 21 papers total.  → The labels make the tape diagram a little easier to use.

**NOTES ON MULTIPLE MEANS OF ENGAGEMENT:**

Support students to work at individualized levels by inviting them to choose to work independently or with a partner to solve additional examples.

## Problem Set  (10 minutes)

Students should do their personal best to complete the Problem Set within the allotted 10 minutes.  Depending on your class, it may be appropriate to modify the assignment by specifying which problems they work on first.  Some problems do not specify a method for solving.  Students should solve these problems using the RDW approach used for Application Problems.

## Student Debrief  (10 minutes)

**Lesson Objective:**  Model division as the unknown factor in multiplication using arrays and tape diagrams.

The Student Debrief is intended to invite reflection and active processing of the total lesson experience.

Invite students to review their solutions for the Problem Set.  They should check work by comparing answers with a partner before going over answers as a class.  Look for misconceptions or misunderstandings that can be addressed in the Debrief.  Guide students in a conversation to debrief the Problem Set and process the lesson.

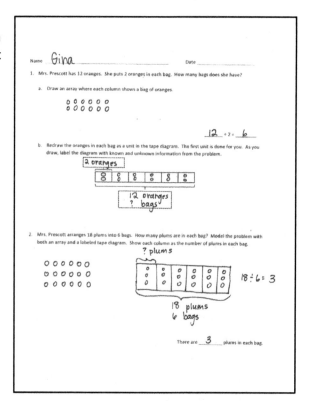

Any combination of the questions below may be used to lead the discussion.

- Compare Problems 1 and 2.  What does the unknown represent in each problem?
- Compare how **units** are represented in tape diagrams and in arrays.
- How can each model represent both types of unknowns?
- Compare the way you solved the Application Problem with the tape diagram model we learned today.

## Exit Ticket  (3 minutes)

After the Student Debrief, instruct students to complete the Exit Ticket.  A review of their work will help with assessing students' understanding of the concepts that were presented in today's lesson and planning more effectively for future lessons.  The questions may be read aloud to the students.

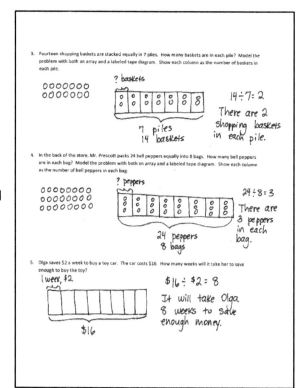

Lesson 11:   Model division as the unknown factor in multiplication using arrays and tape diagrams.

©2015 Great Minds. eureka-math.org
G3-M1-TE-B1-1.3.1-01.2016

151

Multiply.

3 x 1 = _____     3 x 2 = _____     3 x 3 = _____     3 x 4 = _____

3 x 5 = _____     3 x 1 = _____     3 x 2 = _____     3 x 1 = _____

3 x 3 = _____     3 x 1 = _____     3 x 4 = _____     3 x 1 = _____

3 x 5 = _____     3 x 1 = _____     3 x 2 = _____     3 x 3 = _____

3 x 2 = _____     3 x 4 = _____     3 x 2 = _____     3 x 5 = _____

3 x 2 = _____     3 x 1 = _____     3 x 2 = _____     3 x 3 = _____

3 x 1 = _____     3 x 3 = _____     3 x 2 = _____     3 x 3 = _____

3 x 4 = _____     3 x 3 = _____     3 x 5 = _____     3 x 3 = _____

3 x 4 = _____     3 x 1 = _____     3 x 4 = _____     3 x 2 = _____

3 x 4 = _____     3 x 3 = _____     3 x 4 = _____     3 x 5 = _____

3 x 4 = _____     3 x 5 = _____     3 x 1 = _____     3 x 5 = _____

3 x 2 = _____     3 x 5 = _____     3 x 3 = _____     3 x 5 = _____

3 x 4 = _____     3 x 2 = _____     3 x 4 = _____     3 x 3 = _____

3 x 5 = _____     3 x 3 = _____     3 x 2 = _____     3 x 4 = _____

3 x 3 = _____     3 x 5 = _____     3 x 2 = _____     3 x 4 = _____

multiply by 3 (1–5)

**Lesson 11:**     Model division as the unknown factor in multiplication using arrays and tape diagrams.

EUREKA
MATH™

Name _____ Date _____

1. Mrs. Prescott has 12 oranges. She puts 2 oranges in each bag. How many bags does she have?

   a. Draw an array where each column shows a bag of oranges.

   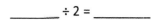
   
   _____ ÷ 2 = _____

   b. Redraw the oranges in each bag as a unit in the tape diagram. The first unit is done for you. As you draw, label the diagram with known and unknown information from the problem.

   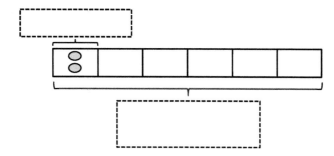

2. Mrs. Prescott arranges 18 plums into 6 bags. How many plums are in each bag? Model the problem with both an array and a labeled tape diagram. Show each column as the number of plums in each bag.

   There are _____ plums in each bag.

**Lesson 11:**    Model division as the unknown factor in multiplication using arrays and tape diagrams.

©2015 Great Minds. eureka-math.org
G3-M1-TE-B1-1.3.1-01.2016

3. Fourteen shopping baskets are stacked equally in 7 piles. How many baskets are in each pile? Model the problem with both an array and a labeled tape diagram. Show each column as the number of baskets in each pile.

4. In the back of the store, Mr. Prescott packs 24 bell peppers equally into 8 bags. How many bell peppers are in each bag? Model the problem with both an array and a labeled tape diagram. Show each column as the number of bell peppers in each bag.

5. Olga saves $2 a week to buy a toy car. The car costs $16. How many weeks will it take her to save enough to buy the toy?

©2015 Great Minds. eureka-math.org
G3-M1-TE-B1-1.3.1-01.2016

Name _____  Date _____

Ms. McCarty has 18 stickers.  She puts 2 stickers on each homework paper and has no more left.  How many homework papers does she have?  Model the problem with both an array and a labeled tape diagram.

**Lesson 11:**     Model division as the unknown factor in multiplication using arrays
and tape diagrams.

©2015 Great Minds. eureka-math.org
G3-M1-TE-B1-1.3.1-01.2016

155

Name _____  Date _____

1.  Fred has 10 pears.  He puts 2 pears in each basket.  How many baskets does he have?

    a.  Draw an array where each column represents the number of pears in each basket.

    _____ ÷ 2 = _____

    b.  Redraw the pears in each basket as a unit in the tape diagram.  Label the diagram with known and unknown information from the problem.

    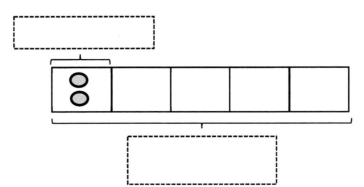

2.  Ms. Meyer organizes 15 clipboards equally into 3 boxes.  How many clipboards are in each box?  Model the problem with both an array and a labeled tape diagram.  Show each column as the number of clipboards in each box.

    There are _____ clipboards in each box.

EUREKA
MATH

3. Sixteen action figures are arranged equally on 2 shelves. How many action figures are on each shelf? Model the problem with both an array and a labeled tape diagram. Show each column as the number of action figures on each shelf.

4. Jasmine puts 18 hats away. She puts an equal number of hats on 3 shelves. How many hats are on each shelf? Model the problem with both an array and a labeled tape diagram. Show each column as the number of hats on each shelf.

5. Corey checks out 2 books a week from the library. How many weeks will it take him to check out a total of 14 books?

**Lesson 11:**   Model division as the unknown factor in multiplication using arrays and tape diagrams.

©2015 Great Minds. eureka-math.org
G3-M1-TE-B1-1.3.1-01.2016

157

# Lesson 12

Objective: Interpret the quotient as the number of groups or the number of objects in each group using units of 2.

## Suggested Lesson Structure

■ Fluency Practice          (13 minutes)
▨ Application Problem        (5 minutes)
▢ Concept Development        (32 minutes)
▨ Student Debrief           (10 minutes)

  **Total Time**            **(60 minutes)**

## Fluency Practice (13 minutes)

- Multiply by 3 Pattern Sheet  **3.OA.7**          (8 minutes)
- Group Counting  **3.OA.1**          (3 minutes)
- Divide  **3.OA.7**          (2 minutes)

### Multiply by 3 Pattern Sheet  (8 minutes)

Materials:  (S) Multiply by 3 (6–10) (Pattern Sheet)

Note: This activity builds fluency with multiplication facts using units of 3. It works toward students knowing from memory all products of two one-digit numbers. See Lesson 9 for the directions for administering a Multiply-By Pattern Sheet.

  T:  (Write $6 \times 3 =$ _____.) Let's skip-count up by threes to solve. (Count with fingers to 6 as students count.)

  S:  3, 6, 9, 12, 15, 18.

  T:  Let's skip-count down to find the answer, too. Start at 30. (Count down with fingers as students count.)

  S:  30, 27, 24, 21, 18.

Repeat the process for $8 \times 3$ and $7 \times 3$.

  T:  Let's practice multiplying by 3. Be sure to work left to right across the page. (Distribute Multiply by 3 Pattern Sheet.)

**Lesson 12:**    Interpret the quotient as the number of groups or the number of objects in each group using units of 2.

EUREKA MATH™

## Group Counting  (3 minutes)

Note:  Group counting reviews interpreting multiplication as repeated addition.  Counting by twos and fours in this activity reviews multiplication with units of 2 from Topic C and anticipates using units of 4 in Topic E.

- T:  Let's count by twos.  (Direct students to count forward and backward to 20.)
- T:  Let's count by fours.  (Direct students to count forward and backward to 36, emphasizing the 20 to 24 and 28 to 32 transitions.)

## Divide  (2 minutes)

Materials:  (S) Personal white board

Note:  This activity builds fluency with multiplication and division.  It works toward the goal of students knowing from memory all products of two one-digit numbers and reviews the objective of Lesson 11.

- T:  (Project a 2 by 4 array of objects.)  Draw an array to match my picture.
- S:  (Draw 2 by 4 array.)
- T:  Skip-count by twos to find how many total objects there are.  (Point as students count.)
- S:  2, 4, 6, 8.
- T:  How many groups of 2 are there?
- S:  4.
- T:  Say the total as a multiplication sentence starting with the number of groups.
- S:  $4 \times 2 = 8$.
- T:  (Write $4 \times 2 = 8$.  Below it, write $8 \div 4 =$ __.)  Fill in the blank to make a true division sentence.  Then, divide your array into 4 equal groups to find the answer.
- S:  (Draw lines separating the array into 4 groups of 2, and write $8 \div 4 = 2$.)
- T:  Erase the lines that divided the array.
- S:  (Erase lines.)
- T:  Show $8 \div 4$ by making groups of 4.
- S:  (Circle 2 groups of 4.)

Repeat process for the following possible sequence:  $9 \div 3$, $12 \div 2$, and $12 \div 3$.

## Application Problem  (5 minutes)

A chef arranges 4 rows of 3 red peppers on a tray.  He adds 2 more rows of 3 yellow peppers.  How many peppers are there altogether?

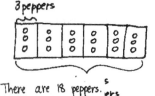

**MP.5**  Note:  Students might solve using an array to model the distributive property (Lesson 10) or a tape diagram (Lesson 11).  If they use the latter strategy, it is likely their first use of a tape diagram to solve multiplication.  The problem is a review that provides an exploratory opportunity for students to select and use appropriate tools.

**EUREKA MATH**

Lesson 12:  Interpret the quotient as the number of groups or the number of objects in each group using units of 2.

©2015 Great Minds. eureka-math.org
G3-M1-TE-B1-1.3.1-01.2016

159

## Concept Development (32 minutes)

Materials: (S) Personal white board

**Problem 1: Model division where the unknown represents the number of objects in each group.**

T: Two students equally share 8 crackers. How many crackers does each student get? Draw to model and solve the problem. Then, explain your thinking to your partner.

S: (Draw and solve.) I gave 1 cracker to each student until I drew 8. → 4 + 4 = 8, so I drew 4 crackers for each student. → It's a multiplication problem with an unknown factor.

T: Write a division sentence to represent your model.

S: (Write 8 ÷ 2 = 4.)

T: (Draw a rectangle.) This diagram represents the total, 8 crackers. In your mind, visualize where we would divide it to make 2 equal parts.

S: (Visualize.)

T: Say "Stop!" when I get to the spot you have in mind. (Move finger from left edge toward middle.)

S: Stop!

T: How does the diagram represent the students?

S: 2 students, 2 parts!

T: What is our unknown?

S: The number of crackers each student gets.

T: Watch how I label the unknown on the diagram. (Bracket and label as shown.) Tell your partner a strategy for finding the unknown using the diagram.

S: I would draw 1 cracker in each part until I drew 8. → Each part has to be equal. 4 + 4 = 8, so 1 part is 4. → I would think 2 × ___ = 8. The question mark is 4.

T: Look at the division sentence you wrote for your first model. Does it represent this diagram too? Explain to your partner.

S: (Discuss.)

### NOTES ON DRAWING TAPE DIAGRAMS:

Students draw to model before or as they solve problems so that the diagram assists them with analysis. The model provides a place aside from the words to think about the problem. It should guide their understanding of the problem and how to find the unknown. They might ask themselves the following questions as they draw.

- Am I looking for a part?
- Am I looking for a number of parts?
- Am I looking for the whole amount?
- What is my model showing me?

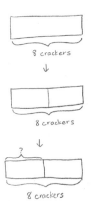

### NOTES ON MULTIPLE MEANS OF REPRESENTATION:

If a natural opportunity presents itself, teach students the word *bracket* so they have specific language with which to refer to the diagram. This may be especially useful for English language learners.

Repeat the process with the following suggested expressions to model division where the quotient represents the number of objects in each group.

- 12 ÷ 2
- 18 ÷ 2

©2015 Great Minds. eureka-math.org
G3-M1-TE-B1-1.3.1-01.2016

**Problem 2:  Model division where the unknown represents the number of groups.**

T:  Let's go back to our original problem, this time changing it a bit.  There are 8 crackers, but this time each student gets 2.  How many students get crackers?

T:  Do we know the size of the groups or the number of groups?

S:  The size of the groups.

T:  We can draw 1 unit of the diagram to represent a group of 2 crackers.  (Draw 1 unit of two.)  What other information does the problem tell us?

S:  The total.

T:  (Estimate the whole and label it *8 crackers*.)  Notice that I drew a dotted line to show the whole diagram.  What is our unknown?

S:  The number of groups.

T:  (Bracket the top part of the diagram and label with a question mark.)  Let's find the number of groups by drawing more units of 2.  How will we know when we've drawn enough units?

S:  We'll get to the total, 8.

T:  Draw along with me on your personal white board.  (Skip-count by two, drawing to add 3 more units.)

S:  (Draw.)

T:  Whisper to your partner the number of students that get crackers.

S:  4 students.

T:  Write a division sentence to match the diagram.

S:  (Write 8 ÷ 2 = 4.)

Repeat the process with the following suggested expressions to model division where the unknown represents the number of groups.

- 12 ÷ 2
- 18 ÷ 2

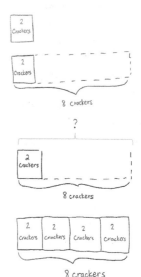

**NOTES ON DRAWING TAPE DIAGRAMS:**

Erasers are important for drawing tape diagrams to model division where the unknown represents the number of groups.  Students may find they have very incorrectly determined the length of the whole.  Encourage them to erase and redraw.

**NOTES ON MULTIPLE MEANS OF ENGAGEMENT:**

Gradually release responsibility to students as the process is repeated with additional examples.  By the third example, students should be working nearly independently.

EUREKA MATH™

Lesson 12:  Interpret the quotient as the number of groups or the number of objects in each group using units of 2.

161

©2015 Great Minds. eureka-math.org
G3-M1-TE-B1-1.3.1-01.2016

In this lesson, three division sentences are each modeled with two types of division.  Use one pair of division sentences for the following reflective dialogue.  (The dialogue is modeled with 8 ÷ 2 = 4.)

T:  The two division sentences for these diagrams are the same, but the tape diagrams are different.  Turn and talk to your partner about why.

S:  The 2 and the 4 represent different things in each problem.  → In the first diagram, we knew how many groups, and in the second, we knew how many in each group.

T:  When we divide, we always know the total number of objects.  We divide either to find the size of the groups, like in the first problem, or the number of groups, like in the second problem.

## Problem Set  (10 minutes)

Students should do their personal best to complete the Problem Set within the allotted 10 minutes.  For some classes, it may be appropriate to modify the assignment by specifying which problems they work on first.  Some problems do not specify a method for solving.  Students should solve these problems using the RDW approach used for Application Problems.

## Student Debrief  (10 minutes)

**Lesson Objective:**  Interpret the quotient as the number of groups or the number of objects in each group using units of 2.

The Student Debrief is intended to invite reflection and active processing of the total lesson experience.

Invite students to review their solutions for the Problem Set.  They should check work by comparing answers with a partner before going over answers as a class.  Look for misconceptions or misunderstandings that can be addressed in the Debrief.  Guide students in a conversation to debrief the Problem Set and process the lesson.

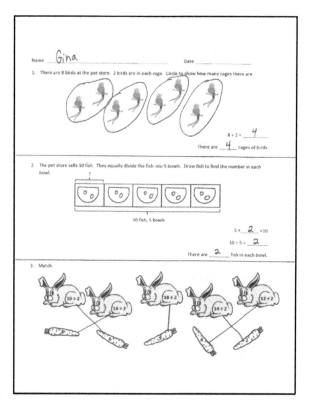

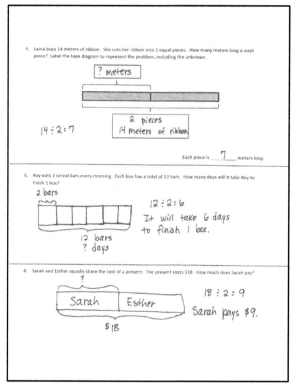

Any combination of the questions below may be used to lead the discussion.

- Describe how you labeled the tape diagram in Problem 4. The number 2 appears in the problem; where do you see it in the diagram?
- Analyze Problems 1 and 2 on the Problem Set to compare different unknowns. (There are 2 birds in each cage in Problem 1, and 2 fish in each bowl in Problem 2.)
- How does what the quotient represents affect the way a tape diagram is drawn?

## Exit Ticket (3 minutes)

After the Student Debrief, instruct students to complete the Exit Ticket. A review of their work will help with assessing students' understanding of the concepts that were presented in today's lesson and planning more effectively for future lessons. The questions may be read aloud to the students.

Lesson 12:    Interpret the quotient as the number of groups or the number of objects in each group using units of 2.

©2015 Great Minds. eureka-math.org
G3-M1-TE-B1-1.3.1-01.2016

163

Multiply.

| | | | |
|---|---|---|---|
| 3 x 1 = _____ | 3 x 2 = _____ | 3 x 3 = _____ | 3 x 4 = _____ |
| 3 x 5 = _____ | 3 x 6 = _____ | 3 x 7 = _____ | 3 x 8 = _____ |
| 3 x 9 = _____ | 3 x 10 = _____ | 3 x 5 = _____ | 3 x 6 = _____ |
| 3 x 5 = _____ | 3 x 7 = _____ | 3 x 5 = _____ | 3 x 8 = _____ |
| 3 x 5 = _____ | 3 x 9 = _____ | 3 x 5 = _____ | 3 x 10 = _____ |
| 3 x 6 = _____ | 3 x 5 = _____ | 3 x 6 = _____ | 3 x 7 = _____ |
| 3 x 6 = _____ | 3 x 8 = _____ | 3 x 6 = _____ | 3 x 9 = _____ |
| 3 x 6 = _____ | 3 x 7 = _____ | 3 x 6 = _____ | 3 x 7 = _____ |
| 3 x 8 = _____ | 3 x 7 = _____ | 3 x 9 = _____ | 3 x 7 = _____ |
| 3 x 8 = _____ | 3 x 6 = _____ | 3 x 8 = _____ | 3 x 7 = _____ |
| 3 x 8 = _____ | 3 x 9 = _____ | 3 x 9 = _____ | 3 x 6 = _____ |
| 3 x 9 = _____ | 3 x 7 = _____ | 3 x 9 = _____ | 3 x 8 = _____ |
| 3 x 9 = _____ | 3 x 8 = _____ | 3 x 6 = _____ | 3 x 9 = _____ |
| 3 x 7 = _____ | 3 x 9 = _____ | 3 x 6 = _____ | 3 x 8 = _____ |
| 3 x 9 = _____ | 3 x 7 = _____ | 3 x 6 = _____ | 3 x 8 = _____ |

multiply by 3 (6–10)

**Lesson 12:** Interpret the quotient as the number of groups or the number of objects in each group using units of 2.

EUREKA MATH™

Name _____  Date _____

1. There are 8 birds at the pet store. Two birds are in each cage. Circle to show how many cages there are.

$8 \div 2 =$ _____

There are _____ cages of birds.

2. The pet store sells 10 fish. They equally divide the fish into 5 bowls. Draw fish to find the number in each bowl.

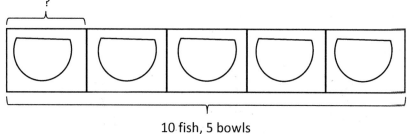

10 fish, 5 bowls

$5 \times$ _____ $= 10$

$10 \div 5 =$ _____

There are _____ fish in each bowl.

3. Match.

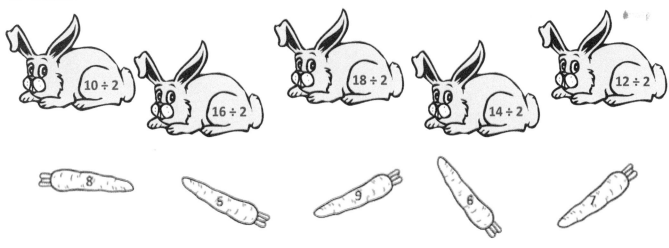

Lesson 12:  Interpret the quotient as the number of groups or the number of objects in each group using units of 2.

©2015 Great Minds. eureka-math.org
G3-M1-TE-B1-1.3.1-01.2016

165

4. Laina buys 14 meters of ribbon. She cuts her ribbon into 2 equal pieces. How many meters long is each piece? Label the tape diagram to represent the problem, including the unknown.

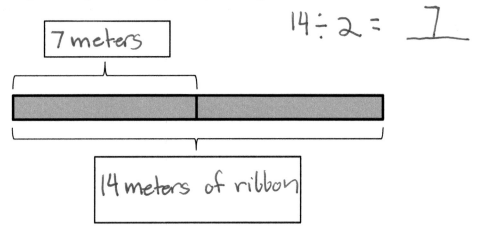

$14 \div 2 = \underline{7}$

| 7 meters |
|---|

| | |
|---|---|

14 meters of ribbon

Each piece is ___7___ meters long.

5. Roy eats 2 cereal bars every morning. Each box has a total of 12 bars. How many days will it take Roy to finish 1 box?

$12 \div 2 = \dfrac{6}{\text{days}}$

total bars   eaten
per box     per morning

| 2 bars | 2 bars | 2 bars | 2 bars | 2 bars | 2 bars |
|---|---|---|---|---|---|

6. Sarah and Esther equally share the cost of a present. The present costs $18. How much does Sarah pay?

**Lesson 12:** Interpret the quotient as the number of groups or the number of objects in each group using units of 2.

©2015 Great Minds. eureka-math.org
G3-M1-TE-B1-1.3.1-01.2016

EUREKA MATH

Name _____     Date _____

There are 14 mints in 1 box.  Cecilia eats 2 mints each day.  How many days does it take Cecilia to eat 1 box of mints?  Draw and label a tape diagram to solve.

It takes Cecilia _____ days to eat 1 box of mints.

Lesson 12:    Interpret the quotient as the number of groups or the number of
              objects in each group using units of 2.

©2015 Great Minds. eureka-math.org
G3-M1-TE-B1-1.3.1-01.2016

167

Name _____   Date _____

1.  Ten people wait in line for the roller coaster.  Two people sit in each car.  Circle to find the total number of cars needed.

$10 \div 2 =$ _____

There are _____ cars needed.

2.  Mr. Ramirez divides 12 frogs equally into 6 groups for students to study.  Draw frogs to find the number in each group.  Label known and unknown information on the tape diagram to help you solve.

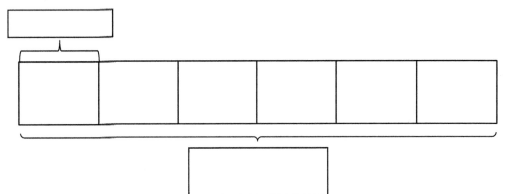

$6 \times$ _____ $= 12$

$12 \div 6 =$ _____

There are _____ frogs in each group.

3.  Match.

Lesson 12:    Interpret the quotient as the number of groups or the number of objects in each group using units of 2.

4. Betsy pours 16 cups of water to equally fill 2 bottles. How many cups of water are in each bottle? Label the tape diagram to represent the problem, including the unknown.

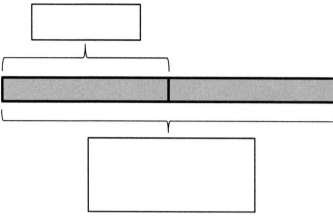

There are _____ cups of water in each bottle.

5. An earthworm tunnels 2 centimeters into the ground each day. The earthworm tunnels at about the same pace every day. How many days will it take the earthworm to tunnel 14 centimeters?

6. Sebastian and Teshawn go to the movies. The tickets cost $16 in total. The boys share the cost equally. How much does Teshawn pay?

Lesson 12: Interpret the quotient as the number of groups or the number of objects in each group using units of 2.

169

©2015 Great Minds. eureka-math.org
G3-M1-TE-B1-1.3.1-01.2016

# Lesson 13

Objective:  Interpret the quotient as the number of groups or the number of objects in each group using units of 3.

## Suggested Lesson Structure

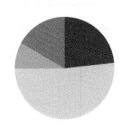

| | |
|---|---|
| ■ Fluency Practice | (14 minutes) |
| ▨ Application Problem | (5 minutes) |
| ▨ Concept Development | (31 minutes) |
| ■ Student Debrief | (10 minutes) |
| **Total Time** | **(60 minutes)** |

## Fluency Practice  (14 minutes)

- Sprint:  Multiply or Divide by 2  **3.OA.7**      (9 minutes)
- Group Counting  **3.OA.1**                              (3 minutes)
- Divide  **3.OA.7**                                            (2 minutes)

### Sprint:  Multiply or Divide by 2  (9 minutes)

Materials:   (S) Multiply or Divide by 2 Sprint

Note: This activity builds fluency with multiplication and division using units of 2.  It works toward students' ability to multiply and divide fluently within 100.  See Lesson 2 for the directions for administering a Sprint.

### Group Counting  (3 minutes)

Note: Group counting reviews interpreting multiplication as repeated addition.  Counting by threes and fours in this activity reviews multiplication with units of 3 from Topic C and anticipates using units of 4 in Topic E.

- T:   Let's count by threes. (Direct students to count forward and backward to 30.)
- T:   Let's count by fours. (Direct students to count forward and backward to 40, emphasizing the 20 to 24 28 to 32, and 36 to 40 transitions.)

©2015 Great Minds. eureka-math.org
G3-M1-TE-B1-1.3.1-01.2016

EUREKA
MATH™

## Divide  (2 minutes)

Materials:   (S) Personal white board

Note:  This activity builds fluency with multiplication and division.  It works toward students knowing from memory all products of two one-digit numbers.

T:    (Write 2 × 3 = ___.)  Say the multiplication sentence.
S:    2 × 3 = 6.
T:    (Write 2 × 3 = 6.  Directly below it, write ___ ÷ 3 = 2.)  On your personal white board, write the equation and fill in the blank.
S:    (Write 6 ÷ 3 = 2.)

Repeat the process for the following possible sequence:  3 × 3, 5 × 3, and 9 × 3.

## Application Problem  (5 minutes)

Mark spends $16 on 2 video games.  Each game costs the same amount.  Find the cost of each game.

Note:  This problem reviews equal groups division from Lesson 12 where the unknown is the number of objects in each group.

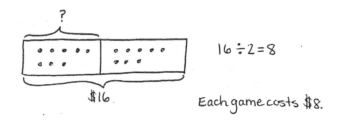

$$16 \div 2 = 8$$

Each game costs $8.

## Concept Development  (31 minutes)

Materials:   (S) Personal white board

**Pictorial:  Draw and analyze tape diagrams to determine the unknown.**

Write or project the following story and the tape diagram drawn below:  Three students equally share a pack of 12 pencils.

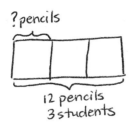

NOTES ON
MULTIPLE MEANS
OF ACTION
AND EXPRESSION:

This lesson is similar to Lesson 12. Depending on performance levels, modify guidance so that students work through pictorial examples quickly, in pairs or independently.  Meet with groups or individuals who need support.  Alternatively, maximize support by skipping the abstract example in favor of slowly working the class through the pictorial.  As an additional scaffold, the teacher may choose to model and have students create tape diagrams with drawings inside of each unit to show the value. Students have used tape diagrams drawn with and without this feature in Grade 2.

Lesson 13:     Interpret the quotient as the number of groups or the number of
               objects in each group using units of 3.

©2015 Great Minds. eureka-math.org
G3-M1-TE-B1-1.3.1-01.2016

171

T: What information do we know from reading the story?

S: The total pencils and the number of students.

T: How does the tape diagram show the story?

S: The whole diagram represents 12 pencils, and it's divided into 3 parts. Those are the students. We don't know how many pencils each student gets. That's what the question mark represents.

**MP.4**

T: Write a division equation to find how many pencils each student gets.

S: (Write 12 ÷ 3 = ___.)

T: Draw my tape diagram on your personal white board. Then, draw to share the 12 pencils equally among the 3 students. Fill in your division equation.

S: (Draw 4 in each unit on the tape diagram. Write 12 ÷ 3 = 4.)

Students can check their work by writing a multiplication sentence.

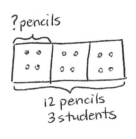

Write or project the following problem and the first tape diagram drawn below: A school buys 12 boxes of pencils. Each classroom gets 3 boxes. How many classrooms get boxes of pencils?

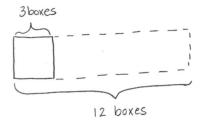

T: What information do we know from the problem?

S: The total boxes and the number of boxes each classroom gets.

T: The box drawn with a solid line represents the number of boxes 1 class gets. I used the dotted line to estimate the total boxes. How should I label the unknown on this diagram?

S: It's the number of classrooms that get boxes.

T: Where can I record my question mark?

S: Under *12 boxes*, write *? classrooms*.

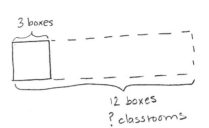

T: (Label the unknown.) On your board, skip-count by threes to draw more units in the tape diagram. How will you know when to stop?

S: We stop when we get to 12. (Draw and count 6, 9, 12.)

T: Use the tape diagram to write and solve a division equation that represents the problem.

S: (Write 12 ÷ 3 = 4.) It's the same division problem as before.

T: What does the 4 represent in this problem?

S: It's the number of classrooms that get boxes of pencils. → It's the number of groups.

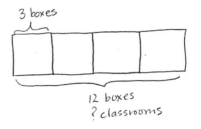

Repeat the process showing division with both types of unknowns using the following suggested expressions.

- 18 ÷ 3
- 21 ÷ 3

Lesson 13:    Interpret the quotient as the number of groups or the number of objects in each group using units of 3.

**Abstract: Interpret tape diagrams to determine the unknown and write division problems.**

Draw or project the following tape diagrams. Students work in pairs.

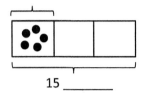 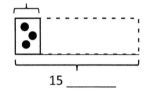

15 _____                           15 _____

- Write division sentences to represent each diagram. (Division sentences should be the same for both diagrams.)
- Label each tape diagram, including the unknown.
- The tape diagrams and division sentences show solutions. Write a word problem to match each solution.
- Save the word problems to compare with other groups during the Student Debrief.

**NOTES ON MULTIPLE MEANS OF REPRESENTATION:**

For the abstract portion of the lesson, some pairs may benefit from looking at word problems completed the previous day to gather ideas and examples upon which to model their work.

**NOTES ON MULTIPLE MEANS OF ENGAGEMENT:**

Have students who need a challenge add a second step to their word problems. Early finishers should solve each other's problems and assess the reasonableness of one another's work.

## Problem Set  (10 minutes)

Students should do their personal best to complete the Problem Set within the allotted 10 minutes. For some classes, it may be appropriate to modify the assignment by specifying which problems they work on first. Some problems do not specify a method for solving. Students should solve these problems using the RDW approach used for Application Problems.

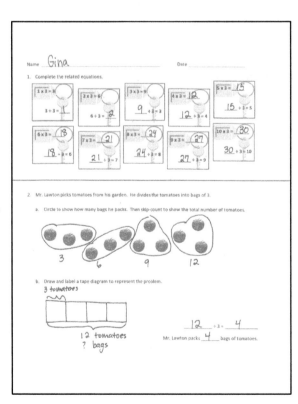

## Student Debrief  (10 minutes)

**Lesson Objective:** Interpret the quotient as the number of groups or the number of objects in each group using units of 3.

The Student Debrief is intended to invite reflection and active processing of the total lesson experience.

Invite students to review their solutions for the Problem Set. They should check work by comparing answers with a partner before going over answers as a class. Look for misconceptions or misunderstandings that can be addressed in the Debrief. Guide students in a conversation to debrief the Problem Set and process the lesson.

Any combination of the questions below may be used to lead the discussion.

- Describe how the model in Problem 2(a) helped for drawing a tape diagram in Problem 2(b).

- How does the Application Problem connect the work we did yesterday to what we did today?

- Share work for Problem 5. The language *some friends* rather than a number may have presented a challenge.

- Compare Problems 4 and 5. How did your approach to drawing the tape diagram change? Why?

- Share word problems from the abstract activity in the Concept Development. The class may solve, or simply discuss, which is the unknown factor. (Guide students to notice how different the contexts are, but that each pair of problems always shows the same two unknowns.)

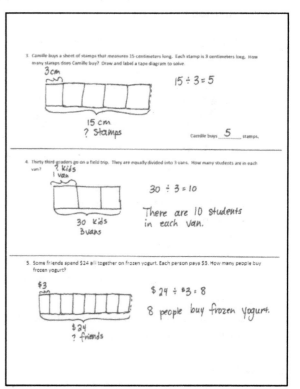

### Exit Ticket  (3 minutes)

After the Student Debrief, instruct students to complete the Exit Ticket. A review of their work will help you assess the students' understanding of the concepts that were presented in the lesson today and plan more effectively for future lessons. You may read the questions aloud to the students.

EUREKA
MATH™

# A

Number Correct: _____

Multiply or Divide by 2

| | | | | | | |
|---|---|---|---|---|---|---|
| 1. | $2 \times 2 =$ | 4 | 23. | $\_\_ \times 2 = 20$ | 10 |
| 2. | $3 \times 2 =$ | 6 | 24. | $\_\_ \times 2 = 4$ | 2 |
| 3. | $4 \times 2 =$ | 8 | 25. | $\_\_ \times 2 = 6$ | 3 |
| 4. | $5 \times 2 =$ | 10 | 26. | $20 \div 2 =$ | 10 |
| 5. | $1 \times 2 =$ | 2 | 27. | $10 \div 2 =$ | 5 |
| 6. | $4 \div 2 =$ | 2 | 28. | $2 \div 1 =$ | 1 |
| 7. | $6 \div 2 =$ | 3 | 29. | $4 \div 2 =$ | 2 |
| 8. | $10 \div 2 =$ | 5 | 30. | $6 \div 2 =$ | 3 |
| 9. | $2 \div 1 =$ | 1 | 31. | $\_\_ \times 2 = 12$ | 6 |
| 10. | $8 \div 2 =$ | 4 | 32. | $\_\_ \times 2 = 14$ | 7 |
| 11. | $6 \times 2 =$ | 12 | 33. | $\_\_ \times 2 = 18$ | 9 |
| 12. | $7 \times 2 =$ | 14 | 34. | $\_\_ \times 2 = 16$ | 8 |
| 13. | $8 \times 2 =$ | 16 | 35. | $14 \div 2 =$ | 7 |
| 14. | $9 \times 2 =$ | 18 | 36. | $18 \div 2 =$ | 9 |
| 15. | $10 \times 2 =$ | 20 | 37. | $12 \div 2 =$ | 6 |
| 16. | $16 \div 2 =$ | 8 | 38. | $16 \div 2 =$ | 8 |
| 17. | $14 \div 2 =$ | 7 | 39. | $11 \times 2 =$ | 22 |
| 18. | $18 \div 2 =$ | 9 | 40. | $22 \div 2 =$ | 11 |
| 19. | $12 \div 2 =$ | 6 | 41. | $12 \times 2 =$ | 24 |
| 20. | $20 \div 2 =$ | 10 | 42. | $24 \div 2 =$ | 12 |
| 21. | $\_\_ \times 2 = 10$ | 5 | 43. | $14 \times 2 =$ | 28 |
| 22. | $\_\_ \times 2 = 12$ | 6 | 44. | $28 \div 2 =$ | 14 |

EUREKA MATH™

Lesson 13:  Interpret the quotient as the number of groups or the number of objects in each group using units of 3.

175

# B

Number Correct: _____

Improvement: _____

Multiply or Divide by 2

| | | | | | | |
|---|---|---|---|---|---|---|
| 1. | $1 \times 2 =$ | 2 | 23. | $\_\_ \times 2 = 4$ | 2 |
| 2. | $2 \times 2 =$ | 4 | 24. | $\_\_ \times 2 = 20$ | 10 |
| 3. | $3 \times 2 =$ | 6 | 25. | $\_\_ \times 2 = 6$ | 3 |
| 4. | $4 \times 2 =$ | 8 | 26. | $4 \div 2 =$ | 2 |
| 5. | $5 \times 2 =$ | 10 | 27. | $2 \div 1 =$ | 1 |
| 6. | $6 \div 2 =$ | 3 | 28. | $20 \div 2 =$ | 10 |
| 7. | $4 \div 2 =$ | 2 | 29. | $10 \div 2 =$ | 5 |
| 8. | $8 \div 2 =$ | 4 | 30. | $6 \div 2 =$ | 3 |
| 9. | $2 \div 1 =$ | 1 | 31. | $\_\_ \times 2 = 12$ | 6 |
| 10. | $10 \div 2 =$ | 5 | 32. | $\_\_ \times 2 = 16$ | 8 |
| 11. | $10 \times 2 =$ | 20 | 33. | $\_\_ \times 2 = 18$ | 9 |
| 12. | $6 \times 2 =$ | 12 | 34. | $\_\_ \times 2 = 14$ | 7 |
| 13. | $7 \times 2 =$ | 14 | 35. | $16 \div 2 =$ | 8 |
| 14. | $8 \times 2 =$ | 16 | 36. | $18 \div 2 =$ | 9 |
| 15. | $9 \times 2 =$ | 18 | 37. | $12 \div 2 =$ | 6 |
| 16. | $14 \div 2 =$ | 7 | 38. | $14 \div 2 =$ | 7 |
| 17. | $12 \div 2 =$ | 6 | 39. | $11 \times 2 =$ | 22 |
| 18. | $16 \div 2 =$ | 8 | 40. | $22 \div 2 =$ | 11 |
| 19. | $20 \div 2 =$ | 10 | 41. | $12 \times 2 =$ | 24 |
| 20. | $18 \div 2 =$ | 9 | 42. | $24 \div 2 =$ | 12 |
| 21. | $\_\_ \times 2 = 12$ | 6 | 43. | $13 \times 2 =$ | 26 |
| 22. | $\_\_ \times 2 = 10$ | 5 | 44. | $26 \div 2 =$ | 13 |

**Lesson 13:** Interpret the quotient as the number of groups or the number of objects in each group using units of 3.

EUREKA MATH

Name _____    Date _____

1.  Fill in the blanks to make true number sentences.

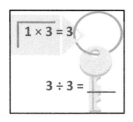
$1 \times 3 = 3$

$3 \div 3 = $ _____

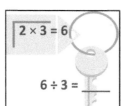
$2 \times 3 = 6$

$6 \div 3 = $ _____

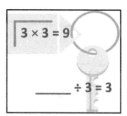
$3 \times 3 = 9$

_____ $\div 3 = 3$

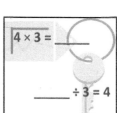
$4 \times 3 = $ _____

_____ $\div 3 = 4$

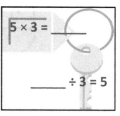
$5 \times 3 = $ _____

_____ $\div 3 = 5$

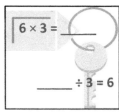
$6 \times 3 = $ _____

_____ $\div 3 = 6$

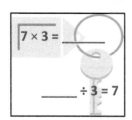
$7 \times 3 = $ _____

_____ $\div 3 = 7$

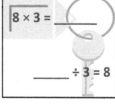
$8 \times 3 = $ _____

_____ $\div 3 = 8$

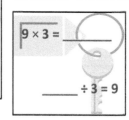
$9 \times 3 = $ _____

_____ $\div 3 = 9$

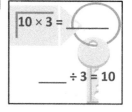
$10 \times 3 = $ _____

_____ $\div 3 = 10$

2.  Mr. Lawton picks tomatoes from his garden.  He divides the tomatoes into bags of 3.

    a.  Circle to show how many bags he packs.  Then, skip-count to show the total number of tomatoes.

12

    b.  Draw and label a tape diagram to represent the problem.

3 tomatoes

| 3 | 3 | 3 | 3 |

12 tomatoes

$\underline{\quad 12 \quad} \div 3 = \underline{\quad 4 \quad}$

Mr. Lawton packs __4__ bags of tomatoes.

EUREKA
MATH

Lesson 13:    Interpret the quotient as the number of groups or the number of
objects in each group using units of 3.

177

©2015 Great Minds. eureka-math.org
G3-M1-TE-B1-1.3.1-01.2016

3. Camille buys a sheet of stamps that measures 15 centimeters long. Each stamp is 3 centimeters long. How many stamps does Camille buy? Draw and label a tape diagram to solve.

Camille buys ____5____ stamps.

4. (30)
Thirty third-graders go on a field trip. They are equally divided into 3 vans. How many students are in each van?

5. Some friends spend $24 altogether on frozen yogurt. Each person pays $3. How many people buy frozen yogurt?

Lesson 13:   Interpret the quotient as the number of groups or the number of objects in each group using units of 3.

EUREKA
MATH

Name _____     Date _____

1. Andrea has 21 apple slices.  She uses 3 apple slices to decorate 1 pie.  How many pies does Andrea make?  Draw and label a tape diagram to solve.

2. There are 24 soccer players on the field.  They form 3 equal teams.  How many players are on each team?

Lesson 13:   Interpret the quotient as the number of groups or the number of objects in each group using units of 3.

©2015 Great Minds. eureka-math.org
G3-M1-TE-B1-1.3.1-01.2016

179

Name _____      Date _____

1. Fill in the blanks to make true number sentences.

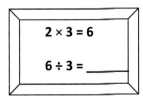
$2 \times 3 = 6$

$6 \div 3 = $ _____

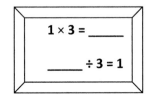
$1 \times 3 = $ _____

_____ $\div 3 = 1$

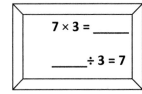
$7 \times 3 = $ _____

_____ $\div 3 = 7$

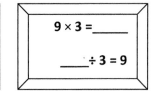
$9 \times 3 = $ _____

_____ $\div 3 = 9$

2. Ms. Gillette's pet fish are shown below. She keeps 3 fish in each tank.

   a. Circle to show how many fish tanks she has. Then, skip-count to find the total number of fish.

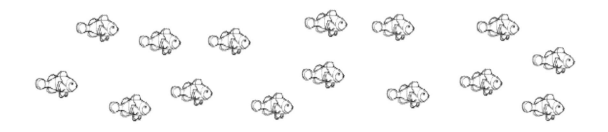

   b. Draw and label a tape diagram to represent the problem.

_____ $\div 3 = $ _____

Ms. Gillette has _____ fish tanks.

EUREKA
MATH

3. Juan buys 18 meters of wire. He cuts the wire into pieces that are each 3 meters long. How many pieces of wire does he cut?

4. A teacher has 24 pencils. They are divided equally among 3 students. How many pencils does each student get?

5. There are 27 third-graders working in groups of 3. How many groups of third-graders are there?

Lesson 13:   Interpret the quotient as the number of groups or the number of
             objects in each group using units of 3.

©2015 Great Minds. eureka-math.org
G3-M1-TE-B1-1.3.1-01.2016

181

**Mathematics Curriculum**

3 GRADE

## Topic E

# Multiplication and Division Using Units of 4

**3.OA.5, 3.OA.7,** 3.OA.1, 3.OA.2, 3.OA.3, 3.OA.4, 3.OA.6

| | | |
|---|---|---|
| **Focus Standard:** | 3.OA.5 | Apply properties of operations as strategies to multiply and divide. *Examples: If 6 × 4 = 24 is known, then 4 × 6 = 24 is also known. (Commutative property of multiplication.) 3 × 5 × 2 can be found by 3 × 5 = 15, then 15 × 2 = 30, or by 5 × 2 = 10, then 3 × 10 = 30. (Associative property of multiplication.) Knowing that 8 × 5 = 40 and 8 × 2 = 16, one can find 8 × 7 as 8 × (5 + 2) = (8 × 5) + (8 × 2) = 40 + 16 = 56. (Distributive property.)* |
| | 3.OA.7 | Fluently multiply and divide within 100, using strategies such as the relationship between multiplication and division (e.g., knowing that 8 × 5 = 40, one knows 40 ÷ 5 = 8) or properties of operations. By the end of Grade 3, know from memory all products of two one-digit numbers. |
| **Instructional Days:** | 4 | |
| **Coherence  -Links from:** | G2–M6 | Foundations of Multiplication and Division |
| **-Links to:** | G4–M3 | Multi-Digit Multiplication and Division |

Topic E begins by introducing students to multiplication by 4 through skip-counting objects in array models in Lesson 14. Students revisit the commutative property in Lesson 15, this time modeling commutativity using both arrays and tape diagrams. For example, students might initially draw a 2 × 4 array and a 4 × 2 array. Then, they see 2 bars of equal length, one with 4 equal parts and the other with 2 equal parts. Now, they have arrays that show (2 × 4) = (4 × 2), as well as tape diagrams that reflect the equality. In Lesson 16, students examine the distributive property in greater depth. This lesson introduces the 5 + *n* pattern as a strategy for finding unknown facts involving 4. For example, students know that 4 × 5 is 20, so 4 × 6 is the same as 20 + 4 more, which totals 24. By Lesson 17, practice of multiplication and division facts is dedicated to modeling the relationship between operations using facts of 4.

**EUREKA MATH**

**A Teaching Sequence Toward Mastery of Multiplication and Division Using Units of 4**

**Objective 1:** Skip-count objects in models to build fluency with multiplication facts using units of 4.
(Lesson 14)

**Objective 2:** Relate arrays to tape diagrams to model the commutative property of multiplication.
(Lesson 15)

**Objective 3:** Use the distributive property as a strategy to find related multiplication facts.
(Lesson 16)

**Objective 4:** Model the relationship between multiplication and division.
(Lesson 17)

# Lesson 14

Objective: Skip-count objects in models to build fluency with multiplication facts using units of 4.

## Suggested Lesson Structure

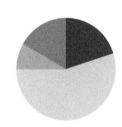

- ■ Fluency Practice      (12 minutes)
- ■ Application Problem      (5 minutes)
- ■ Concept Development      (33 minutes)
- ■ Student Debrief      (10 minutes)

     **Total Time**      **(60 minutes)**

## Fluency Practice  (12 minutes)

- ▪ Sprint: Multiply or Divide by 3 **3.OA.7**      (9 minutes)
- ▪ Read Tape Diagrams **3.OA.3**      (3 minutes)

### Sprint: Multiply or Divide by 3  (9 minutes)

Materials:   (S) Multiply or Divide by 3 Sprint

Note: This activity builds fluency with multiplication and division using units of 3.  It works toward students' fluency within 100.  See Lesson 2 for the directions for administering a Sprint.

Instead of movement exercises between Sprints, have students:

- ▪ Count by twos to 20 forward and backward.
- ▪ Count by fours to 40 forward and backward.

### Read Tape Diagrams  (3 minutes)

Materials:   (S) Personal white board

Note: Students practice *reading* the difference between the value of the unit (the size of the groups) and the number of units.  The activity anticipates using the tape diagram as a model for commutativity.

- T: (Project a tape diagram partitioned into 5 equal units, drawing 2 stars in the first unit.)  What is the value of each unit?
- S: 2 stars.
- T: How many units are there?
- S: 5 units.

Lesson 14:    Skip-count objects in models to build fluency with multiplication facts using units of 4.

**EUREKA MATH**™

T: Write a multiplication sentence for this tape diagram.

S: (Write 5 × 2 = 10.)

Repeat the process, alternating between finding the number of groups and the size of the groups, for 4 × 3 = 12, 8 ÷ 4 = 2, and 15 ÷ 3 = 5.

## Application Problem (5 minutes)

Jackie buys 21 pizzas for a party. She places 3 pizzas on each table. How many tables are there?

Note: This problem reviews division from Lesson 13 where the unknown is the number of groups. In preparation for today's lesson, the teacher might choose to have students solve by skip-counting to add units until they reach the total of 21.

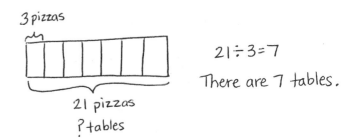

$$21 \div 3 = 7$$

There are 7 tables.

## Concept Development (33 minutes)

Materials: (S) Personal white board, fours array (Template) (pictured below)

**Problem 1: Skip-count by fours using an array to multiply.**

Students start with the template inserted into their personal white board.

T: Let's count to 40 using the array. Hum the number you count as you point to each dot. For the last dot in each row, say the number out loud and write it to the right of the row.

S: Hum, hum, hum, 4. (Write 4. Continue counting in this manner to 40.)

T: At the signal, tell what unit we counted by. (Signal.)

S: Fours!

T: I will say a multiplication expression. You find the answer on your array. Write the expression and an equal sign next to the answer to make an equation. (Say expressions that correspond to the array out of order, for example, 4 × 4, 9 × 4, etc.)

S: (Write expressions and equal signs next to each answer.)

T: I will say the answer; you say the equation. 20.

S: 20 = 5 × 4.

### NOTES ON MULTIPLE MEANS OF REPRESENTATION:

It may be tempting to skip the template for this problem; however, the template helps visual learners connect spoken numbers with their physical value. It illustrates the relationship between counting by fours and multiplying with units of 4.

*Fours Array Template (Labeled)*

Lesson 14: Skip-count objects in models to build fluency with multiplication facts using units of 4.

185

©2015 Great Minds. eureka-math.org
G3-M1-TE-B1-1.3.1-01.2016

**Problem 2: Use a tape diagram to model and solve multiplication.**

T: Draw a tape diagram that represents the number of groups shown on the array template.

S: (Draw a rectangle partitioned into 10 units and label it as *10 groups*.)

T: Tell your partner the number of objects in each group, and then draw and label that information on your diagram.

S: There are 4 objects in each group. (Label 1 unit as *4 objects*.)

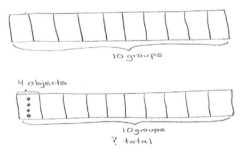

**NOTES ON MULTIPLE MEANS OF ACTION AND EXPRESSION:**

This is the first formal experience in Grade 3 using a tape diagram to model multiplication. Some students may have used one to solve the Application Problem in Lesson 12. If they need additional help identifying known and unknown information, prompt them to look back at the array, and then have them articulate the meaning of each factor.

T: Label the unknown on your diagram. Check your work with your partner's.

S: (Label the total unknown and check with a partner.)

T: Skip-count units to find the total value of your tape diagram.

S: 4, 8, 12, 16, 20, 24, 28, 32, 36, 40.

T: Write and solve an equation to represent the problem.

S: (Write 10 × 4 = 40.)

Repeat the process using 7 × 4 and 4 × 5. Consider asking students to draw the arrays, or vary practice by adding context to one or both of these problems.

## Problem Set (10 minutes)

Students should do their personal best to complete the Problem Set within the allotted 10 minutes. For some classes, it may be appropriate to modify the assignment by specifying which problems they work on first. Some problems do not specify a method for solving. Students should solve these problems using the RDW approach used for Application Problems.

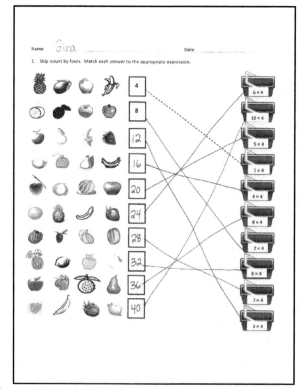

**Lesson 14:**    Skip-count objects in models to build fluency with multiplication facts using units of 4.

EUREKA MATH

## Student Debrief  (10 minutes)

**Lesson Objective:** Skip-count objects in models to build fluency with multiplication facts using units of 4.

The Student Debrief is intended to invite reflection and active processing of the total lesson experience.

Invite students to review their solutions for the Problem Set.  They should check work by comparing answers with a partner before going over answers as a class.  Look for misconceptions or misunderstandings that can be addressed in the Debrief.  Guide students in a conversation to debrief the Problem Set and process the lesson.

Any combination of the questions below may be used to lead the discussion.

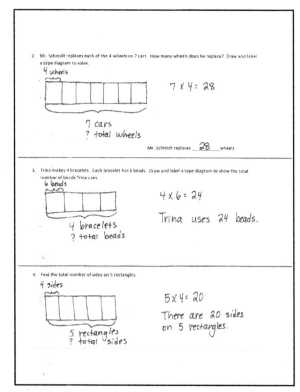

- **MP.4**
  - Discuss differences between the tape diagrams and unknowns in Problems 2 and 3.  (In Problem 2, the value of the unit is four, and in Problem 3, the number 4 represents the number of units.)

- If you were to skip-count to solve Problem 3, what would you skip-count by?  How would that be different from a skip-counting strategy to solve Problem 4?

- Could you skip-count Problem 4 without drawing a model?  How?

- How did the array in Problem 1 help you solve the other problems on the Problem Set?

## Exit Ticket  (3 minutes)

After the Student Debrief, instruct students to complete the Exit Ticket.  A review of their work will help with assessing students' understanding of the concepts that were presented in today's lesson and planning more effectively for future lessons.  The questions may be read aloud to the students.

---

Lesson 14:    Skip-count objects in models to build fluency with multiplication facts using units of 4.

187

©2015 Great Minds. eureka-math.org
G3-M1-TE-B1-1.3.1-01.2016

## A

Number Correct: _____

Multiply or Divide by 3

| | | | | | | |
|---|---|---|---|---|---|---|
| 1. | 2 × 3 = | 6 | 23. | __ × 3 = 30 | 10 |
| 2. | 3 × 3 = | 9 | 24. | __ × 3 = 6 | 2 |
| 3. | 4 × 3 = | 12 | 25. | __ × 3 = 9 | 3 |
| 4. | 5 × 3 = | 15 | 26. | 30 ÷ 3 = | 10 |
| 5. | 1 × 3 = | 3 | 27. | 15 ÷ 3 = | 5 |
| 6. | 6 ÷ 3 = | 2 | 28. | 3 ÷ 1 = | 3 |
| 7. | 9 ÷ 3 = | 3 | 29. | 6 ÷ 3 = | 2 |
| 8. | 15 ÷ 3 = | 5 | 30. | 9 ÷ 3 = | 3 |
| 9. | 3 ÷ 1 = | 3 | 31. | __ × 3 = 18 | 6 |
| 10. | 12 ÷ 3 = | 4 | 32. | __ × 3 = 21 | 7 |
| 11. | 6 × 3 = | 18 | 33. | __ × 3 = 27 | 9 |
| 12. | 7 × 3 = | 21 | 34. | __ × 3 = 24 | 8 |
| 13. | 8 × 3 = | 24 | 35. | 21 ÷ 3 = | 7 |
| 14. | 9 × 3 = | 27 | 36. | 27 ÷ 3 = | 9 |
| 15. | 10 × 3 = | 30 | 37. | 18 ÷ 3 = | 6 |
| 16. | 24 ÷ 3 = | 8 | 38. | 24 ÷ 3 = | 8 |
| 17. | 21 ÷ 3 = | 7 | 39. | 11 × 3 = | 33 |
| 18. | 27 ÷ 3 = | 9 | 40. | 33 ÷ 3 = | 11 |
| 19. | 18 ÷ 3 = | 6 | 41. | 12 × 3 = | 36 |
| 20. | 30 ÷ 3 = | 10 | 42. | 36 ÷ 3 = | 12 |
| 21. | __ × 3 = 15 | 5 | 43. | 13 × 3 = | 39 |
| 22. | __ × 3 = 12 | 4 | 44. | 39 ÷ 3 = | 13 |

Lesson 14: Skip-count objects in models to build fluency with multiplication facts using units of 4.

EUREKA MATH™

# B

Number Correct: _____

Improvement: _____

Multiply or Divide by 3

| | | |
|---|---|---|
| 1. | 1 × 3 = | 3 |
| 2. | 2 × 3 = | 6 |
| 3. | 3 × 3 = | 9 |
| 4. | 4 × 3 = | 12 |
| 5. | 5 × 3 = | 15 |
| 6. | 9 ÷ 3 = | 3 |
| 7. | 6 ÷ 3 = | 2 |
| 8. | 12 ÷ 3 = | 4 |
| 9. | 3 ÷ 1 = | 3 |
| 10. | 15 ÷ 3 = | 5 |
| 11. | 10 × 3 = | 30 |
| 12. | 6 × 3 = | 18 |
| 13. | 7 × 3 = | 21 |
| 14. | 8 × 3 = | 24 |
| 15. | 9 × 3 = | 27 |
| 16. | 21 ÷ 3 = | 7 |
| 17. | 18 ÷ 3 = | 6 |
| 18. | 24 ÷ 3 = | 8 |
| 19. | 30 ÷ 3 = | 10 |
| 20. | 27 ÷ 3 = | 9 |
| 21. | __ × 3 = 12 | 4 |
| 22. | __ × 3 = 15 | 5 |

| | | |
|---|---|---|
| 23. | __ × 3 = 6 | 2 |
| 24. | __ × 3 = 30 | 10 |
| 25. | __ × 3 = 9 | 3 |
| 26. | 6 ÷ 3 = | 2 |
| 27. | 3 ÷ 1 = | 3 |
| 28. | 30 ÷ 3 = | 10 |
| 29. | 15 ÷ 3 = | 5 |
| 30. | 9 ÷ 3 = | 3 |
| 31. | __ × 3 = 18 | 6 |
| 32. | __ × 3 = 24 | 8 |
| 33. | __ × 3 = 27 | 9 |
| 34. | __ × 3 = 21 | 7 |
| 35. | 24 ÷ 3 = | 8 |
| 36. | 27 ÷ 3 = | 9 |
| 37. | 18 ÷ 3 = | 6 |
| 38. | 21 ÷ 3 = | 7 |
| 39. | 11 × 3 = | 33 |
| 40. | 33 ÷ 3 = | 11 |
| 41. | 12 × 3 = | 36 |
| 42. | 36 ÷ 3 = | 12 |
| 43. | 13 × 3 = | 39 |
| 44. | 39 ÷ 3 = | 13 |

EUREKA
MATH™

Lesson 14: Skip-count objects in models to build fluency with multiplication facts using units of 4.

189

©2015 Great Minds. eureka-math.org
G3-M1-TE-B1-1.3.1-01.2016

Name _____ Date _____

1. Skip-count by fours. Match each answer to the appropriate expression.

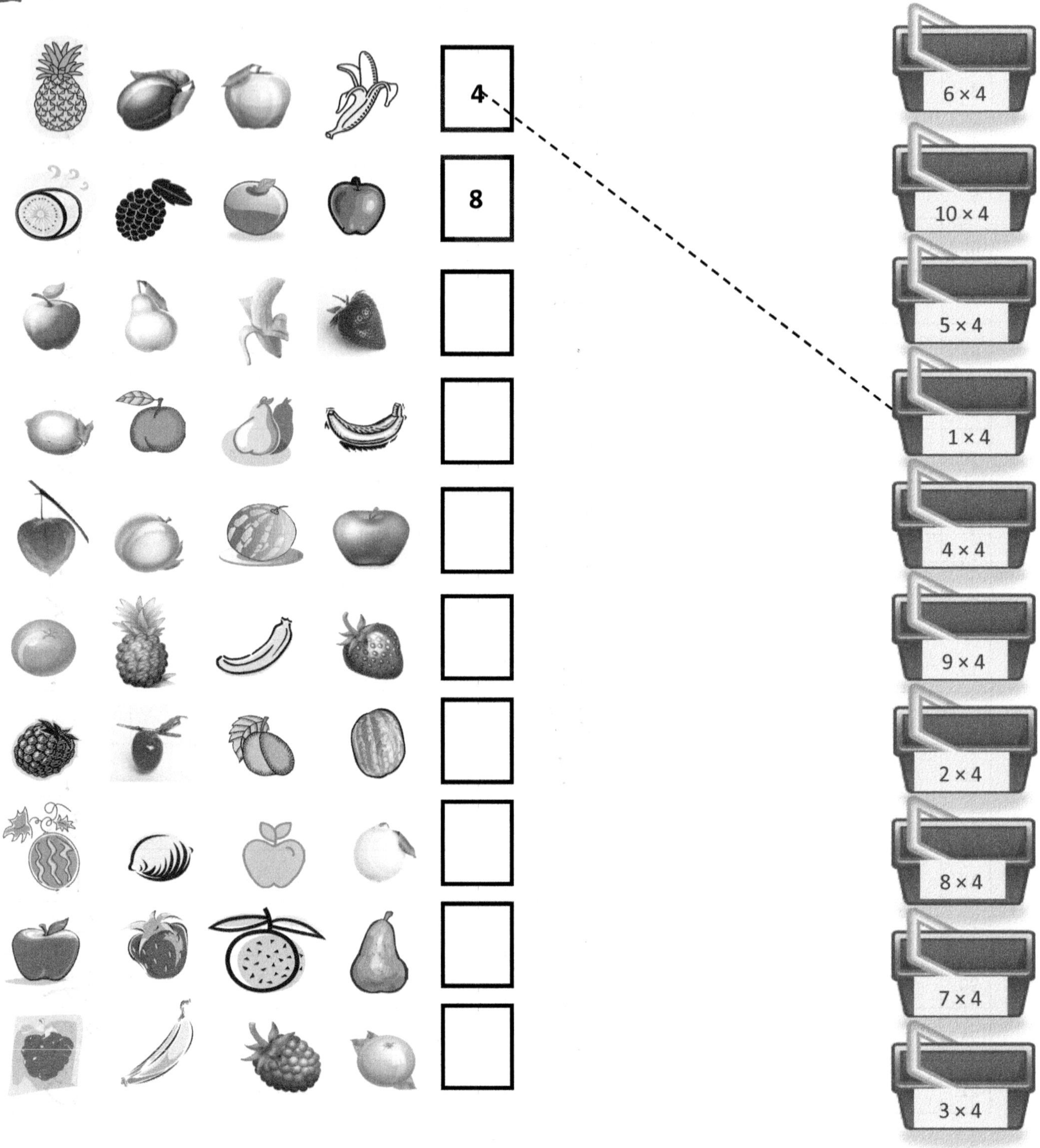

| | |
|---|---|
| 4 | |
| 8 | |
| | |
| | |
| | |
| | |
| | |
| | |
| | |
| | |

6 × 4

10 × 4

5 × 4

1 × 4

4 × 4

9 × 4

2 × 4

8 × 4

7 × 4

3 × 4

Lesson 14:    Skip-count objects in models to build fluency with multiplication facts using units of 4.

EUREKA MATH

2. Mr. Schmidt replaces each of the 4 wheels on 7 cars. How many wheels does he replace? Draw and label a <u>tape diagram</u> to solve.

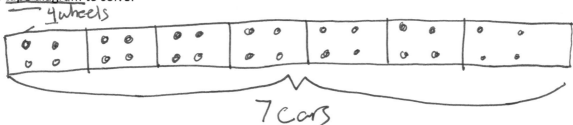

4 wheels

7 cars

Mr. Schmidt replaces ____28____ wheels.

3. Trina makes 4 bracelets. Each bracelet has 6 beads. Draw and label a tape diagram to show the total number of beads Trina uses.

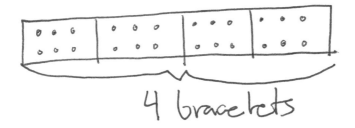

4 bracelets

$4 \times 6 = 24$ beads

4. Find the total number of sides on 5 rectangles.

Name _____ Date _____

Arthur has 4 boxes of chocolates.  Each box has 6 chocolates inside.  How many chocolates does Arthur have altogether?  Draw and label a tape diagram to solve.

Name _____   Date _____

1.  Skip-count by fours.  Match each answer to the appropriate expression.

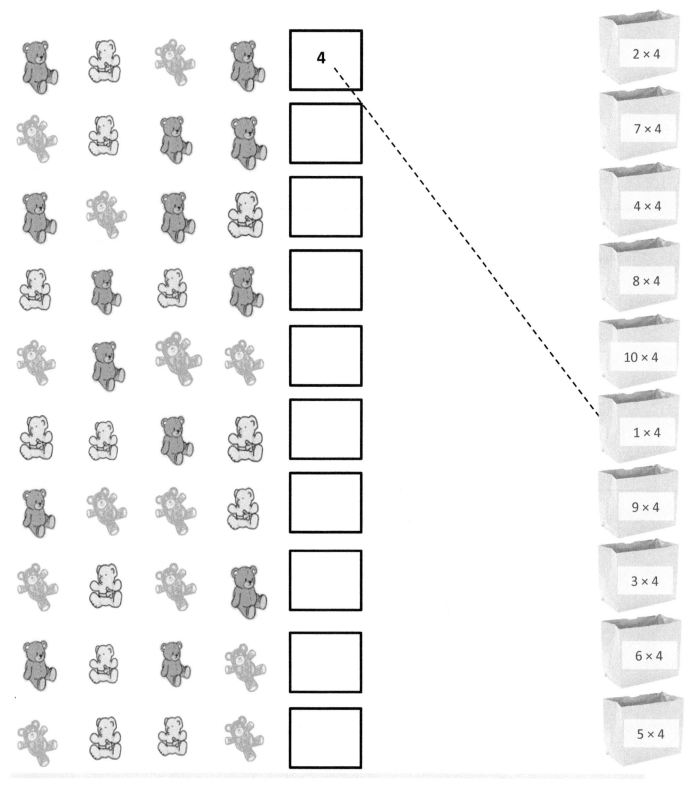

**Lesson 14:**   Skip-count objects in models to build fluency with multiplication facts
using units of 4.

©2015 Great Minds. eureka-math.org
G3-M1-TE-B1-1.3.1-01.2016

**193**

2. Lisa places 5 rows of 4 juice boxes in the refrigerator. Draw an array and skip-count to find the total number of juice boxes.

There are _____ juice boxes in total.

3. Six folders are placed on each table. How many folders are there on 4 tables? Draw and label a tape diagram to solve.

4. Find the total number of corners on 8 squares.

Lesson 14: Skip-count objects in models to build fluency with multiplication facts using units of 4.

©2015 Great Minds. eureka-math.org
G3-M1-TE-B1-1.3.1-01.2016

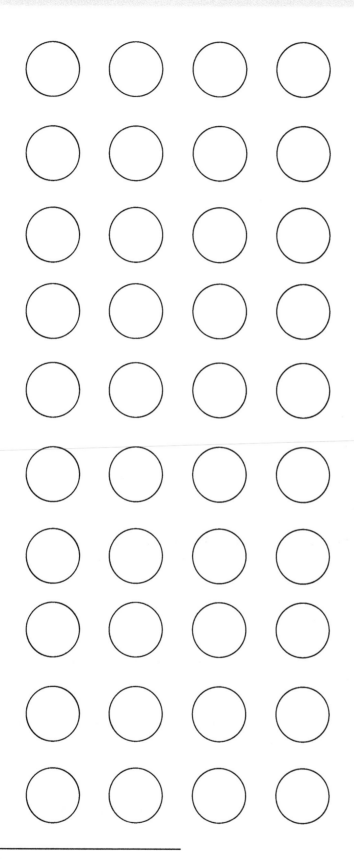

fours array

Lesson 14:   Skip-count objects in models to build fluency with multiplication facts using units of 4.

195

©2015 Great Minds. eureka-math.org
G3-M1-TE-B1-1.3.1-01.2016

# Lesson 15

Objective: Relate arrays to tape diagrams to model the commutative property of multiplication.

## Suggested Lesson Structure

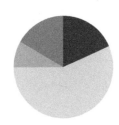

■ Fluency Practice          (11 minutes)
■ Application Problem        (5 minutes)
□ Concept Development        (34 minutes)
■ Student Debrief           (10 minutes)
  **Total Time**            **(60 minutes)**

## Fluency Practice  (11 minutes)

- Multiply by 4 Pattern Sheet  **3.OA.7**          (8 minutes)
- Group Counting  **3.OA.1**                       (3 minutes)

## Multiply by 4  (8 minutes)

Materials:   (S) Multiply by 4 (1–5) (Pattern Sheet)

Note: This activity builds fluency with multiplication facts using units of 4. It works toward the goal of students knowing from memory all products of two one-digit numbers. See Lesson 9 for the directions for administering a Multiply-By Pattern Sheet.

  T:   (Write 5 × 4 = _____.) Let's skip-count up by fours to find the answer. (Count with fingers to 5 as students count. Record the skip-count answers on the board.)

  S:   4, 8, 12, 16, 20.

  T:   (Circle 20 and write 5 × 4 = 20 above it. Write 4 × 4 = _____.) Let's skip-count up by fours again. (Count with fingers to 4 as students count.)

  S:   4, 8, 12, 16.

  T:   Let's see how we can skip-count down to find the answer to 4 × 4. Start at 20. (Count down with fingers as students say numbers.)

  S:   20, 16.

Repeat the process for 3 × 4.

  T:   Let's practice multiplying by 4. Be sure to work left to right across the page. (Distribute Multiply by 4 Pattern Sheet.)

## Group Counting  (3 minutes)

Note:  Group counting reviews interpreting multiplication as repeated addition.  Counting by twos and threes in this activity reviews multiplication with units of 2 and 3 from Topics C and D.

- T:   Let's count by twos.  (Direct students to count forward and backward to 20.)
- T:   Let's count by threes.  (Direct students to count forward and backward to 30.)

## Application Problem  (5 minutes)

A cell phone is about 4 inches long.  About how long are 9 cell phones laid end to end?

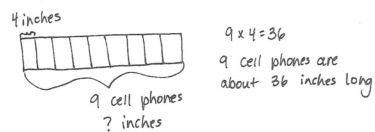

Note:  This problem reviews multiplication using units of 4 from Lesson 14.  It provides an opportunity to review using tape diagrams as tools for solving multiplication problems, which students further explore in today's lesson.

## Concept Development  (34 minutes)

Materials:  (S) Personal white board, blank paper with $\frac{1}{3}$ folded (shown to the right)

**Pictorial:  Relate arrays to tape diagrams.**

Each student starts with one piece of blank, folded paper (shown to the right).

- T:   Draw an array with 2 rows and 4 columns above the fold on your paper.  Use the array to remind your partner about what the commutative property is.  Turn your paper if you need to.
- S:   (May rotate array 90 degrees.)  The factors can switch places or trade meanings, but the total stays the same.
- T:   Use the commutative property to write two multiplication equations for the array.  Write them on the left side of the paper below the fold, one above the other.
- S:   (Write 2 × 4 = 8 and 4 × 2 = 8.)
- T:   Next to each equation, draw and label a tape diagram to match.  Make sure the diagrams are the same size because they both represent the same total.

S:  (Draw two diagrams, shown to the right.)

T:  Explain to a partner how your tape diagrams relate to the array.

S:  (Discuss.)

T:  The array shows commutativity, and so do the tape diagrams as we **MP.7** compare them.  Why is that true?

S:  What the factors represent in the tape diagrams changes to number of units or size of units.  It depends on what the factors represent in the equations or in the array.  → The tape diagrams are just a different way to represent the multiplication.

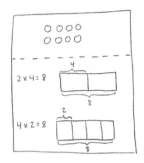

Repeat the process with 9 × 4.  To facilitate comparing tape diagrams, remind students to draw diagrams of the same size.

**Pictorial–Abstract:  Model commutativity using arrays and tape diagrams.**

Provide students with two examples:  5 × 4 and 4 × 7.

Make further practice less guided.  Ask students to do the following:

- Draw arrays to match the expressions.
- Write two equations for each array.
- Draw and label tape diagrams to represent the commutativity for each set of facts.

After they have completed both examples, invite students to share and discuss their work.

T:  Why is it that an array can show two multiplication sentences, but a tape diagram can only show one multiplication sentence?

S:  Because if you turn the tape diagram, the number of units and their size doesn't change. They just look different.  → That's why we need two tape diagrams to model the commutativity of one array.

## Problem Set  (10 minutes)

Students should do their personal best to complete the Problem Set within the allotted 10 minutes.  For some classes, it may be appropriate to modify the assignment by specifying which problems they work on first.  Some problems do not specify a method for solving.  Students should solve these problems using the RDW approach used for Application Problems.

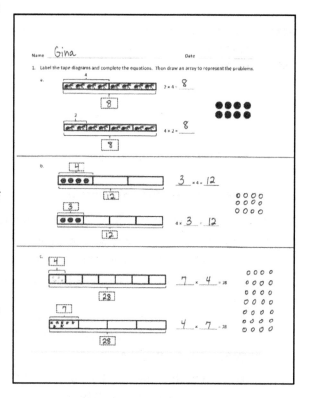

198          Lesson 15:      Relate arrays to tape diagrams to model the commutative property of
                                   multiplication.

                    ©2015 Great Minds. eureka-math.org
                    G3-M1-TE-B1-1.3.1-01.2016

EUREKA MATH™

## Student Debrief  (10 minutes)

**Lesson Objective:** Relate arrays to tape diagrams to model the commutative property of multiplication.

The Student Debrief is intended to invite reflection and active processing of the total lesson experience.

Invite students to review their solutions for the Problem Set. They should check work by comparing answers with a partner before going over answers as a class. Look for misconceptions or misunderstandings that can be addressed in the Debrief. Guide students in a conversation to debrief the Problem Set and process the lesson.

Any combination of the questions below may be used to lead the discussion.

- Students may have drawn different arrays for Problems 1(a), 1(b), and 1(c). Compare differences and discuss why both arrays reflect both diagrams.

- Compare Problems 3 and 4. Notice the model of commutativity even with different contexts.

- How do the array and the two tape diagrams show commutativity?

- How does the commutative property help us learn new multiplication facts?

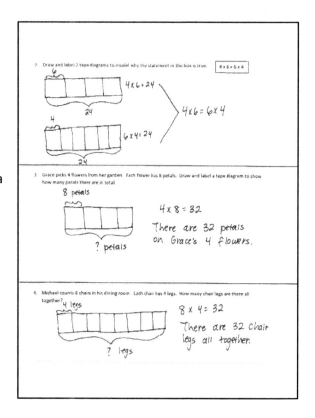

## Exit Ticket  (3 minutes)

After the Student Debrief, instruct students to complete the Exit Ticket. A review of their work will help with assessing students' understanding of the concepts that were presented in today's lesson and planning more effectively for future lessons. The questions may be read aloud to the students.

NOTES ON
MULTIPLE MEANS
OF ENGAGEMENT:

The last bullet anticipates **3.OA.9**, not formally taught until Module 3. Students who need a challenge may use the commutative property to write known facts using units of 2, 3, 4, 5, and 10. They will realize they already know more than half of their facts!

Lesson 15:  Relate arrays to tape diagrams to model the commutative property of multiplication.

199

©2015 Great Minds. eureka-math.org
G3-M1-TE-B1-1.3.1-01.2016

Multiply.

| | | | |
|---|---|---|---|
| 4 x 1 = _____ | 4 x 2 = _____ | 4 x 3 = _____ | 4 x 4 = _____ |
| 4 x 5 = _____ | 4 x 1 = _____ | 4 x 2 = _____ | 4 x 1 = _____ |
| 4 x 3 = _____ | 4 x 1 = _____ | 4 x 4 = _____ | 4 x 1 = _____ |
| 4 x 5 = _____ | 4 x 1 = _____ | 4 x 2 = _____ | 4 x 3 = _____ |
| 4 x 2 = _____ | 4 x 4 = _____ | 4 x 2 = _____ | 4 x 5 = _____ |
| 4 x 2 = _____ | 4 x 1 = _____ | 4 x 2 = _____ | 4 x 3 = _____ |
| 4 x 1 = _____ | 4 x 3 = _____ | 4 x 2 = _____ | 4 x 3 = _____ |
| 4 x 4 = _____ | 4 x 3 = _____ | 4 x 5 = _____ | 4 x 3 = _____ |
| 4 x 4 = _____ | 4 x 1 = _____ | 4 x 4 = _____ | 4 x 2 = _____ |
| 4 x 4 = _____ | 4 x 3 = _____ | 4 x 4 = _____ | 4 x 5 = _____ |
| 4 x 4 = _____ | 4 x 5 = _____ | 4 x 1 = _____ | 4 x 5 = _____ |
| 4 x 2 = _____ | 4 x 5 = _____ | 4 x 3 = _____ | 4 x 5 = _____ |
| 4 x 4 = _____ | 4 x 2 = _____ | 4 x 4 = _____ | 4 x 3 = _____ |
| 4 x 5 = _____ | 4 x 3 = _____ | 4 x 2 = _____ | 4 x 4 = _____ |
| 4 x 3 = _____ | 4 x 5 = _____ | 4 x 2 = _____ | 4 x 4 = _____ |

multiply by 4 (1–5)

**Lesson 15:** Relate arrays to tape diagrams to model the commutative property of multiplication.

EUREKA
MATH™

Name _____    Date _____

1.  Label the tape diagrams and complete the equations.  Then, draw an array to represent the problems.

a.

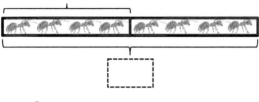

$2 \times 4 =$ _____

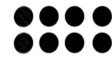

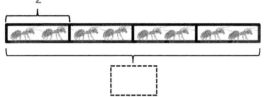

$4 \times 2 =$ _____

b.

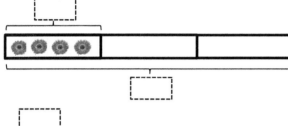

_____ $\times 4 =$ _____

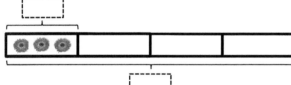

$4 \times$ _____ $=$ _____

 c.

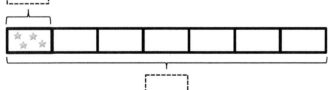

_____ $\times$ _____ $= 28$

_____ $\times$ _____ $= 28$

Lesson 15:    Relate arrays to tape diagrams to model the commutative property of multiplication.

201

2.  Draw and label 2 tape diagrams to model why the statement in the box is true.

$$4 \times 6 = 6 \times 4$$

3.  Grace picks 4 flowers from her garden.  Each flower has 8 petals.  Draw and label a tape diagram to show how many petals there are in total.

4.  Michael counts 8 chairs in his dining room.  Each chair has 4 legs.  How many chair legs are there altogether?

202        Lesson 15:        Relate arrays to tape diagrams to model the commutative property of
                              multiplication.

©2015 Great Minds. eureka-math.org
G3-M1-TE-B1-1.3.1-01.2016

EUREKA
MATH

Name _____     Date _____

Draw and label 2 tape diagrams to show that 4 × 3 = 3 × 4.  Use your diagrams to explain how you know the statement is true.

**Lesson 15:**     Relate arrays to tape diagrams to model the commutative property of multiplication.

©2015 Great Minds. eureka-math.org
G3-M1-TE-B1-1.3.1-01.2016

203

Name _____ Date _____

1. Label the tape diagrams and complete the equations. Then, draw an array to represent the problems.

a.

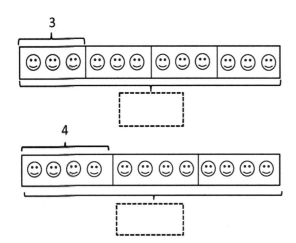

$4 \times 3 =$ _____

$3 \times 4 =$ _____

b.

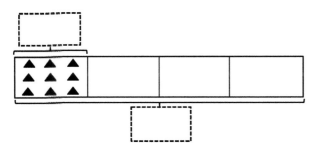

$4 \times$ _____ $=$ _____

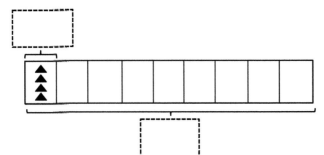

_____ $\times 4 =$ _____

Lesson 15: Relate arrays to tape diagrams to model the commutative property of multiplication.

EUREKA MATH

c.

_____ × 4 = _____

4 × _____ = _____

2. Seven clowns hold 4 balloons each at the fair.  Draw and label a tape diagram to show the total number of balloons the clowns hold.

3. George swims 7 laps in the pool each day.  How many laps does George swim after 4 days?

Lesson 15:   Relate arrays to tape diagrams to model the commutative property of multiplication.

205

©2015 Great Minds. eureka-math.org
G3-M1-TE-B1-1.3.1-01.2016

# Lesson 16

Objective:  Use the distributive property as a strategy to find related multiplication facts.

## Suggested Lesson Structure

■ Fluency Practice            (14 minutes)
▨ Application Problem         (5 minutes)
▢ Concept Development         (31 minutes)
■ Student Debrief            (10 minutes)

**Total Time**               **(60 minutes)**

## Fluency Practice  (14 minutes)

- Multiply by 4 Pattern Sheet  **3.OA.7**        (8 minutes)
- Group Counting  **3.OA.1**                     (3 minutes)
- Read Tape Diagrams  **3.OA.3**                 (3 minutes)

## Multiply by 4 Pattern Sheet  (8 minutes)

Materials:   (S) Multiply by 4 (6–10) (Pattern Sheet)

Note:  This activity builds fluency with multiplication facts using units of 4.  It works toward the goal of students knowing from memory all products of two one-digit numbers.  See Lesson 9 for the directions for administering a Multiply-By Pattern Sheet.

  T:   (Write 7 × 4 = _____.)  Let's skip-count up by fours to solve.  (Count with fingers to 7 as students count.)

  S:   4, 8, 12, 16, 20, 24, 28.

  T:   Let's skip-count up by fours starting at 5 fours or 20.

  S:   (Show 5 fingers to represent 5 fours, or 20.)  20, 24, 28.  (Count with fingers up to 7 fours as students count.)

  T:   Let's skip-count down to find the answer to 7 × 4.  Start at 10 fours or 40.  (Count down with fingers as students say numbers.)

  S:   40, 36, 32, 28.

Repeat the process of skip-counting up from 5 fours and down from 10 fours to solve 9 × 4 and 8 × 4. Distribute Multiply by 4 Pattern Sheet (6–10).

EUREKA
MATH™

## Group Counting (3 minutes)

Note: Group counting reviews interpreting multiplication as repeated addition. Counting by twos and threes in this activity reviews multiplication with units of 2 and 3 from Topics C and D.

- T: Let's count by twos. (Direct students to count forward and backward to 20.)
- T: Let's count by threes. (Direct students to count forward and backward to 30. Whisper the numbers between threes and speak each three out loud. For example, whisper 1, whisper 2, say 3, whisper 4, whisper 5, say 6, and so on.)

## Read Tape Diagrams (3 minutes)

Materials: (S) Personal white board

Note: Students practice reading the difference between the value of the unit (the size of the groups) and the number of units. The activity reviews using the tape diagram as a model for commutativity.

- T: (Project a tape diagram partitioned into 2 equal units. Draw 8 stars in each unit, and bracket the total with a question mark.) Say the addition sentence.
- S: 8 + 8 = 16.
- T: Say the multiplication sentence starting with the number of groups.
- S: 2 × 8 = 16.
- T: Draw the tape diagram, and label units with numbers instead of stars. Label the missing total. Beneath the diagram, write a multiplication sentence.
- S: (Draw a tape diagram with 8 written inside both units and 16 written as the total. Beneath the diagram, write 2 × 8 = 16.)

Repeat the process for 3 × 7 and 4 × 6.

## Application Problem (5 minutes)

Ms. Williams draws the array below to show the class seating chart. She sees the students in 4 rows of 7 when she teaches at Board 1. Use the commutative property to show how Ms. Williams sees the class when she teaches at Board 2.

Extension: On Monday, 6 students are absent. How many students are in class on Monday?

The first array shows 4 rows of 7. This array shows 7 rows of 4.

Extension: 7 × 4 = 28

28 − 6 = 22. There are 22 students in class on Monday.

Board 1

Board 2

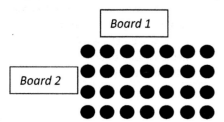

**EUREKA MATH**

**Lesson 16:** Use the distributive property as a strategy to find related multiplication facts.

207

©2015 Great Minds. eureka-math.org
G3-M1-TE-B1-1.3.1-01.2016

Note:  This problem reviews the commutative property from Lesson 15.  Students may use a tape diagram to show their solution.  The inclusion of the extension anticipates the two-step problem in the Lesson 17 Problem Set.  If appropriate for the class, present the extension.

## Concept Development  (31 minutes)

Materials:   (S) Personal white board, fours array (Lesson 14 Template) (pictured below)

**Problem 1:  Model the 5 + *n* pattern as a strategy for multiplying using units of 4.**

*Fours Array Template*

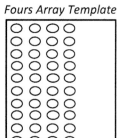

T:   Shade the part of the array that shows 5 × 4.

S:   (Shade 5 rows of 4.)

T:   Talk to your partner about how to box an array that shows (5 × 4) + (1 × 4), and then box it.

S:   The box should have one more row than what's shaded.  (Box 6 × 4.)

T:   What expression does the boxed array represent?

S:   6 × 4.

T:   Label the shaded and un-shaded arrays in your box with equations.

S:   (Write 5 × 4 = 20 and 1 × 4 = 4.)

T:   How can we combine our two multiplication equations to find the total number of dots?

S:   6 × 4 = 24, or 20 + 4 = 24.

Repeat the process with the following suggested examples:

- 5 × 4 and 2 × 4 to model 7 × 4
- 5 × 4 and 4 × 4 to model 9 × 4

T:   What expression did we use to help us solve all three problems?

S:   5 × 4.

T:   Talk to your partner.  Why do you think I asked you to solve using 5 × 4 each time?

S:   You can just count by fives to solve it.  → It equals 20.  It's easy to add other numbers to 20.

T:   Compare using 5 × 4 to solve your fours with 5 × 6 to solve your sixes and 5 × 8 to solve your eights.

S:   (Discuss.  Identify the ease of skip-counting and that the products are multiples of 10.)

T:   Now that you know how to use your fives, you have a way to solve 7 sixes as 5 sixes and 2 sixes or 7 eights as 5 eights and 2 eights.

**NOTES ON TEACHER BOARD:**

Keep track of the equations for all three examples.  As students reflect, they can refer to the visual on the class board to see that 5 × 4 is the consistent expression.

**NOTES ON MULTIPLE MEANS OF ACTION AND EXPRESSION:**

Minimize instructional changes as you repeat with different numbers.  Scaffolding problems using the same method allows students to generalize skills more easily.

Lesson 16:    Use the distributive property as a strategy to find related multiplication facts.

**Problem 2:  Apply the 5 + *n* pattern to decompose and solve larger facts.**

Students work in pairs.

T: Fold the template so that only 8 of the 10 rows are showing. We'll use the array that's left. What multiplication expression are we finding?

S: (Fold two rows away.) 8 × 4.

T: Use the strategy we practiced today to solve 8 × 4.

S: (Demonstrate one possible solution.) Let's shade and label 5 × 4. → Then, we can label the un-shaded part. → That's 3 × 4. → 5 × 4 = 20 and 3 × 4 = 12. → 20 + 12 = 32. → There are 32 in total.

T: (Write 8 × 4 = (5 × 4) + (3 × 4).) Talk with your partner about how you know this is true.

S: (Discuss.)

T: We can break a larger fact into two smaller facts to help us solve it. (Draw number bond shown to the right.) Here, we broke apart 8 fours into 5 fours and 3 fours to solve. So, we can write an equation, 8 fours = 5 fours + 3 fours. (Write equation on the board.)

T: (5 + 3) × 4 is another way of writing (5 × 4) + (3 × 4). Talk with your partner about why these expressions are the same.

S: (Discuss.)

T: True or false? In 5 × 4 and 3 × 4, the size of the groups is the same.

S: True!

T: Four represents the size of the groups. The expression (5 × 4) + (3 × 4) shows how we **distribute** the groups of 4. Since the size of the groups is the same, we can add the 5 fours and 3 fours to make 8 fours.

Repeat the process with the following suggested example:

- 10 × 4, modeled by doubling the product of 5 × 4

> **NOTES ON MULTIPLE MEANS OF ENGAGEMENT:**
>
> Have students who need an additional challenge decompose the same problem using facts other than 5 × 4. They should see that other strategies work as well. Compare strategies to prove the efficiency of 5 × 4.

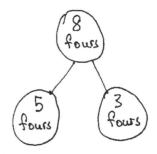

8 fours = 5 fours + 3 fours

8 × 4 = (5 × 4) + (3 × 4)

= (5 + 3) × 4

## Problem Set  (10 minutes)

Students should do their personal best to complete the Problem Set within the allotted 10 minutes. For some classes, it may be appropriate to modify the assignment by specifying which problems they work on first. Some problems do not specify a method for solving. Students should solve these problems using the RDW approach used for Application Problems.

**EUREKA MATH™**

Lesson 16:   Use the distributive property as a strategy to find related multiplication facts.

©2015 Great Minds. eureka-math.org
G3-M1-TE-B1-1.3.1-01.2016

**209**

## Student Debrief (10 minutes)

**Lesson Objective:** Use the distributive property as a strategy to find related multiplication facts.

The Student Debrief is intended to invite reflection and active processing of the total lesson experience.

Invite students to review their solutions for the Problem Set. They should check work by comparing answers with a partner before going over answers as a class. Look for misconceptions or misunderstandings that can be addressed in the Debrief. Guide students in a conversation to debrief the Problem Set and process the lesson.

Any combination of the questions below may be used to lead the discussion.

- Review vocabulary term **distribute**.
- Explain how breaking apart or finding the products of two smaller arrays helps find the product of a larger array in Problem 1(d).
- Share strategies for solving Problem 2.
- Explain the following sequence:

  $(5 + 3) \times 4 =$

  $(5 \times 4) + (3 \times 4) =$

  5 fours + 3 fours =

  8 fours =

  $8 \times 4 =$

- How does the sequence above show a number being distributed?
- Could the strategy we learned today change your approach to finding the total students in our Application Problem? Why or why not?
- Why would the strategy we learned today be helpful for solving an even larger fact like 15 × 4?

## Exit Ticket (3 minutes)

After the Student Debrief, instruct students to complete the Exit Ticket. A review of their work will help with assessing students' understanding of the concepts that were presented in today's lesson and planning more effectively for future lessons. The questions may be read aloud to the students.

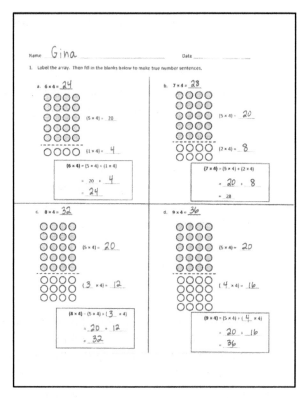

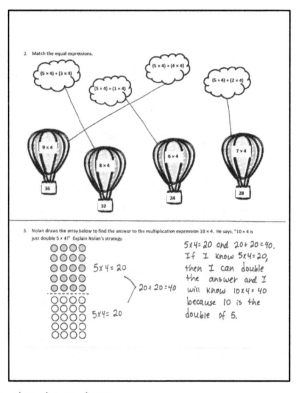

Lesson 16:   Use the distributive property as a strategy to find related multiplication facts.

©2015 Great Minds. eureka-math.org
G3-M1-TE-B1-1.3.1-01.2016

**EUREKA MATH**

Practice pg. 35

Multiply.

| | | | |
|---|---|---|---|
| 4 x 1 = _____ | 4 x 2 = _____ | 4 x 3 = _____ | 4 x 4 = _____ |
| **4 x 5 =** _____ | **4 x 6 =** _____ | **4 x 7 =** _____ | **4 x 8 =** _____ |
| 4 x 9 = _____ | 4 x 10 = _____ | 4 x 6 = _____ | 4 x 7 = _____ |
| **4 x 6 =** _____ | **4 x 8 =** _____ | **4 x 6 =** _____ | **4 x 9 =** _____ |
| 4 x 6 = _____ | 4 x 10 = _____ | 4 x 6 = _____ | 4 x 7 = _____ |
| **4 x 6 =** _____ | **4 x 7 =** _____ | **4 x 8 =** _____ | **4 x 7 =** _____ |
| 4 x 9 = _____ | 4 x 7 = _____ | 4 x 10 = _____ | 4 x 7 = _____ |
| **4 x 8 =** _____ | **4 x 6 =** _____ | **4 x 8 =** _____ | **4 x 7 =** _____ |
| 4 x 8 = _____ | 4 x 9 = _____ | 4 x 8 = _____ | 4 x 10 = _____ |
| **4 x 8 =** _____ | **4 x 9 =** _____ | **4 x 6 =** _____ | **4 x 9 =** _____ |
| 4 x 7 = _____ | 4 x 9 = _____ | 4 x 8 = _____ | 4 x 9 = _____ |
| **4 x 10 =** _____ | **4 x 9 =** _____ | **4 x 10 =** _____ | **4 x 6 =** _____ |
| 4 x 10 = _____ | 4 x 7 = _____ | 4 x 10 = _____ | 4 x 8 = _____ |
| **4 x 10 =** _____ | **4 x 9 =** _____ | **4 x 10 =** _____ | **4 x 6 =** _____ |
| 4 x 8 = _____ | 4 x 10 = _____ | 4 x 7 = _____ | 4 x 9 = _____ |

multiply by 4 (6–10)

EUREKA
MATH™

**Lesson 16:** Use the distributive property as a strategy to find related multiplication facts.

211

©2015 Great Minds. eureka-math.org
G3-M1-TE-B1-1.3.1-01.2016

Name _____  Date _____

1.  Label the array.  Then, fill in the blanks below to make true number sentences.

a.  **6 × 4 = _____**

(5 × 4) = __20__

(1 × 4) = _____

| **(6 × 4)** = (5 × 4) + (1 × 4) |
| --- |
| = __20__ + _____ |
| = _____ |

b.  **7 × 4 = _____**

(5 × 4) = _____

(2 × 4) = _____

| **(7 × 4)** = (5 × 4) + (2 × 4) |
| --- |
| = _____ + _____ |
| = __28__ |

c.  **8 × 4 = _____**

(5 × 4) = _____

(___ × 4) = _____

| **(8 × 4)** = (5 × 4) + (___ × 4) |
| --- |
| = _____ + _____ |
| = _____ |

d.  **9 × 4 = _____**

(5 × 4) = _____

(___ × 4) = _____

| **(9 × 4)** = (5 × 4) + (___ × 4) |
| --- |
| = _____ + _____ |
| = _____ |

**Lesson 16:**  Use the distributive property as a strategy to find related multiplication facts.

**EUREKA MATH**™

2. Match the equal expressions.

(5 × 4) + (3 × 4)

(5 × 4) + (1 × 4)

(5 × 4) + (4 × 4)

(5 × 4) + (2 × 4)

9 × 4

36

8 × 4

32

6 × 4

24

7 × 4

28

---

3. Nolan draws the array below to find the answer to the multiplication expression 10 × 4. He says, "10 × 4 is just double 5 × 4." Explain Nolan's strategy.

○ ○ ○ ○
○ ○ ○ ○
○ ○ ○ ○
○ ○ ○ ○
○ ○ ○ ○
- - - - - - - -
○ ○ ○ ○
○ ○ ○ ○
○ ○ ○ ○
○ ○ ○ ○
○ ○ ○ ○

EUREKA
MATH™

Lesson 16:    Use the distributive property as a strategy to find related multiplication facts.

213

©2015 Great Minds. eureka-math.org
G3-M1-TE-B1-1.3.1-01.2016

Name _____   Date _____

Destiny says, "I can use 5 × 4 to find the answer to 7 × 4." Use the array below to explain Destiny's strategy using words and numbers.

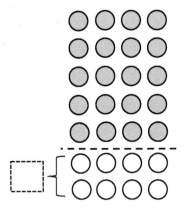

| (7 × 4) = (5 × 4) + (2 × 4) |
| --- |
| = _____ + _____ |
| = _____ |

**Lesson 16:**   Use the distributive property as a strategy to find related multiplication facts.

EUREKA MATH™

Name _____    Date _____

1.  Label the array.  Then, fill in the blanks below to make true number sentences.

a.  **6 × 4 =** $\underline{24}$

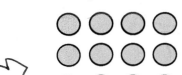

$(5 \times 4) = \underline{20}$

$(\underline{1} \times 4) = \underline{4}$

**(6 × 4) = (5 × 4) + (** $\underline{1}$ **× 4)**

= $\underline{20}$ + $\underline{4}$

= $\underline{24}$

b.  **8 × 4 =** _____

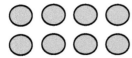

$(5 \times 4) =$ _____

$(\underline{\quad} \times 4) =$ _____

**(8 × 4) = (5 × 4) + (** _____ **× 4)**

= _____ + _____

= _____

EUREKA
MATH™

Lesson 16:    Use the distributive property as a strategy to find related multiplication
             facts.

215

©2015 Great Minds. eureka-math.org
G3-M1-TE-B1-1.3.1-01.2016

2.  Match the multiplication expressions with their answers.

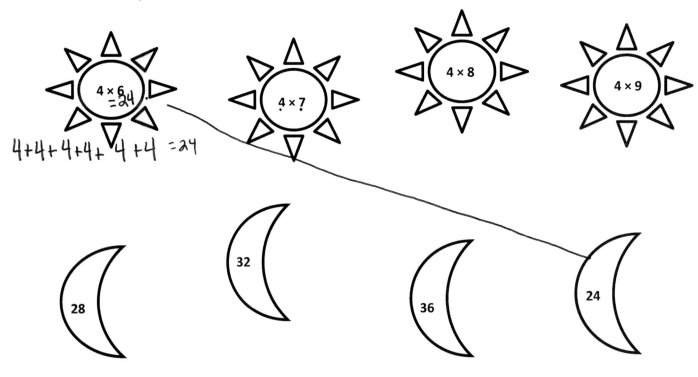

4×6
=24

4+4+4+4+4+4 =24

4×7

4×8

4×9

32

28

36

24

3.  The array below shows one strategy for solving 9 × 4. Explain the strategy using your own words.

(5 × 4) = _____

(4 × 4) = _____

Lesson 16:     Use the distributive property as a strategy to find related multiplication facts.

EUREKA
MATH

# Lesson 17

Objective:  Model the relationship between multiplication and division.

## Suggested Lesson Structure

■ Fluency Practice          (9 minutes)
▓ Application Problem        (5 minutes)
░ Concept Development        (36 minutes)
▨ Student Debrief           (10 minutes)
   **Total Time**            **(60 minutes)**

## Fluency Practice  (9 minutes)

▪ Sprint:  Multiply or Divide by 4  **3.OA.7**          (9 minutes)

### Sprint:  Multiply or Divide by 4  (9 minutes)

Materials:   (S) Multiply or Divide by 4 Sprint

Note:  Framing division through missing factors in multiplication sentences builds a strong foundation for understanding the relationships between multiplication and division.  See Lesson 2 for directions for administering a Sprint.

Between Sprints, include the following group counts in place of movement exercises.

  ▪ Count by twos to 20 forward and backward.
  ▪ Count by threes to 30, hum/talk forward and backward.  (Hum as you think 1, 2, say 3, hum 4, 5, say 6, etc.)
  ▪ Count by fives to 50 forward and backward.

## Application Problem  (5 minutes)

Mrs. Peacock bought 4 packs of yogurt.  She had exactly enough to give each of her 24 students 1 yogurt cup.  How many yogurt cups are there in 1 pack?

Note:  This problem is designed to lead into the Concept Development.  In Problem 1, students will analyze how a number bond represents the division expression 24 ÷ 4.

## Concept Development  (36 minutes)

Materials:   (S) Personal white board

**Problem 1:  Use the number bond to relate multiplication and division.**

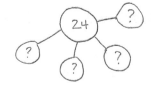

T:   (Draw or project the number bond shown to the right.) The number bond represents the division equation you wrote to solve the Application Problem.  Turn and tell your partner how it shows 24 ÷ 4.

S:   (Discuss.)

T:   Look back at the Application Problem.  Is the unknown in the number bond the same as the unknown in the division problem?  What does it represent?

S:   They're the same.  The unknown represents the size of the groups.

T:   (Project a second number bond where the total and one part are drawn.  Write __ × 4 = 24.) Skip-count by fours to find the unknown factor.  Each time you say a four, I will make a new part of my number bond.  (Draw the parts as students count.)

S:   4, 8, 12, 16, 20, 24.

T:   How many fours make 24?

S:   6 fours!

T:   So, 24 ÷ 4 equals…?

S:   6.

T:   The division equations are the same.  How do the quotients in the two number bonds represent different things?

S:   The 6 in the first number bond represents the size of the groups.  The 6 in the second number bond represents the number of groups.

Repeat the process with 32 ÷ 4.  (Model how the quotient can represent the number of groups or the size of the groups.)

T:   How do the multiplication and division equations relate in each example?

S:   I thought of the division equation like a multiplication equation with an unknown factor and skip-counted by fours until I reached the total.

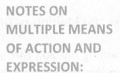

**NOTES ON MULTIPLE MEANS OF ACTION AND EXPRESSION:**

The expression 32 ÷ 4 is also used in Problem 3 of the Problem Set.  Because of the duplication, the suggested process for completing the Problem Set is to save Problem 3 until the end.  However, for some classes, it may prove useful to preview the example here and have students complete it as one of the first problems they do independently on the Problem Set.  This will build confidence by giving students an immediate sense of success.

**Problem 2:  Solve word problems to illustrate the relationship between multiplication and division.**

Write or project the following problem:  A classroom has tables that seat a total of 20 students.  Four students are seated at each table.  How many tables are in the classroom?

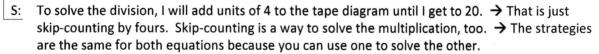

| | | |
|---|---|---|
| T: | Draw and label a tape diagram to represent the problem. | |
| S: | (Draw diagram shown to the right.) | |
| T: | Without solving, write a division equation and a multiplication | |
| **MP.2** | equation with an unknown factor to represent your drawing. | |
| S: | (Write 20 ÷ 4 = __ and __ × 4 = 20.) | |
| T: | What does the unknown in both problems represent? | |
| S: | The number of groups. | |
| T: | Tell your partner your strategy for solving each equation. | |
| S: | To solve the division, I will add units of 4 to the tape diagram until I get to 20.  → That is just skip-counting by fours.  Skip-counting is a way to solve the multiplication, too.  → The strategies are the same for both equations because you can use one to solve the other. | |
| T: | Solve both equations now. | |

Repeat the process with 16 ÷ 4.  (Problem 2 models division where the quotient represents the number of groups.)

## Problem Set  (10 minutes)

Students should do their personal best to complete the Problem Set within the allotted 10 minutes.  For some classes, it may be appropriate to modify the assignment by specifying which problems they work on first.  Some problems do not specify a method for solving.  Students should solve these problems using the RDW approach used for Application Problems.

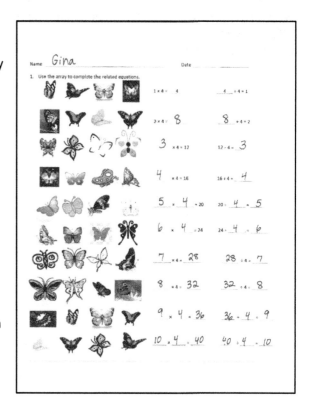

## Student Debrief  (10 minutes)

**Lesson Objective:**  Model the relationship between multiplication and division.

The Student Debrief is intended to invite reflection and active processing of the total lesson experience.

Invite students to review their solutions for the Problem Set.  They should check work by comparing answers with a partner before going over answers as a class.  Look for misconceptions or misunderstandings that can be addressed in the Debrief.  Guide students in a conversation to debrief the Problem Set and process the lesson.

Any combination of the questions below may be used to lead the discussion.

- In the first problem on the Problem Set, what patterns did you notice in the array?
- How did the patterns you noticed help you solve the multiplication and division sentences?
- Share student work from Problems 3 and 4. Students may have solved using number bonds or tape diagrams, multiplication, or division. Compare approaches.
- How can a number bond show both multiplication and division?
- Discuss: Division is an *unknown factor* problem.
- In Problems 3 and 4, the unknown is the size of each group. What is different about Problem 4? (It is a two-step problem.)

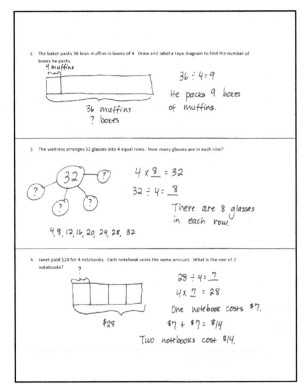

## Exit Ticket  (3 minutes)

After the Student Debrief, instruct students to complete the Exit Ticket. A review of their work will help with assessing students' understanding of the concepts that were presented in today's lesson and planning more effectively for future lessons. The questions may be read aloud to the students.

EUREKA MATH™

Practice: 11/13/19
Pg 37

Number Correct: _____

# A

Multiply or Divide by 4

| 1. | $2 \times 4 =$ | 8 |
|---|---|---|
| 2. | $3 \times 4 =$ | 12 |
| 3. | $4 \times 4 =$ | 16 |
| 4. | $5 \times 4 =$ | 20 |
| 5. | $1 \times 4 =$ | 4 |
| 6. | $8 \div 4 =$ | 2 |
| 7. | $12 \div 4 =$ | 3 |
| 8. | $20 \div 4 =$ | 5 |
| 9. | $4 \div 1 =$ | 4 |
| 10. | $16 \div 4 =$ | 4 |
| 11. | $6 \times 4 =$ | 24 |
| 12. | $7 \times 4 =$ | 28 |
| 13. | $8 \times 4 =$ | 32 |
| 14. | $9 \times 4 =$ | 36 |
| 15. | $10 \times 4 =$ | 40 |
| 16. | $32 \div 4 =$ | 8 |
| 17. | $28 \div 4 =$ | 7 |
| 18. | $36 \div 4 =$ | 9 |
| 19. | $24 \div 4 =$ | 6 |
| 20. | $40 \div 4 =$ | 10 |
| 21. | $\_\_ \times 4 = 20$ | 5 |
| 22. | $\_\_ \times 4 = 24$ | 6 |

| 23. | $\_\_ \times 4 = 40$ | 10 |
|---|---|---|
| 24. | $\_\_ \times 4 = 8$ | 2 |
| 25. | $\_\_ \times 4 = 12$ | 3 |
| 26. | $40 \div 4 =$ | 10 |
| 27. | $20 \div 4 =$ | 5 |
| 28. | $4 \div 1 =$ | 4 |
| 29. | $8 \div 4 =$ | 2 |
| 30. | $12 \div 4 =$ | 3 |
| 31. | $\_\_ \times 4 = 16$ | 4 |
| 32. | $\_\_ \times 4 = 28$ | 7 |
| 33. | $\_\_ \times 4 = 36$ | 9 |
| 34. | $\_\_ \times 4 = 32$ | 8 |
| 35. | $28 \div 4 =$ | 7 |
| 36. | $36 \div 4 =$ | 9 |
| 37. | $24 \div 4 =$ | 6 |
| 38. | $32 \div 4 =$ | 8 |
| 39. | $11 \times 4 =$ | 44 |
| 40. | $44 \div 4 =$ | 11 |
| 41. | $12 \div 4 =$ | 3 |
| 42. | $48 \div 4 =$ | 12 |
| 43. | $14 \times 4 =$ | 56 |
| 44. | $56 \div 4 =$ | 14 |

# B

Number Correct: _____

Improvement: _____

**Multiply or Divide by 4**

| | | | | | | |
|---|---|---|---|---|---|---|
| 1. | $1 \times 4 =$ | 4 | 23. | $\_\_ \times 4 = 8$ | 2 |
| 2. | $2 \times 4 =$ | 8 | 24. | $\_\_ \times 4 = 40$ | 10 |
| 3. | $3 \times 4 =$ | 12 | 25. | $\_\_ \times 4 = 12$ | 3 |
| 4. | $4 \times 4 =$ | 16 | 26. | $8 \div 4 =$ | 2 |
| 5. | $5 \times 4 =$ | 20 | 27. | $4 \div 1 =$ | 4 |
| 6. | $12 \div 4 =$ | 3 | 28. | $40 \div 4 =$ | 10 |
| 7. | $8 \div 4 =$ | 2 | 29. | $20 \div 4 =$ | 5 |
| 8. | $16 \div 4 =$ | 4 | 30. | $12 \div 4 =$ | 3 |
| 9. | $4 \div 1 =$ | 4 | 31. | $\_\_ \times 4 = 12$ | 3 |
| 10. | $20 \div 4 =$ | 5 | 32. | $\_\_ \times 4 = 24$ | 6 |
| 11. | $10 \times 4 =$ | 40 | 33. | $\_\_ \times 4 = 36$ | 9 |
| 12. | $6 \times 4 =$ | 24 | 34. | $\_\_ \times 4 = 28$ | 7 |
| 13. | $7 \times 4 =$ | 28 | 35. | $32 \div 4 =$ | 8 |
| 14. | $8 \times 4 =$ | 32 | 36. | $36 \div 4 =$ | 9 |
| 15. | $9 \times 4 =$ | 36 | 37. | $24 \div 4 =$ | 6 |
| 16. | $28 \div 4 =$ | 7 | 38. | $28 \div 4 =$ | 7 |
| 17. | $24 \div 4 =$ | 6 | 39. | $11 \times 4 =$ | 44 |
| 18. | $32 \div 4 =$ | 8 | 40. | $44 \div 4 =$ | 11 |
| 19. | $40 \div 4 =$ | 10 | 41. | $12 \times 4 =$ | 48 |
| 20. | $36 \div 4 =$ | 9 | 42. | $48 \div 4 =$ | 12 |
| 21. | $\_\_ \times 4 = 16$ | 4 | 43. | $13 \times 4 =$ | 52 |
| 22. | $\_\_ \times 4 = 20$ | 5 | 44. | $52 \div 4 =$ | 13 |

Lesson 17: Model the relationship between multiplication and division.

**EUREKA MATH**™

Name _____ Date _____

1. Use the array to complete the related equations.

$1 \times 4 = \underline{\quad 4 \quad}$          $\underline{\quad 4 \quad} \div 4 = 1$

$2 \times 4 = \underline{\qquad}$          $\underline{\qquad} \div 4 = 2$

$\underline{\qquad} \times 4 = 12$          $12 \div 4 = \underline{\qquad}$

$\underline{\qquad} \times 4 = 16$          $16 \div 4 = \underline{\qquad}$

$\underline{\qquad} \times \underline{\qquad} = 20$          $20 \div \underline{\qquad} = \underline{\qquad}$

$\underline{\qquad} \times \underline{\qquad} = 24$          $24 \div \underline{\qquad} = \underline{\qquad}$

    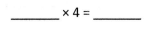

$\underline{\qquad} \times 4 = \underline{\qquad}$          $\underline{\qquad} \div 4 = \underline{\qquad}$

$\underline{\qquad} \times 4 = \underline{\qquad}$          $\underline{\qquad} \div 4 = \underline{\qquad}$

$\underline{\qquad} \times \underline{\qquad} = \underline{\qquad}$          $\underline{\qquad} \div \underline{\qquad} = \underline{\qquad}$

$\underline{\qquad} \times \underline{\qquad} = \underline{\qquad}$          $\underline{\qquad} \div \underline{\qquad} = \underline{\qquad}$

2. The baker packs 36 bran muffins in boxes of 4. Draw and label a tape diagram to find the number of boxes he packs.

3. The waitress arranges 32 glasses into 4 equal rows. How many glasses are in each row?

4. Janet paid $28 for 4 notebooks. Each notebook costs the same amount. What is the cost of 2 notebooks?

Lesson 17:    Model the relationship between multiplication and division.

EUREKA MATH

Name _____     Date _____

1. Mr. Thomas organizes 16 binders into stacks of 4.   How many stacks does he make?  Draw and label a number bond to solve.

2. The chef uses 28 avocados to make 4 batches of guacamole.  How many avocados are in 2 batches of guacamole?  Draw and label a tape diagram to solve.

Name _____   Date _____

1.  Use the array to complete the related equations.

1 × 4 = _____          _____ ÷ 4 = 1

2 × 4 = _____          _____ ÷ 4 = 2

_____ × 4 = 12          12 ÷ 4 = _____

_____ × 4 = 16          16 ÷ 4 = _____

_____ × _____ = 20          20 ÷ _____ = _____

_____ × _____ = 24          24 ÷ _____ = _____

_____ × 4 = _____          _____ ÷ 4 = _____

_____ × 4 = _____          _____ ÷ 4 = _____

_____ × _____ = _____          _____ ÷ _____ = _____

_____ × _____ = _____          _____ ÷ _____ = _____

Model the relationship between multiplication and division.

EUREKA
MATH

2.  The teacher puts 32 students into groups of 4. How many groups does she make? Draw and label a tape diagram to solve.

3.  The store clerk arranges 24 toothbrushes into 4 equal rows. How many toothbrushes are in each row?

4.  An art teacher has 40 paintbrushes. She divides them equally among her 4 students. She finds 8 more brushes and divides these equally among the students, as well. How many brushes does each student receive?

# Mathematics Curriculum

Topic F

# Distributive Property and Problem Solving Using Units of 2–5 and 10

**3.OA.3, 3.OA.5, 3.OA.7, 3.OA.8**, 3.OA.1, 3.OA.2, 3.OA.4, 3.OA.6

| | | |
|---|---|---|
| **Focus Standard:** | 3.OA.3 | Use multiplication and division within 100 to solve word problems in situations involving equal groups, arrays, and measurement quantities, e.g., by using drawings and equations with a symbol for the unknown number to represent the problem. |
| | 3.OA.5 | Apply properties of operations as strategies to multiply and divide. *Examples: If 6 × 4 = 24 is known, then 4 × 6 = 24 is also known. (Commutative property of multiplication.)  3 × 5 × 2 can be found by 3 × 5 = 15, then 15 × 2 = 30, or by 5 × 2 = 10, then 3 × 10 = 30. (Associative property of multiplication.)  Knowing that 8 × 5 = 40 and 8 × 2 = 16, one can find 8 × 7 as 8 × (5 + 2) = (8 × 5) + (8 × 2) = 40 + 16 = 56. (Distributive property.)* |
| | 3.OA.7 | Fluently multiply and divide within 100, using strategies such as the relationship between multiplication and division (e.g., knowing that 8 × 5 = 40, one knows 40 ÷ 5 = 8) or properties of operations.  By the end of Grade 3, know from memory all products of two one-digit numbers. |
| | 3.OA.8 | Solve two-step word problems using the four operations.  Represent these problems using equations with a letter standing for the unknown quantity.  Assess the reasonableness of answers using mental computation and estimation strategies including rounding. |
| **Instructional Days:** | 4 | |
| **Coherence  -Links from:** | G2–M6 | Foundations of Multiplication and Division |
| **-Links to:** | G4–M3 | Multi-Digit Multiplication and Division |

Topic F introduces the factors 5 and 10, familiar from skip-counting in Grade 2. Students apply the multiplication and division strategies they have learned to mixed practice with all of the factors included in Module 1. Students model relationships between factors and decompose numbers as they further explore the relationship between multiplication and division. This culminates in Lessons 18 and 19 as students decompose the dividend in a division sentence to practice the distributive property with division. For example, students decompose $28 \div 4$ as $(20 \div 4) + (8 \div 4) = 5 + 2 = 7$. In the final lessons of the module, students apply the tools, representations, and concepts they have learned to solve multi-step word problems. They demonstrate the flexibility of their thinking as they assess the reasonableness of their answers for a variety of problem types. Lesson 20 focuses on word problems involving multiplication and division, while Lesson 21 increases the complexity of problem solving by including word problems involving all four operations.

| A Teaching Sequence Toward Mastery of Distributive Property and Problem Solving Using Units of 2–5 and 10 |
| --- |
| **Objective 1:** Apply the distributive property to decompose units. (Lessons 18–19) |
| **Objective 2:** Solve two-step word problems involving multiplication and division, and assess the reasonableness of answers. (Lesson 20) |
| **Objective 3:** Solve two-step word problems involving all four operations, and assess the reasonableness of answers. (Lesson 21) |

# Lesson 18

Objective:  Apply the distributive property to decompose units.

## Suggested Lesson Structure

■ Fluency Practice          (9 minutes)
▨ Application Problem        (5 minutes)
▢ Concept Development        (36 minutes)
■ Student Debrief           (10 minutes)

**Total Time**              **(60 minutes)**

### Fluency Practice  (9 minutes)

▪ Sprint:  Add or Subtract Using 5  **2.NBT.5**       (9 minutes)

### Sprint:  Add or Subtract Using 5  (9 minutes)

Materials:   (S) Add or Subtract using 5 Sprint

Note:  This activity builds a foundation for multiplication using units of 5 through reviewing skip-counting from Grade 2.  See Lesson 2 for the directions for administering a Sprint.

Between Sprints, include the following group counts in place of movement exercises.

- Count by threes to 30, think/talk forward and backward.
- Count by sixes to 30, forward and backward.
- Count by fours to 40, forward and backward.

### Application Problem  (5 minutes)

A parking structure has 10 levels.  There are 3 cars parked on each level.  How many cars are parked in the structure?

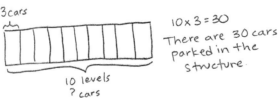

Note:  $10 \times 3 = 30$ is the same problem used in Problem 2 of the Concept Development, only without the context provided here.  Solving the problem ahead of time de-emphasizes the answer so that students more easily focus attention on the new concept of decomposing with number bonds.

©2015 Great Minds. eureka-math.org
G3-M1-TE-B1-1.3.1-01.2016

## Concept Development  (36 minutes)

Materials:   (S) Personal white board

**Problem 1:  Use number bonds to decompose numbers and apply the distributive property.**

Project an array for 7 × 3 with a line drawn as shown.  Write 7 × 3 next to the array.

T:   How many threes?

S:   7 threes.

T:   The dotted line shows a way to break apart the array.
     The 7 threes are broken into…?

S:   5 threes and 2 threes.

T:   Let's draw our number bonds.

S:   (Draw the number bond shown to the right.)

T:   Write the equation that shows how to add the two
     parts.

S:   (Write 5 threes + 2 threes = 7 threes.)

T:   Whisper to a partner the two multiplication sentences
     you used to help you solve 7 × 3.

S:   (Whisper 5 × 3 = 15 and 2 × 3 = 6.)

T:   (Draw a second number bond using the expressions
     (5 × 3) and (2 × 3).)  The number bond is another way to
     show breaking apart.  This shows how we partitioned
     the array and wrote the number bond using our number
     sentences.

T:   Let's rewrite this as the addition of two products using
     my frame.  (Point to the equation below.)

         (__ × 3) + (__ × 3) = ___ × 3

         _____ + _____ = _____

S:   (Write.)

         (5 × 3) + (2 × 3) = 7 × 3

             15 + 6 = 21

T:   How does the number sentence show the number
     bond?

S:   It shows the 7 broken into 5 and 2. → And, the threes
     are shared with both parts. → Yes, 5 threes and 2
     threes. → One part has 5 threes, and the other part
     has 2 threes.

Repeat the process with 9 × 4.

T:   Let's call it the break apart and distribute strategy.  The
     number bond helps us see that we can find the total by
     adding two smaller parts together.

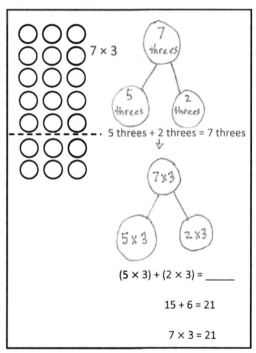

*Sample Teacher Board*

7 × 3

7 threes

5 threes     2 threes

5 threes + 2 threes = 7 threes

7×3

5 × 3     2 ×3

(5 × 3) + (2 × 3) = _____

15 + 6 = 21

7 × 3 = 21

NOTES ON
MULTIPLE MEANS
OF ACTION AND
EXPRESSION:

Encourage students who need extra
support to draw an array before using
the number bond to decompose.

**Problem 2:  Use number bonds and the distributive property.**

T:  (Write 10 × 3.)  How many threes?

S:  10 threes.

T:  What are some ways we can break apart 10?

S:  5 and 5.  → 6 and 4.  → 7 and 3.  → 8 and 2.

T:  So, if we were counting apples, that would be 5 apples and 5 apples or 6 apples and 4 apples?

S:  Yes.

T:  But we aren't counting apples.  What are we counting?

S:  Threes.

T:  So, that would be 6 threes and…?

S:  4 threes.

T:  Let's draw our number bonds.

S:  (Draw number bond shown to the right.)

T:  Write the equation that shows how to add the two parts.  Start with 6 threes and 4 threes.

S:  (Write 6 threes + 4 threes = 10 threes.)

T:  Rewrite this as the addition of two products using my frame.  (Point to the equation below.)

$$(\_ \times 3) + (\_ \times 3) = \_\_ \times 3$$

$$_____ + _____ = _____$$

S:  (Write.)

$$(6 \times 3) + (4 \times 3) = 10 \times 3$$

$$18 + 12 \qquad = 30$$

Repeat the process with 8 × 4.

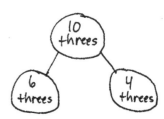

6 threes + 4 threes = 10 threes
(6 × 3) + (4 × 3) = 10 × 3
18 + 12 = 30

## Problem Set  (10 minutes)

Students should do their personal best to complete the Problem Set within the allotted 10 minutes.  For some classes, it may be appropriate to modify the assignment by specifying which problems they work on first.  Some problems do not specify a method for solving.  Students should solve these problems using the RDW approach used for Application Problems.

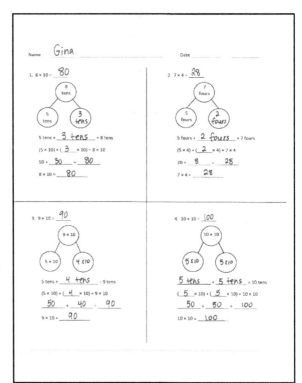

EUREKA
MATH

## Student Debrief  (10 minutes)

**Lesson Objective**:  Apply the distributive property to decompose units.

The Student Debrief is intended to invite reflection and active processing of the total lesson experience.

Invite students to review their solutions for the Problem Set.  They should check work by comparing answers with a partner before going over answers as a class.  Look for misconceptions or misunderstandings that can be addressed in the Debrief.  Guide students in a conversation to debrief the Problem Set and process the lesson.

Any combination of the questions below may be used to lead the discussion.

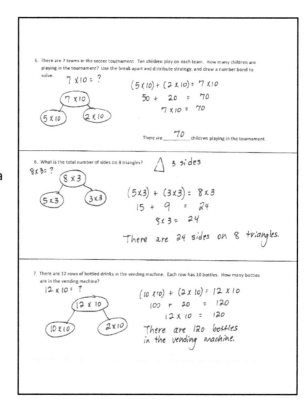

- Compare the number bond and array models for showing the break apart and distribute strategy.

- Share work for Problem 4.  Compare students' number choices.

- Why do you think we use the number bond as a method for breaking a total into two parts?  How was this strategy helpful to find the answer to a larger fact in Problem 7?

- How does Problem 1 in the Concept Development relate to today's Application Problem?

- In anticipation of using the distributive property with division in Lesson 19, ask the following:  Do you think the break apart and distribute strategy can be used with division?  What might that look like?

## Exit Ticket  (3 minutes)

After the Student Debrief, instruct students to complete the Exit Ticket.  A review of their work will help with assessing students' understanding of the concepts that were presented in today's lesson and planning more effectively for future lessons.  The questions may be read aloud to the students.

# A

Number Correct: _____

Add or Subtract Using 5

| | | | | | | |
|---|---|---|---|---|---|---|
| 1. | 0 + 5 = | | 23. | 10 + 5 = | |
| 2. | 5 + 5 = | | 24. | 15 + 5 = | |
| 3. | 10 + 5 = | | 25. | 20 + 5 = | |
| 4. | 15 + 5 = | | 26. | 25 + 5 = | |
| 5. | 20 + 5 = | | 27. | 30 + 5 = | |
| 6. | 25 + 5 = | | 28. | 35 + 5 = | |
| 7. | 30 + 5 = | | 29. | 40 + 5 = | |
| 8. | 35 + 5 = | | 30. | 45 + 5 = | |
| 9. | 40 + 5 = | | 31. | 0 + 50 = | |
| 10. | 45 + 5 = | | 32. | 50 + 50 = | |
| 11. | 50 − 5 = | | 33. | 50 + 5 = | |
| 12. | 45 − 5 = | | 34. | 55 + 5 = | |
| 13. | 40 − 5 = | | 35. | 60 − 5 = | |
| 14. | 35 − 5 = | | 36. | 55 − 5 = | |
| 15. | 30 − 5 = | | 37. | 60 + 5 = | |
| 16. | 25 − 5 = | | 38. | 65 + 5 = | |
| 17. | 20 − 5 = | | 39. | 70 − 5 = | |
| 18. | 15 − 5 = | | 40. | 65 − 5 = | |
| 19. | 10 − 5 = | | 41. | 100 + 50 = | |
| 20. | 5 − 5 = | | 42. | 150 + 50 = | |
| 21. | 5 + 0 = | | 43. | 200 − 50 = | |
| 22. | 5 + 5 = | | 44. | 150 − 50 = | |

Lesson 18:  Apply the distributive property to decompose units.

EUREKA MATH

# B

Number Correct: _____

Improvement: _____

Add or Subtract Using 5

| | | |
|---|---|---|
| 1. | 5 + 0 = | |
| 2. | 5 + 5 = | |
| 3. | 5 + 10 = | |
| 4. | 5 + 15 = | |
| 5. | 5 + 20 = | |
| 6. | 5 + 25 = | |
| 7. | 5 + 30 = | |
| 8. | 5 + 35 = | |
| 9. | 5 + 40 = | |
| 10. | 5 + 45 = | |
| 11. | 50 − 5 = | |
| 12. | 45 − 5 = | |
| 13. | 40 − 5 = | |
| 14. | 35 − 5 = | |
| 15. | 30 − 5 = | |
| 16. | 25 − 5 = | |
| 17. | 20 − 5 = | |
| 18. | 15 − 5 = | |
| 19. | 10 − 5 = | |
| 20. | 5 − 5 = | |
| 21. | 0 + 5 = | |
| 22. | 5 + 5 = | |

| | | |
|---|---|---|
| 23. | 10 + 5 = | |
| 24. | 15 + 5 = | |
| 25. | 20 + 5 = | |
| 26. | 25 + 5 = | |
| 27. | 30 + 5 = | |
| 28. | 35 + 5 = | |
| 29. | 40 + 5 = | |
| 30. | 45 + 5 = | |
| 31. | 50 + 0 = | |
| 32. | 50 + 50 = | |
| 33. | 5 + 50 = | |
| 34. | 5 + 55 = | |
| 35. | 60 − 5 = | |
| 36. | 55 − 5 = | |
| 37. | 5 + 60 = | |
| 38. | 5 + 65 = | |
| 39. | 70 − 5 = | |
| 40. | 65 − 5 = | |
| 41. | 50 + 100 = | |
| 42. | 50 + 150 = | |
| 43. | 200 − 50 = | |
| 44. | 150 − 50 = | |

EUREKA
MATH™

Lesson 18:     Apply the distributive property to decompose units.

235

©2015 Great Minds. eureka-math.org
G3-M1-TE-B1-1.3.1-01.2016

Page 111-112

Name _____ Date _____

1. 8 × 10 = _____

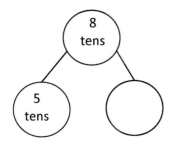

5 tens + _____ = 8 tens

(5 × 10) + (_____ × 10) = 8 × 10

50 + _____ = _____

8 × 10 = _____

2. 7 × 4 = ___28___

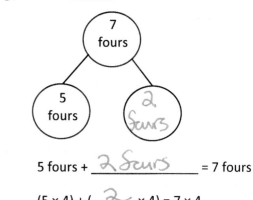

5 fours + _2 fours_ = 7 fours

(5 × 4) + (_2_ × 4) = 7 × 4

20 + _8_ = _28_

7 × 4 = _28_

3. 9 × 10 = _____

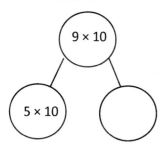

5 tens + _____ = 9 tens

(5 × 10) + (_____ × 10) = 9 × 10

_____ + _____ = _____

9 × 10 = _____

4. 10 × 10 = _____

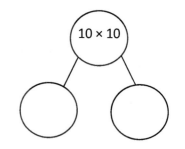

_____ + _____ = 10 tens

(_____ × 10) + (_____ × 10) = 10 × 10

_____ + _____ = _____

10 × 10 = _____

Lesson 18:    Apply the distributive property to decompose units.

EUREKA MATH™

5. There are 7 teams in the soccer tournament. Ten children play on each team. How many children are playing in the tournament? Use the break apart and distribute strategy, and draw a number bond to solve.

There are _____ children playing in the tournament.

6. What is the total number of sides on 8 triangles?

7. There are 12 rows of bottled drinks in the vending machine. Each row has 10 bottles. How many bottles are in the vending machine?

Name _____ Date _____

Dylan used the break apart and distribute strategy to solve a multiplication problem.  Look at his work below, write the multiplication problem Dylan solved, and complete the number bond.

Dylan's work:

$(5 \times 4) + (1 \times 4) =$

$20 + 4 = 24$

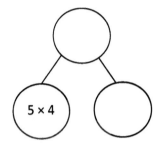

_____ × _____ = _____

**Lesson 18:** Apply the distributive property to decompose units.

EUREKA MATH

Name _____  Date _____

1.  Match.

2.  9 × 4 = _____

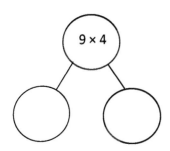

( _____ × 4) + ( _____ × 4) = 9 × 4

_____ + _____ = _____

9 × 4 = _____

EUREKA
MATH™

Lesson 18:  Apply the distributive property to decompose units.

239

©2015 Great Minds. eureka-math.org
G3-M1-TE-B1-1.3.1-01.2016

3.  Lydia makes 10 pancakes. She tops each pancake with 4 blueberries. How many blueberries does Lydia use in all? Use the break apart and distribute strategy, and draw a number bond to solve.

Lydia uses _____ blueberries in all.

4.  Steven solves 7 × 3 using the break apart and distribute strategy. Show an example of what Steven's work might look like below.

5.  There are 7 days in 1 week. How many days are there in 10 weeks?

Lesson 18:     Apply the distributive property to decompose units.

©2015 Great Minds. eureka-math.org
G3-M1-TE-B1-1.3.1-01.2016

# Lesson 19

Objective: Apply the distributive property to decompose units.

## Suggested Lesson Structure

| | |
|---|---|
| ■ Fluency Practice | (14 minutes) |
| ▨ Application Problem | (5 minutes) |
| ▢ Concept Development | (31 minutes) |
| ▨ Student Debrief | (10 minutes) |
| **Total Time** | **(60 minutes)** |

## Fluency Practice  (14 minutes)

- Group Counting  **3.OA.1**              (3 minutes)
- Commutative Multiplying  **3.OA.7**       (3 minutes)
- Decompose and Multiply  **3.OA.5**       (4 minutes)
- Compose and Multiply  **3.OA.5**         (4 minutes)

### Group Counting  (3 minutes)

Note:  Group counting reviews interpreting multiplication as repeated addition.  Counting by threes, fours, fives, and sixes in this activity reviews multiplication with units of 3, 4, and 5 and anticipates multiplication with units of 6 in Module 3.

- T:  Let's count by fives.  (Direct students to count forward and backward to 50.)
- T:  Let's count by fours.  (Direct students to count forward and backward to 40.)
- T:  Let's count by threes.  (Direct students to count forward and backward to 30.)
- T:  Let's count by sixes.  (Direct students to count forward and backward to 36, emphasizing the 24 to 30 transition.)

### Commutative Multiplying  (3 minutes)

Note:  This activity reviews the commutativity of multiplication, learned in Lessons 7, 8, and 15.

- T:  (Write $3 \times 2 =$ ___.)  Say the multiplication sentence.
- S:  $3 \times 2 = 6$.
- T:  Flip it.
- S:  $2 \times 3 = 6$.

Repeat the process for $5 \times 2$, $5 \times 3$, $3 \times 4$, $2 \times 8$, and $3 \times 7$.

## Decompose and Multiply  (4 minutes)

Materials:  (S) Personal white board

Note:  This activity anticipates multiplication using units of 6, 7, 8, and 9 by decomposing larger facts into smaller known facts.  It reviews the break apart and distribute strategy.

> T:  (Write $7 \times 4 =$ ___.)  Rewrite the equation in unit form.
>
> S:  (Write 7 fours = ___.)
>
> T:  (Write 7 fours = (5 fours) + (___fours) = ___.)  7 fours
>      is the same as 5 fours and how many fours?
>
> S:  2 fours.
>
> T:  (Write (5 fours) + (2 fours) = ___.  Below it, write
>      20 + ___ = ___.)  Fill in the blanks.
>
> S:  (Write 20 + 8 = 28.)
>
> T:  $7 \times 4$ equals?
>
> S:  28!

*Sample Teacher board*

```
7 × 4 = ___

7 fours = (5 fours) + (___ fours) = ___

          (5 fours) + (2    fours) = ___

             20   +   ___    =  ___
```

Repeat for the following possible sequence: $8 \times 3$, $9 \times 2$, and $6 \times 4$.  Change the unknowns that students need to fill in.

## Compose and Multiply  (4 minutes)

Materials:  (S) Personal white board

Note:  This activity anticipates multiplication using units of 6, 7, 8, and 9 by composing smaller known facts into larger unknown facts.  It reviews the break apart and distribute strategy.

> T:  (Write $(5 \times 3) + (2 \times 3) =$ ___.)  Fill in the blank to write a true multiplication sentence on your
>      personal white board.  Below the multiplication sentence, write an addition sentence.
>
> S:  (Write $(5 \times 3) + (2 \times 3) = 21$.  Below it, write 15 + 6 = 21.)
>
> T:  Write $(5 \times 3) + (2 \times 3)$ as a single multiplication sentence.
>
> S:  (Write $7 \times 3 = 21$.)

Repeat for the following possible sequence:  $8 \times 2$ and $9 \times 4$.

## Application Problem  (5 minutes)

Henrietta works in a shoe store.  She uses 2 shoelaces to lace each pair of shoes.  She has a total of 24 laces.  How many pairs of shoes can Henrietta lace?

Note:  This problem reviews material from Lesson 18 but intentionally previews 24 ÷ 2, which is used in the first example of the Concept Development.  Students may choose to solve the Application Problem with division or as an *unknown factor* multiplication problem.  Use these variations in method to spark discussion.

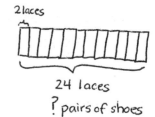

**Lesson 19:**     Apply the distributive property to decompose units.

**EUREKA MATH**™

©2015 Great Minds. eureka-math.org
G3-M1-TE-B1-1.3.1-01.2016

## Concept Development (31 minutes)

**Materials:** (S) Personal white board

**Problem 1: Model break apart and distribute using an array as a strategy for division.**

Draw or project a 12 × 2 array and write 24 ÷ 2 = _____ above it.

- T: Let's use the array to help us solve 24 ÷ 2 = _____. There are 24 dots total. (Draw a line after the tenth row.) This shows one way to break apart the array.
- T: Write division equations to represent the part of the array above the line and the part of the array below the line.
- S: (Write 20 ÷ 2 = 10 and 4 ÷ 2 = 2.)
- T: How many twos are above the line?
- S: 10 twos.
- T: How many twos are below the line?
- S: 2 twos.
- T: Let's rewrite this as the addition of two quotients. Use my equations.

$$(\underline{\quad} \div 2) + (\underline{\quad} \div 2) = \underline{\quad} \div 2$$

$$\underline{\quad} + \underline{\quad} = \underline{\quad}$$

$$24 \div 2 = \underline{\quad}$$

$$20 \div 2 = 10$$

$$4 \div 2 = 2$$

$$24 \div 2 = (20 \div 2) + (4 \div 2)$$

- S: (Line 1: Fill in totals. Line 2: Write 10 + 2 = 12.)
- T: Explain to your partner the process we used to solve 24 ÷ 2.
- S: We added the quotients of two smaller facts to find the quotient of a larger one.

Repeat the process with a 13 × 2 array to show 26 ÷ 2. Break it into 20 ÷ 2 and 6 ÷ 2.

**Problem 2: Use break apart and distribute as a strategy for division.**

- T: (Write 27 ÷ 3 = _____.) What are we focused on when we break apart to divide? Breaking up the number of groups (or rows), like in multiplication, or breaking up the total?
- S: Breaking up the total.
- T: Let's break up 27 into 15 and another number. Fifteen plus what equals 27?
- S: 12.
- T: Work with a partner to draw an array that shows 27 ÷ 3 where 3 is the number of columns.
- S: (Draw a 9 × 3 array.)
- T: Box the part of your array that shows a total of 15.
- S: (Box the first 5 rows.)
- T: Write a division equation for the boxed portion to the right of the array.
- S: (Write 15 ÷ 3 = 5.)

T:   Box the part of your array that shows a total of 12.

S:   (Box the remaining 4 rows.)

T:   Now, write a division equation for that part of the array.

S:   (Write $12 \div 3 = 4$.)

T:   Tell your partner how you will use the equations to help you solve the original equation, $27 \div 3 =$ __.

S:   I'll add the quotients of the two smaller facts.

T:   (Write the following.) Complete the following sequence to solve $27 \div 3$ with your partner.

$$27 \div 3 = (15 \div 3) + (12 \div 3)$$

$$= \underline{\hspace{1cm}} + \underline{\hspace{1cm}}$$

$$= \underline{\hspace{1cm}}$$

**NOTES ON MULTIPLE MEANS OF ENGAGEMENT:**

Add a challenge by asking students to think about other ways of breaking apart 27. A student will most likely choose parts that are not evenly divisible by 3. This will lead to a discussion that gets students to realize that, with division, the strategy relies on the decomposition being such that the dividends must be evenly divisible by the divisor.

Repeat the process with $33 \div 3$. Students can break apart 33 by using the number pair 30 and 3.

## Problem Set (10 minutes)

Students should do their personal best to complete the Problem Set within the allotted 10 minutes. For some classes, it may be appropriate to modify the assignment by specifying which problems they work on first. Some problems do not specify a method for solving. Students should solve these problems using the RDW approach used for Application Problems.

**NOTES ON MULTIPLE MEANS OF REPRESENTATION:**

If appropriate, encourage the class or individual students to solve $33 \div 3$ without using an array.

## Student Debrief (10 minutes)

**Lesson Objective:** Apply the distributive property to decompose units.

The Student Debrief is intended to invite reflection and active processing of the total lesson experience.

Invite students to review their solutions for the Problem Set. They should check work by comparing answers with a partner before going over answers as a class. Look for misconceptions or misunderstandings that can be addressed in the Debrief. Guide students in a conversation to debrief the Problem Set and process the lesson.

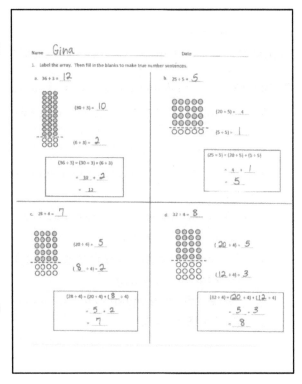

EUREKA MATH

Any combination of the questions below may be used to lead the discussion.

- Compare Nell's strategy in Problem 3 to the strategy for solving 24 ÷ 2 in the Concept Development.

- Yesterday, we used the break apart and distribute strategy with multiplication. How is the method we learned today similar?

- How is the break apart and distribute strategy different for multiplication than for division? (This strategy works for division when the total is broken into 2 parts that are evenly divisible by the divisor. For example, to solve 33 ÷ 8, decomposing 33 into 25 and 8 is not effective at this level because neither 25 nor 8 is evenly divisible by 3.)

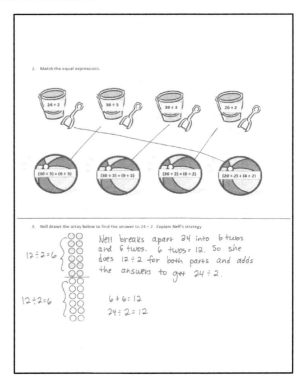

## Exit Ticket  (3 minutes)

After the Student Debrief, instruct students to complete the Exit Ticket. A review of their work will help with assessing students' understanding of the concepts that were presented in today's lesson and planning more effectively for future lessons. The questions may be read aloud to the students.

Name _____    Date _____

1. Label the array. Then, fill in the blanks to make true number sentences.

   a.   36 ÷ 3 = _____

   (30 ÷ 3) = _____

   (6 ÷ 3) = _____

   | (36 ÷ 3) = (30 ÷ 3) + (6 ÷ 3) |
   |---|
   | = __10__ + _____ |
   | = __12__ |

   b.   25 ÷ 5 = _5_

   (20 ÷ 5) = __4__

   (5 ÷ 5) = _1_

   | (25 ÷ 5) = (20 ÷ 5) + (5 ÷ 5) |
   |---|
   | = __4__ + __1__ |
   | = __5__ |

   c.   28 ÷ 4 = _7_

   (20 ÷ 4) = _5_

   (_8_ ÷ 4) = _2_

   rows

   | (28 ÷ 4) = (20 ÷ 4) + (_8_ ÷ 4) |
   |---|
   | = _5_ + _2_ |
   | = _7_ |

   d.   32 ÷ 4 = _____

   (_____ ÷ 4) = _____

   (_____ ÷ 4) = _____

   | (32 ÷ 4) = (_____ ÷ 4) + (_____ ÷ 4) |
   |---|
   | = _____ + _____ |
   | = _____ |

Lesson 19:     Apply the distributive property to decompose units.

**EUREKA MATH**

©2015 Great Minds. eureka-math.org
G3-M1-TE-B1-1.3.1-01.2016

2.  Match the equal expressions.

24 ÷ 2      36 ÷ 3      39 ÷ 3      26 ÷ 2

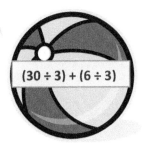 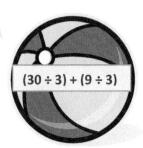 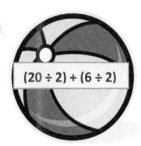 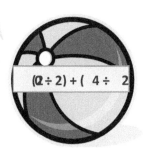

(30 ÷ 3) + (6 ÷ 3)      (30 ÷ 3) + (9 ÷ 3)      (20 ÷ 2) + (6 ÷ 2)      (2 ÷ 2) + ( 4 ÷ 2

3.  Nell draws the array below to find the answer to 24 ÷ 2.  Explain Nell's strategy.

Name _____     Date _____

Complete the equations below to solve 22 ÷ 2 = _____.

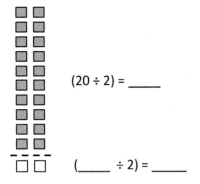

(20 ÷ 2) = _____

(_____ ÷ 2) = _____

(22 ÷ 2) = (20 ÷ 2) + (_____ ÷ 2)

= _____ + _____

= _____

**Lesson 19:**     Apply the distributive property to decompose units.

EUREKA
MATH™

Name _____  Date _____

1. Label the array.  Then, fill in the blanks to make true number sentences.

a.  18 ÷ 3 = _____

△ △ △
△ △ △   (9 ÷ 3) = 3
△ △ △
- - - - - - - - -
△ △ △
△ △ △   (9 ÷ 3) = _____
△ △ △

(18 ÷ 3) = (9 ÷ 3) + (9 ÷ 3)

= __3__ + _____

= __6__

b.  21 ÷ 3 = _____

△ △ △
△ △ △
△ △ △   (15 ÷ 3) = 5
△ △ △
△ △ △
- - - - - - - - -
△ △ △
△ △ △   (6 ÷ 3) = _____

(21 ÷ 3) = (15 ÷ 3) + (6 ÷ 3)

= __5__ + _____

= _____

c.  24 ÷ 4 = _____

△ △ △ △
△ △ △ △
△ △ △ △   (20 ÷ 4) = _____
△ △ △ △
△ △ △ △
- - - - - - - - -
△ △ △ △   (4 ÷ 4) = _____

(24 ÷ 4) = (20 ÷ 4) + (_____ ÷ 4)

= _____ + _____

= _____

d.  36 ÷ 4 = _____

△ △ △ △
△ △ △ △
△ △ △ △   (20 ÷ 4) = _____
△ △ △ △
△ △ △ △
- - - - - - - - -
△ △ △ △
△ △ △ △
△ △ △ △   (16 ÷ 4) = _____
△ △ △ △

(36 ÷ 4) = (___ ÷ 4) + (___ ÷ 4)

= _____ + _____

= _____

2. Match equal expressions.

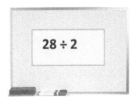      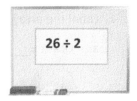

$28 \div 2$    $33 \div 3$    $36 \div 3$    $26 \div 2$

$(30 \div 3) + (3 \div 3)$    $(20 \div 2) + (6 \div 2)$    $(30 \div 3) + (6 \div 3)$    $(20 \div 2) + (8 \div 2)$

---

3. Alex draws the array below to find the answer to $35 \div 5$. Explain Alex's strategy.

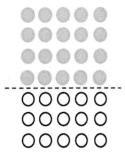

Lesson 19:    Apply the distributive property to decompose units.

EUREKA
MATH

# Lesson 20

Objective: Solve two-step word problems involving multiplication and division, and assess the reasonableness of answers.

## Suggested Lesson Structure

■ Fluency Practice       (9 minutes)
░ Application Problem     (8 minutes)
░ Concept Development     (33 minutes)
▓ Student Debrief        (10 minutes)
   **Total Time**        **(60 minutes)**

## Fluency Practice (9 minutes)

▪ Sprint: Skip-Count by 5  **2.NBT.2**       (9 minutes)

### Sprint: Skip-Count by 5 (9 minutes)

Materials:   (S) Skip-Count by 5 Sprint

Note: This activity builds a foundation for multiplication using units of 5 through reviewing skip-counting from Grade 2. See Lesson 2 for the directions for administering a Sprint.

Between Sprints, include the following group counting in place of movement exercises:

- Count by fours to 40, hum/talk forward and backward. (Hum as you think 1, 2, 3; say 4. Hum as you think 5, 6, 7; say 8, etc.)
- Count by sixes to 42 forward and backward, emphasizing the 24 to 30 and 36 to 42 transitions.
- Count by threes to 30 forward and backward.

## Application Problem (8 minutes)

Red, orange, and blue scarves are on sale for $4 each. Nina buys 2 scarves of each color. How much does she spend altogether?

$4
Scarves | R | R | o | o | B | B |
                  ?

2 + 2 + 2 = 6 scarves
6 × $4 = $24
Nina spends $24.

Note: This problem reviews multiplication using units of 4. It also leads into Problem 1 of the Concept Development.

**Lesson 20:**    Solve two-step word problems involving multiplication and division, and assess the reasonableness of answers.

©2015 Great Minds. eureka-math.org
G3-M1-TE-B1-1.3.1-01.2016

251

## Concept Development  (33 minutes)

Materials:   (S) Personal white board

**Problem 1:  Model a two-step problem with a tape diagram.**

Write or project the following story:  Red, orange, and blue scarves are on sale for $4 each.  Nina buys 2 scarves of each color.  She also buys a hat that costs $4.  How much does she spend altogether?

NOTES ON
MULTIPLE MEANS
OF REPRESENTATION:

The vignette follows the *I do, we do, you do* process to guide students through the two-step word problems. Adjust the level of support for each problem according to the needs students demonstrate. Consider working with a small group to solve Problem 3.

T:   Compare this new problem with the Application Problem you just solved.  What is different?

S:   The question is still the same, but the new problem adds the cost of a hat to the total.

T:   Turn and talk to your partner:  How can we use our answer from the Application Problem to help solve the new problem?

S:   In our Application Problem, we found the cost of the 6 scarves.  → We just have to add the cost of the hat to the total.

T:   (Draw tape diagram.)  This tape diagram shows the Application Problem.

T:   Each of these boxes is 1 unit.  Tell me what 1 unit represents.

S:   1 scarf.

T:   What is the value of 1 unit?

S:   $4.

T:   What do the 6 units represent?

S:   6 scarves.

T:   How did you label the 6 units?

S:   With a question mark.

T:   What equation did you use to find the total of all the items?

S:   6 × $4 = $24.

T:   Watch as I add to our model to represent the new problem.

T:   (Draw and label diagram as shown.)  Now, I add the cost of the hat, $4, to the total cost of the scarves, $24, (write $4 + $24 = _____), which is…?

S:   $28.

T:   How many units did we add together to find the total of both items?

S:   7 units.  → 1 unit + 6 units.

T:   Tell your partner a multiplication sentence you could use to find the total cost of the scarves and hat without finding the value of the scarves first.

S:   7 units of $4 = $28.  → 7 × $4 = $28.

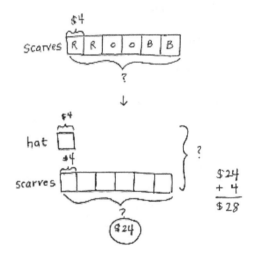

Lesson 20:   Solve two-step word problems involving multiplication and division, and assess the reasonableness of answers.

**Problem 2:  Use the tape diagram to solve a two-step problem.**

Write or project the following story:  Mr. Lim buys 7 plants for his garden.  Each plant costs $5.  The next day, he buys a rose bush that also costs $5.  How much more do the 7 plants cost than the rose bush?

T:   What information is known from reading the story?

S:   The cost of each plant is $5.  We also know the rose bush costs $5.

T:   What information is unknown?

S:   We don't know the total cost of the 7 plants, so we don't know how much more the plants cost than the rose bush.

T:   Notice there are two unknowns in our problem. Let's first draw and label a tape diagram to model the unknown as the cost of the 7 plants.

S:   (Draw and label tape diagram.)

T:   Tell me how to find the cost of the plants.

S:   We multiply 7 × $5.

T:   The plants cost…?

S:   $35.

T:   Have we answered the question?

S:   No.

T:   What is the question we are trying to answer?

S:   How much more the plants cost than the rose bush.

T:   (Label the second question mark.)  Tell your partner what strategy you might use to answer the question.

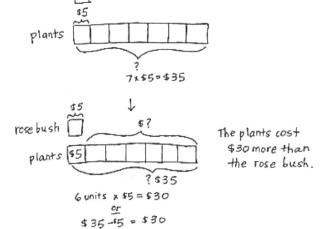

S:   I might subtract the cost of the rose bush from the total cost of the 7 plants.  → I might do 6 × $5 because the plants have 6 units more than the rose bush.  → I'll skip-count the 6 extra fives on the plants diagram.

T:   Write an equation and solve the problem on your personal white board.

S:   (Possibly write:  $35 – $5 = $30, 6 × $5 = $30, $5 + $5 + $5 + $5 + $5 + $5 = $30.)

T:   Reread the question.  Have we answered it?

S:   (Reread and confirm.)

T:   Is $30 a reasonable answer?  Why or why not?

S:   Yes, 7 plants are expensive!  $5 is a lot less than $35, so $30 less makes sense.  → I checked with addition.  $30 + $5 = $35.

T:   (Erase the first diagram and the $35 that marks the total value on the second diagram.)  We first drew two models because the problem has two steps.  How does this model represent the whole problem on its own?

S:   (Discuss).

T:   We know that 1 unit is $5.  How many units represent the additional cost of the plants?

Lesson 20:    Solve two-step word problems involving multiplication and division, and assess the reasonableness of answers.

253

©2015 Great Minds. eureka-math.org
G3-M1-TE-B1-1.3.1-01.2016

S:    6 units.

T:    Given what you know, is it necessary to find the total cost of the plants?  Why or why not?

S:    You can just do 6 × $5 without having to know about $35.

T:    Explain to your partner the difference between the two ways of solving this problem.

**Problem 3:  Work with a partner to model and solve a two-step problem.**

Write or project the following story:  Ten children equally share 40 almonds.  How many almonds will 3 children get?

T:    What information is known?

S:    The total amount of almonds and the number of children.

T:    What is unknown?

S:    How many almonds 3 children get.

T:    In order to solve, what do you need to find first?

S:    The amount of almonds 1 child gets.

T:    With a partner, model and solve the problem.  Make sure to reread the question to see if you have answered the question.  Then, think about whether or not the answer makes sense.  This is how we check the reasonableness of the answer.

> **NOTES ON**
> **MULTIPLE MEANS**
> **OF ENGAGEMENT:**
>
> Scaffold Problem 3 by providing a tape diagram with no labels.  This allows students to see the problem and analyze the steps they need to take to solve the problem.

## Problem Set  (10 minutes)

Students should do their personal best to complete the Problem Set within the allotted 10 minutes.  For some classes, it may be appropriate to modify the assignment by specifying which problems they work on first.  Some problems do not specify a method for solving.  Students should solve these problems using the RDW approach used for Application Problems.

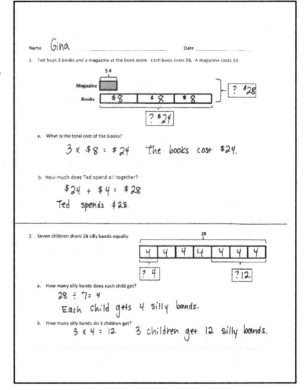

**Lesson 20:**    Solve two-step word problems involving multiplication and division, and assess the reasonableness of answers.

## Student Debrief  (10 minutes)

**Lesson Objective:** Solve two-step word problems involving multiplication and division, and assess the reasonableness of answers.

The Student Debrief is intended to invite reflection and active processing of the total lesson experience.

Invite students to review their solutions for the Problem Set. They should check work by comparing answers with a partner before going over answers as a class. Look for misconceptions or misunderstandings that can be addressed in the Debrief. Guide students in a conversation to debrief the Problem Set and process the lesson.

Any combination of the questions below may be used to lead the discussion.

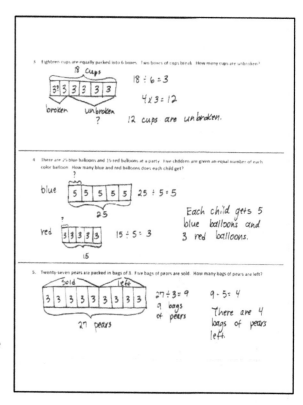

- Compare the structure of Problems 1 and 2 to the rest of the Problem Set. Problems 1 and 2 explicitly ask two questions to scaffold the two-step word problems. Problems 3–5 still require two steps but only ask one question.

- Compare Problems 3 and 5. What do the unknowns represent? How are these problems similar? How are they different?

- Have students share their models. In Problems 3 and 5, how did you show the boxes of broken cups and the bags of pears sold?

- How did you check the reasonableness of your answers to each problem?

## Exit Ticket  (3 minutes)

After the Student Debrief, instruct students to complete the Exit Ticket. A review of their work will help with assessing students' understanding of the concepts that were presented in today's lesson and planning more effectively for future lessons. The questions may be read aloud to the students.

Lesson 20:    Solve two-step word problems involving multiplication and division, and assess the reasonableness of answers.

255

# A

Number Correct: _____

Skip-Count by 5

| | | |
|---|---|---|
| 1. | 0, 5, __ | |
| 2. | 5, 10, __ | |
| 3. | 10, 15, __ | |
| 4. | 15, 20, __ | |
| 5. | 20, 25, __ | |
| 6. | 25, 30, __ | |
| 7. | 30, 35, __ | |
| 8. | 35, 40, __ | |
| 9. | 40, 45, __ | |
| 10. | 50, 45, __ | |
| 11. | 45, 40, __ | |
| 12. | 40, 35, __ | |
| 13. | 35, 30, __ | |
| 14. | 30, 25, __ | |
| 15. | 25, 20, __ | |
| 16. | 20, 15, __ | |
| 17. | 15, 10, __ | |
| 18. | 0, __, 10 | |
| 19. | 25, __, 35 | |
| 20. | 5, __, 15 | |
| 21. | 30, __, 40 | |
| 22. | 10, __, 20 | |

| | | |
|---|---|---|
| 23. | 35, __, 45 | |
| 24. | 15, __, 25 | |
| 25. | 40, __, 50 | |
| 26. | 25, __, 15 | |
| 27. | 50, __, 40 | |
| 28. | 20, __, 10 | |
| 29. | 45, __, 35 | |
| 30. | 15, __, 5 | |
| 31. | 40, __, 30 | |
| 32. | 10, __, 0 | |
| 33. | 35, __, 25 | |
| 34. | __, 10, 5 | |
| 35. | __, 35, 30 | |
| 36. | __, 15, 10 | |
| 37. | __, 40, 35 | |
| 38. | __, 20, 15 | |
| 39. | __, 45, 40 | |
| 40. | 50, 55, __ | |
| 41. | 45, 50, __ | |
| 42. | 65, __, 55 | |
| 43. | 55, 60, __ | |
| 44. | 60, 65, __ | |

Lesson 20:    Solve two-step word problems involving multiplication and division, and assess the reasonableness of answers.

EUREKA
MATH™

# B

Skip-Count by 5

| | | |
|---|---|---|
| 1. | 5, 10, ___ | |
| 2. | 10, 15, ___ | |
| 3. | 15, 20, ___ | |
| 4. | 20, 25, ___ | |
| 5. | 25, 30, ___ | |
| 6. | 30, 35, ___ | |
| 7. | 35, 40, ___ | |
| 8. | 40, 45, ___ | |
| 9. | 50, 45, ___ | |
| 10. | 45, 40, ___ | |
| 11. | 40, 35, ___ | |
| 12. | 35, 30, ___ | |
| 13. | 30, 25, ___ | |
| 14. | 25, 20, ___ | |
| 15. | 20, 15, ___ | |
| 16. | 15, 10, ___ | |
| 17. | 0, ___, 10 | |
| 18. | 25, ___, 35 | |
| 19. | 5, ___, 15 | |
| 20. | 30, ___, 40 | |
| 21. | 10, ___, 20 | |
| 22. | 35, ___, 45 | |

| | | |
|---|---|---|
| 23. | 15, ___, 25 | |
| 24. | 35, ___, 45 | |
| 25. | 20, ___, 30 | |
| 26. | 25, ___, 15 | |
| 27. | 50, ___, 60 | |
| 28. | 20, ___, 10 | |
| 29. | 45, ___, 35 | |
| 30. | 15, ___, 5 | |
| 31. | 35, ___, 25 | |
| 32. | 10, ___, 0 | |
| 33. | 35, ___, 25 | |
| 34. | ___, 15, 10 | |
| 35. | ___, 40, 35 | |
| 36. | ___, 20, 15 | |
| 37. | ___, 45, 40 | |
| 38. | ___, 10, 5 | |
| 39. | ___, 35, 30 | |
| 40. | 45, 50, ___ | |
| 41. | 50, 55, ___ | |
| 42. | 55, 60, ___ | |
| 43. | 65, ___, 55 | |
| 44. | ___, 60, 55 | |

**Lesson 20:** Solve two-step word problems involving multiplication and division, and assess the reasonableness of answers.

**257**

©2015 Great Minds. eureka-math.org
G3-M1-TE-B1-1.3.1-01.2016

Name _____   Date _____

1.  Ted buys 3 books and a magazine at the book store.  Each book costs $8.  A magazine costs $4.

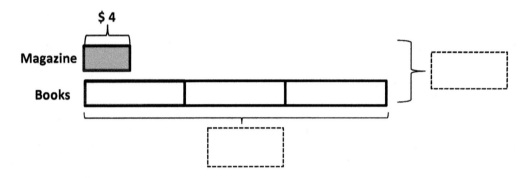

    a.   What is the total cost of the books?

    b.   How much does Ted spend altogether?

2.  Seven children share 28 silly bands equally.

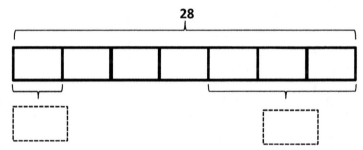

    a.   How many silly bands does each child get?

    b.   How many silly bands do 3 children get?

**Lesson 20:**      Solve two-step word problems involving multiplication and division, and assess the reasonableness of answers.

©2015 Great Minds. eureka-math.org
G3-M1-TE-B1-1.3.1-01.2016

**EUREKA MATH**

3.  Eighteen cups are equally packed into 6 boxes.  Two boxes of cups break.  How many cups are unbroken?

---

4.  There are 25 blue balloons and 15 red balloons at a party.  Five children are given an equal number of each color balloon.  How many blue and red balloons does each child get?

---

5.  Twenty-seven pears are packed in bags of 3.  Five bags of pears are sold.  How many bags of pears are left?

**Lesson 20:**    Solve two-step word problems involving multiplication and division, and assess the reasonableness of answers.

©2015 Great Minds. eureka-math.org
G3-M1-TE-B1-1.3.1-01.2016

259

Name _____     Date _____

1.  Thirty-two jelly beans are shared by 8 students.

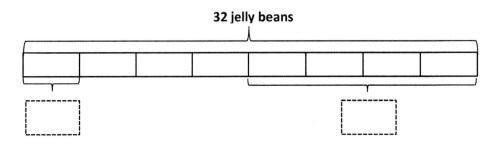

    a.  How many jelly beans will each student get?

    b.  How many jelly beans will 4 students get?

2.  The teacher has 30 apple slices and 20 pear slices.  Five children equally share all of the fruit slices.  How many fruit slices does each child get?

©2015 Great Minds. eureka-math.org
G3-M1-TE-B1-1.3.1-01.2016

EUREKA
MATH™

Name _____     Date _____

1.  Jerry buys a pack of pencils that costs $3.  David buys 4 sets of markers.  Each set of markers also costs $3.

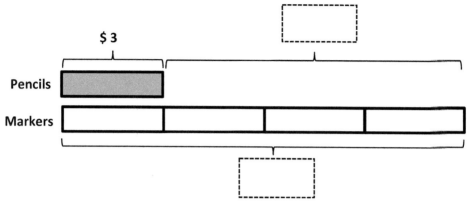

a.  What is the total cost of the markers?

b.  How much more does David spend on 4 sets of markers than Jerry spends on a pack of pencils?

---

2.  Thirty students are eating lunch at 5 tables.  Each table has the same number of students.

a.  How many students are sitting at each table?

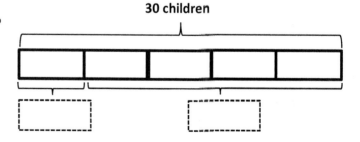

**30 children**

b.  How many students are sitting at 4 tables?

**EUREKA MATH**    **Lesson 20:**   Solve two-step word problems involving multiplication and division,    **261**
                   and assess the reasonableness of answers.

©2015 Great Minds. eureka-math.org
G3-M1-TE-B1-1.3.1-01.2016

3. The teacher has 12 green stickers and 15 purple stickers. Three students are given an equal number of each color sticker. How many green and purple stickers does each student get?

---

4. Three friends go apple picking. They pick 13 apples on Saturday and 14 apples on Sunday. They share the apples equally. How many apples does each person get?

---

5. The store has 28 notebooks in packs of 4. Three packs of notebooks are sold. How many packs of notebooks are left?

**Lesson 20:**    Solve two-step word problems involving multiplication and division, and assess the reasonableness of answers.

©2015 Great Minds. eureka-math.org
G3-M1-TE-B1-1.3.1-01.2016

EUREKA MATH

# Lesson 21

Objective:  Solve two-step word problems involving all four operations, and assess the reasonableness of answers.

## Suggested Lesson Structure

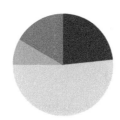

| | |
|---|---|
| ■ Fluency Practice | (14 minutes) |
| ■ Application Problem | (5 minutes) |
| ■ Concept Development | (31 minutes) |
| ■ Student Debrief | (10 minutes) |
| **Total Time** | **(60 minutes)** |

## Fluency Practice  (14 minutes)

- Group Counting  **3.OA.1**                        (3 minutes)
- Multiply by 5 Pattern Sheet  **3.OA.7**       (8 minutes)
- Commutative Multiplying  **3.OA.7**           (3 minutes)

### Group Counting  (3 minutes)

Note: Group counting reviews interpreting multiplication as repeated addition.  Counting by threes, fours, and sixes in this activity reviews multiplication with units of 3 and 4 and anticipates multiplication with units of 6 in Module 3.

  T:   Let's count by threes.  (Direct students to count forward and backward to 30.)

  T:   Let's count by fours, think/talk forward and backward.  (Direct students to count forward and backward to 40.  Think 1, 2, 3; say 4.  Think 5, 6, 7; say 8, etc.)

  T:   Let's count by sixes.  (Direct students to count forward and backward to 48, emphasizing the 24 to 30 and 36 to 42 transitions.)

### Multiply by 5 Pattern Sheet  (8 minutes)

Materials:   (S) Multiply by 5 (1–5) (Pattern Sheet)

Note: This activity builds fluency with multiplication facts using units of 5.  It works toward students knowing from memory all products of two one-digit numbers.  See Lesson 9 for the directions for administering a Multiply-By Pattern Sheet.

  T:   (Write $5 \times 5 = $ ____.)  Let's skip-count up by fives to solve.  (Count with fingers to 5 as students count.  Record skip-count answers on the board.)

  S:   5, 10, 15, 20, 25.

Lesson 21:    Solve two-step word problems involving all four operations, and assess
the reasonableness of answers.

263

T: (Circle 25 and write 5 × 5 = 25 above it.  Write 3 × 5 = _____.)  Let's skip-count up by fives again.  (Count with fingers to 3 as students count.)

S: 5, 10, 15.

T: Let's see how we can skip-count down to find the answer, too.  Start at 25.  (Count down with fingers as students say numbers.)

S: 25, 20, 15.

Repeat the process for 9 × 5 and 8 × 5.

T: Let's practice multiplying by 5.  Be sure to work left to right across the page.  (Distribute Multiply by 5 Pattern Sheet.)

## Commutative Multiplying  (3 minutes)

Note:  This activity reviews the commutativity of multiplication, learned in Lessons 7, 8, and 15.

T: (Write 4 × 2 = ___.)  Say the multiplication sentence.

S: 4 × 2 = 8.

T: Flip it.

S: 2 × 4 = 8.

Repeat the process for 5 × 3, 9 × 2, 4 × 3, 2 × 7, and 3 × 8.

## Application Problem  (5 minutes)

There are 4 boxes with 6 binders in each one.  Three brothers share the binders.  How many binders does each brother get?

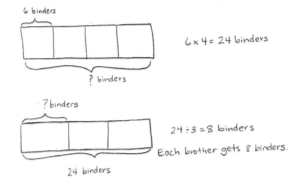

Note:  This two-step problem reviews Lesson 20's objective.  Students self-select an approach and independently solve.  Practicing a two-step problem here scaffolds the difference between the structured practice in Lesson 20 and the open-ended practice in Lesson 21.  Prepare students for today's exploration by guiding them to evaluate their methods for solving and assessing the reasonableness of their answers.

Lesson 21:  Solve two-step word problems involving all four operations, and assess the reasonableness of answers.

**EUREKA MATH**

©2015 Great Minds. eureka-math.org
G3-M1-TE-B1-1.3.1-01.2016

## Concept Development (31 minutes)

Materials: (S) Chart paper, markers, paper strips (optional for representing tape diagrams), glue

Today's lesson is a culminating exploration that follows the following process:

- Divide the class into groups no larger than four students.
- Assign each group one word problem from the Problem Set. (Cut the Problem Set so that initially each group only receives the problem they are assigned. More than one group may work on the same problem.)
- Each group collaborates to model and solve their assigned problem.
- Each group prepares to present their problem to the class, describing their method for solving and explaining the reasonableness of their answer.

Each group needs one set of the materials listed in the materials section.

Directions (similar to RDW process):

1. Read and analyze together to determine known and unknown information.
2. Discuss how to model.
3. Model and label diagrams.
4. Discuss and agree on the steps needed to solve.
5. Write equations and solve.
6. Assess the reasonableness of the solution. (Ask, "Does **MP.1** our answer make sense? How do we know?")
7. Write a complete sentence to answer the question.
8. Prepare a mini-presentation to explain each step of your work. Prepare to answer clarifying questions from the group.

Each group presents to the class. Audience members should be prepared to ask clarifying questions, challenge each other's work, and offer compliments. If more than one group solves the same problem, discussion might include similarities and differences between problem-solving approaches.

## Problem Set (5 minutes)

When all groups have presented, pass out the entire Problem Set, and have students solve the problems independently. The time allotment is short, as they have just seen and discussed every problem.

> **NOTES ON MULTIPLE MEANS OF ACTION AND EXPRESSION:**
>
> The first two problems on the Problem Set have diagrams drawn to scaffold instructions. These diagrams may be removed for the exploration to adjust the level of support for the groups who solve them.
>
> A visual representation of the CCLS Tables 1–2 could be used to help students determine the known and unknown information.

> **NOTES ON MULTIPLE MEANS OF REPRESENTATION:**
>
> Consider assigning roles so that group members participate and each student remains accountable for learning. This is particularly important with regard to each group's presentation. Set the expectation that each member actively contributes.
>
> Another option is to reconfigure the groups and partner share the process and solution, encouraging the use of precise language (e.g., equation, product, and quotient).

Lesson 21: Solve two-step word problems involving all four operations, and assess the reasonableness of answers.

265

©2015 Great Minds. eureka-math.org
G3-M1-TE-B1-1.3.1-01.2016

## Student Debrief  (10 minutes)

**Lesson Objective:**  Solve two-step word problems involving all four operations, and assess the reasonableness of answers.

After the presentations and discussion of the Problem Set during the lesson, today's Debrief culminates the module with a celebration.  Students reflect on their progress in learning to multiply and divide using units of 2, 3, 4, 5, and 10.

Students are seated with a personal white board.  Select one student to stand behind someone seated.  Say an expression or give a word problem.  Of the pair, the first student to solve it correctly and lift his board wins the round.  That student rotates one seat to the right.  The goal is for a single child to work her way back to the seat behind which she originally stood.  The game is very fast-paced to build excitement.  Given the time constraint, the game is unlikely to finish.  The winner can be the student who moves the most spaces.

Sample expressions or word problems:

- How many legs are there on 5 dogs?
- $4 \times 3$
- $6 \times 2$
- Write a related division fact for $5 \times 3$.
- $18 \div 3$

## Exit Ticket  (3 minutes)

After the Student Debrief, instruct students to complete the Exit Ticket.  A review of their work will help with assessing students' understanding of the concepts that were presented in today's lesson and planning more effectively for future lessons.  The questions may be read aloud to the students.

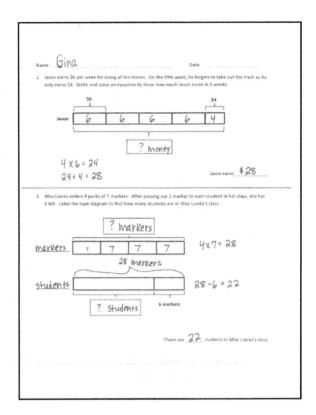

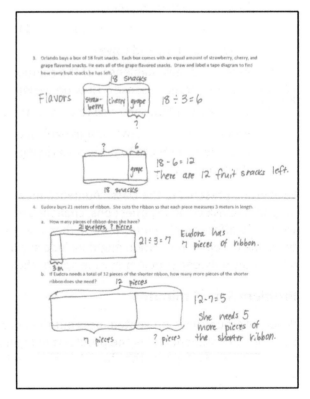

**Lesson 21:**   Solve two-step word problems involving all four operations, and assess the reasonableness of answers.

Multiply.

5 x 1 = _____     5 x 2 = _____     5 x 3 = _____     5 x 4 = _____

5 x 5 = _____     5 x 1 = _____     5 x 2 = _____     5 x 1 = _____

5 x 3 = _____     5 x 1 = _____     5 x 4 = _____     5 x 1 = _____

5 x 5 = _____     5 x 1 = _____     5 x 2 = _____     5 x 3 = _____

5 x 2 = _____     5 x 4 = _____     5 x 2 = _____     5 x 5 = _____

5 x 2 = _____     5 x 1 = _____     5 x 2 = _____     5 x 3 = _____

5 x 1 = _____     5 x 3 = _____     5 x 2 = _____     5 x 3 = _____

5 x 4 = _____     5 x 3 = _____     5 x 5 = _____     5 x 3 = _____

5 x 4 = _____     5 x 1 = _____     5 x 4 = _____     5 x 2 = _____

5 x 4 = _____     5 x 3 = _____     5 x 4 = _____     5 x 5 = _____

5 x 4 = _____     5 x 5 = _____     5 x 1 = _____     5 x 5 = _____

5 x 2 = _____     5 x 5 = _____     5 x 3 = _____     5 x 5 = _____

5 x 4 = _____     5 x 2 = _____     5 x 4 = _____     5 x 3 = _____

5 x 5 = _____     5 x 3 = _____     5 x 2 = _____     5 x 4 = _____

5 x 3 = _____     5 x 5 = _____     5 x 2 = _____     5 x 4 = _____

multiply by 5 (1–5)

**Lesson 21:** Solve two-step word problems involving all four operations, and assess the reasonableness of answers.

267

Name _____   Date _____

1. Jason earns $6 per week for doing all his chores. On the fifth week, he forgets to take out the trash, so he only earns $4. Write and solve an equation to show how much Jason earns in 5 weeks.

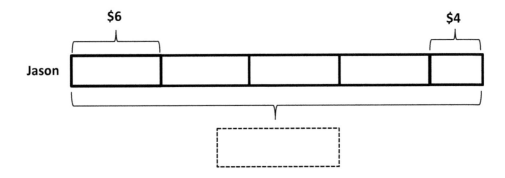

Jason earns _____.

_____

2. Miss Lianto orders 4 packs of 7 markers. After passing out 1 marker to each student in her class, she has 6 left. Label the tape diagram to find how many students are in Miss Lianto's class.

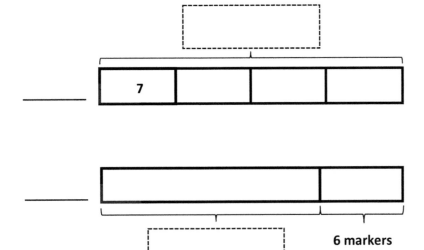

There are _____ students in Miss Lianto's class.

**Lesson 21:**   Solve two-step word problems involving all four operations, and assess the reasonableness of answers.

EUREKA
MATH™

3. Orlando buys a box of 18 fruit snacks. Each box comes with an equal number of strawberry-, cherry-, and grape-flavored snacks. He eats all of the grape-flavored snacks. Draw and label a tape diagram to find how many fruit snacks he has left.

4. Eudora buys 21 meters of ribbon. She cuts the ribbon so that each piece measures 3 meters in length.

   a. How many pieces of ribbon does she have?

   b. If Eudora needs a total of 12 pieces of the shorter ribbon, how many more pieces of the shorter ribbon does she need?

EUREKA
MATH™

Lesson 21:    Solve two-step word problems involving all four operations, and assess
              the reasonableness of answers.

©2015 Great Minds. eureka-math.org
G3-M1-TE-B1-1.3.1-01.2016

269

Name _____  Date _____

Ms. Egeregor buys 27 books for her classroom library. She buys an equal number of fiction, nonfiction, and poetry books. She shelves all of the poetry books first. Draw and label a tape diagram to show how many books Ms. Egeregor has left to shelve.

Lesson 21:     Solve two-step word problems involving all four operations, and assess the reasonableness of answers.

EUREKA MATH

©2015 Great Minds. eureka-math.org
G3-M1-TE-B1-1.3.1-01.2016

Name _____    Date _____

1.  Tina eats 8 crackers for a snack each day at school.  On Friday, she drops 3 and only eats 5.  Write and solve an equation to show the total number of crackers Tina eats during the week.

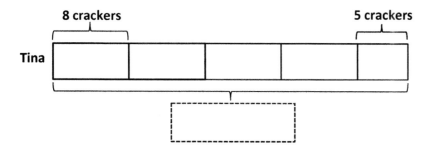

Tina eats _____ crackers.

2.  Ballio has a reading goal.  He checks 3 boxes of 9 books out from the library.  After finishing them, he realizes that he beat his goal by 4 books!  Label the tape diagrams to find Ballio's reading goal.

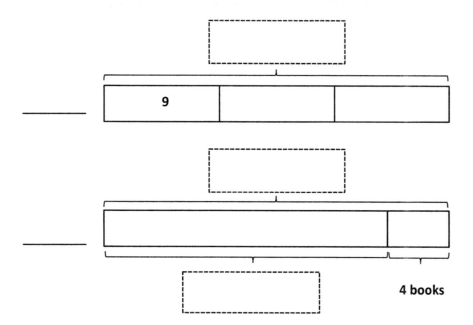

Ballio's goal is to read _____ books.

Lesson 21:  Solve two-step word problems involving all four operations, and assess the reasonableness of answers.

271

©2015 Great Minds. eureka-math.org
G3-M1-TE-B1-1.3.1-01.2016

3. Mr. Nguyen plants 24 trees around the neighborhood pond. He plants equal numbers of maple, pine, spruce, and birch trees. He waters the spruce and birch trees before it gets dark. How many trees does Mr. Nguyen still need to water? Draw and label a tape diagram.

_____

4. Anna buys 24 seeds and plants 3 in each pot. She has 5 pots. How many more pots does Anna need to plant all of her seeds?

Lesson 21: Solve two-step word problems involving all four operations, and assess the reasonableness of answers.

EUREKA
MATH™

Name _____     Date _____

1.  Mr. Lewis arranges all the desks in his classroom into 6 equal groups of 4.  How many desks are in his classroom?  Show a picture and multiplication sentence in your work.

 

 

 

 

     a.  What does the product in your multiplication sentence represent?

 

 

 

 

     b.  Fill in the blanks below to complete a related division sentence.

         _____ ÷ 4 = _____

 

 

 

     c.  What does the quotient in Part (b) represent?

2. a. Draw an array that shows 9 rows of 2. Write a multiplication sentence to represent the array, and circle the factor that represents the number of rows.

b. Draw another array that shows 2 rows of 9. Write a different multiplication sentence, and circle the factor that represents the size of the row.

c. Explain the relationship between the two arrays using number sentences and words.

**Module 1:** Properties of Multiplication and Division and Solving Problems with Units 2–5 and 10

EUREKA MATH

3.   Ms. Park buys a tray of apples for a class party. There are 5 rows of 4 red apples. There is 1 row of 4 green apples.

    a.   The picture below shows Ms. Park's apples. Fill in the blanks to complete the expressions.

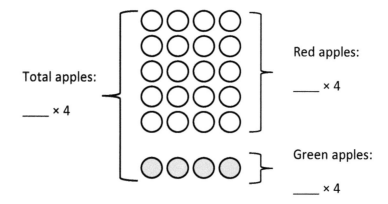

Total apples:

____ × 4

Red apples:

____ × 4

Green apples:

____ × 4

    b.   Fill in the unknowns in the equation below to match the picture of the apples in Part (a). Use the break apart and distribute strategy to find the total number of apples Ms. Park bought.

       _____ × 4 = _____ × 4 + _____ × 4

Ms. Park bought _____ apples.

    c.   Lilly brings 8 green apples for the class party. Show Lilly's green apples on the picture in Part (a). Then, fill in the unknowns in the equation below to match the new picture. Solve to find the total number of apples.

       _____ × 4 = _____ × 4 + _____ × 4

There are _____ apples in all.

4.  Mr. Myer's class plays a game.  The class earns 5 points each time they answer a question correctly.  The class earns 50 points playing the game on Monday.

    a.  How many questions did the class answer correctly?  Show a picture and division sentence in your work.

    b.  Mr. Myer uses the equation 5 × _____ = 50 to find how many questions the class answered correctly.  Is his method correct?  Why or why not?

    c.  The class answered 7 questions correctly on Tuesday.  What is the total number of points the class earned on both days?

EUREKA
MATH™

5. Complete as many problems as you can in 100 seconds.  Your teacher will time you and tell you when to stop.

| | | | | |
|---|---|---|---|---|
| 4 x 1 = _____ | 3 ÷ 1 = _____ | 10 x _____ = 20 | 2 x 3 = _____ | 10 ÷ 5 = _____ |
| 4 ÷ 2 = _____ | 2 x _____ = 4 | 15 ÷ 5 = _____ | 10 x 3 = _____ | 4 x _____ = 12 |
| 3 x 3 = _____ | 5 x _____ = 15 | 16 ÷ 4 = _____ | 2 x _____ = 8 | 10 x 4 = _____ |
| 2 x 4 = _____ | 12 ÷ 4 = _____ | 4 x _____ = 20 | 5 x 5 = _____ | 50 ÷ 10 = _____ |
| 15 ÷ 3 = _____ | 2 x _____ = 10 | 24 ÷ 4 = _____ | 10 x 6 = _____ | 5 x _____ = 30 |
| 2 x 6 = _____ | 4 x _____ = 24 | 35 ÷ 5 = _____ | 3 x _____ = 21 | 10 x 7 = _____ |
| 4 x 7 = _____ | 14 ÷ 2 = _____ | 3 x _____ = 24 | 5 x 8 = _____ | 80 ÷ 10 = _____ |
| 32 ÷ 4 = _____ | 10 x _____ = 80 | 27 ÷ 3 = _____ | 2 x 9 = _____ | 5 x _____ = 45 |

©2015 Great Minds. eureka-math.org
G3-M1-TE-B1-1.3.1-01.2016

**Represent and solve problems involving multiplication and division.**

**3.OA.1**    Interpret products of whole numbers, e.g., interpret $5 \times 7$ as the total number of objects in 5 groups of 7 objects each. *For example, describe a context in which a total number of objects can be expressed as $5 \times 7$.*

**3.OA.2**    Interpret whole-number quotients of whole numbers, e.g., interpret $56 \div 8$ as the number of objects in each share when 56 objects are partitioned equally into 8 shares, or as a number of shares when 56 objects are partitioned into equal shares of 8 objects each. *For example, describe a context in which a number of shares or a number of groups can be expressed as $56 \div 8$.*

**3.OA.3**    Use multiplication and division within 100 to solve word problems in situations involving equal groups, arrays, and measurement quantities, e.g., by using drawings and equations with a symbol for the unknown number to represent the problem. (See Glossary, Table 2.)

**3.OA.4**    Determine the unknown whole number in a multiplication or division equation relating three whole numbers. *For example, determine the unknown number that makes the equation true in each of the equations $8 \times ? = 48$, $5 = \_ \div 3$, $6 \times 6 = ?$*

**Understand properties of multiplication and the relationship between multiplication and division.**

**3.OA.5**    Apply properties of operations as strategies to multiply and divide. (Students need not use formal terms for these properties.) *Examples: If $6 \times 4 = 24$ is known, then $4 \times 6 = 24$ is also known. (Commutative property of multiplication.) $3 \times 5 \times 2$ can be found by $3 \times 5 = 15$, then $15 \times 2 = 30$, or by $5 \times 2 = 10$, then $3 \times 10 = 30$. (Associative property of multiplication.) Knowing that $8 \times 5 = 40$ and $8 \times 2 = 16$, one can find $8 \times 7$ as $8 \times (5 + 2) = (8 \times 5) + (8 \times 2) = 40 + 16 = 56$. (Distributive property.)*

**3.OA.6**    Understand division as an unknown-factor problem. *For example, find $32 \div 8$ by finding the number that makes 32 when multiplied by 8.*

**Multiply and divide within 100.**

**3.OA.7**    Fluently multiply and divide within 100, using strategies such as the relationship between multiplication and division (e.g., knowing that $8 \times 5 = 40$, one knows $40 \div 5 = 8$) or properties of operations. By the end of Grade 3, know from memory all products of two one-digit numbers.

**Solve problems involving the four operations, and identify and explain patterns in arithmetic.**

**3.OA.8**    Solve two-step word problems using the four operations. Represent these problems using equations with a letter standing for the unknown quantity. Assess the reasonableness of answers using the mental computation and estimation strategies including rounding. (This standard is limited to problems posed with whole numbers and having whole-number answers; students should know how to perform operations in the conventional order when there are no parentheses to specify a particular order, i.e., Order of Operations.)

**Module 1:**    Properties of Multiplication and Division and Solving Problems with Units 2–5 and 10

## Evaluating Student Learning Outcomes

A Progression Toward Mastery is provided to describe steps that illuminate the gradually increasing understandings that students develop *on their way to proficiency*. In this chart, this progress is presented from left (Step 1) to right (Step 4) for Problems 1–4. The learning goal for students is to achieve Step 4 mastery. These steps are meant to help teachers and students identify and celebrate what the students CAN do now, and what they need to work on next. Problem 5 is scored differently since it is a timed assessment of fluency. Students complete as many problems as they can in 2 minutes. Although this page of the assessment contains 40 questions, answering 30 correct within the time limit is considered passing.

| A Progression Toward Mastery | | | | |
|---|---|---|---|---|
| **Assessment Task Item and Standards Addressed** | **STEP 1** Little evidence of reasoning without a correct answer. | **STEP 2** Evidence of some reasoning without a correct answer. | **STEP 3** Evidence of some reasoning with a correct answer or evidence of solid reasoning with an incorrect answer. | **STEP 4** Evidence of solid reasoning with a correct answer. |
| | **(1 Point)** | **(2 Points)** | **(3 Points)** | **(4 Points)** |
| **1** <br><br> 3.OA.1 <br> 3.OA.2 <br> 3.OA.3 <br> 3.OA.4 | Student is unable to answer any question correctly. The attempt shows the student may not understand the meaning of the questions. | Student answers at least one question correctly. Mistakes may include those listed in the box to the right, and/or: <br> ▪ Finds the incorrect total number of desks. <br> ▪ Does not show understanding of the meaning of the product. <br> ▪ Places the numbers incorrectly in the division sentence. <br> ▪ Does not show understanding of the meaning of the quotient. | Student answers at least two questions correctly. Mistakes may include the following: <br> ▪ Finds the correct total number of desks but does not draw an accurate picture. <br> ▪ Incorrectly completes the related division sentence but understands that the quotient represents the number of groups. | Student correctly: <br> ▪ Draws a picture, calculates the total number of desks, 24, and writes a multiplication sentence ($6 \times 4 = 24$ or $4 \times 6 = 24$). <br> ▪ Explains that the product, 24, represents the total number of desks. <br> ▪ Fills in the blanks to complete the related division sentence ($24 \div 4 = 6$). <br> ▪ Explains that the quotient, 6, represents the number of groups. |

## A Progression Toward Mastery

| **2**<br><br>**3.OA.3**<br>**3.OA.5** | Student is unable to answer any question correctly. The attempt shows the student may not understand the meaning of the questions. | Student answers at least one question correctly. Mistakes may include those listed in the box to the right, and/or:<br><br>■ Draws incorrect arrays in Part (a) and/or in Part (b).<br><br>■ Writes an incorrect multiplication sentence in either Part (a) or Part (b). Inaccurately explains the relationship between the two arrays. | Student answers at least two questions correctly. Mistakes may include the following:<br><br>■ Incorrectly circles 2 in Part (a) or Part (b).<br><br>■ Explanation of the relationship between the two arrays includes some inaccuracies. | Student correctly:<br><br>■ Draws an array with 9 rows of 2, writes a multiplication sentence (9 × 2 = 18 or 2 × 9 = 18), and circles 9.<br><br>■ Draws an array with 2 rows of 9, writes a different multiplication sentence (2 × 9 = 18 or 9 × 2 = 18), and circles 9.<br><br>■ Provides an accurate explanation of the commutative property in Part (c). |
|---|---|---|---|---|
| **3**<br><br>**3.OA.3**<br>**3.OA.5** | Student is unable to answer any question correctly. The attempt shows the student may not understand the meaning of the questions. | Student answers at least one question correctly. Mistakes may include those listed in the box to the right, and/or:<br><br>■ Incorrectly fills in the blanks in the expressions in Part (a).<br><br>■ Incorrectly fills in the unknowns in Part (b) and/or in Part (c).<br><br>■ Inaccurately shows Lilly's 8 apples in the picture in Part (a). | Student answers at least two questions correctly. Mistakes may include the following:<br><br>■ Incorrectly fills in the blank for the total apples in Part (a).<br><br>■ Correctly fills in the unknowns in Part (b) and/or Part (c) but incorrectly calculates the total number of apples.<br><br>■ Correctly calculates the total number of apples in Part (b) but does not use the distributive property. | Student correctly:<br><br>■ Fills in the blanks to complete the expressions in Part (a). (Total apples: 6 × 4, red apples: 5 × 4, and green apples: 1 × 4.)<br><br>■ Fills in the unknowns in the equation (6, 5, 1) and uses the distributive property to calculate the total number of apples as 24.<br><br>■ Draws two more rows of green apples in the array in Part (a), fills in the unknowns (8, 5, 3), and calculates the total number of apples as 32. |

   **Module 1:**   Properties of Multiplication and Division and Solving Problems with Units 2–5 and 10

EUREKA MATH™

## A Progression Toward Mastery

| 4<br><br>3.OA.3<br>3.OA.6<br>3.OA.8 | Student is unable to answer any question correctly. The attempt shows the student may not understand the meaning of the questions. | Student answers at least one question correctly. Mistakes may include those listed in the box to the right, and/or:<br><br>▪ Draws an inaccurate picture.<br><br>▪ Writes an incorrect division sentence.<br><br>▪ Identifies that Mr. Myer's method is correct but explanation includes inaccuracies. Incorrectly calculates the total number of points earned on both days in Part (c). | Student answers at least two questions correctly. Mistakes may include the following:<br><br>▪ Explanation for Part (b) includes some limitations but no inaccuracies.<br><br>▪ Correctly calculates the number of points earned on Tuesday but does not find the total for both days. | Student correctly:<br><br>▪ Draws a picture, and writes a division sentence and calculates the number of questions (50 ÷ 5 = 10).<br><br>▪ Explains division as an unknown factor problem in Part (b).<br><br>▪ Calculates the total number of points the class earned on both days in Part (c) as 85. |
|---|---|---|---|---|
| 5<br><br>3.OA.7 | Use the attached sample work to correct students' answers on the fluency page of the assessment.<br><br>Students who answer 30 or more questions correctly within the allotted time pass this portion of the assessment. They are ready to move on to the more complicated fluency page given with the Module 2 End-of-Module Assessment. For students who do not pass, you may choose to re-administer this fluency page with each subsequent End-of-Module Assessment until they are successful.<br><br>Analyze the mistakes students make on this assessment to further guide your fluency instruction. Possible questions to ask as you analyze are:<br><br>▪ Did this student struggle with multiplication, division, or both?<br><br>▪ Did this student struggle with a particular factor?<br><br>▪ Did this student consistently miss problems with the unknown in a particular position? | | | |

Name _Gina_____    Date _____

1.  Mr. Lewis arranges all the desks in his classroom into 6 equal groups of 4. How many desks are in his classroom? Show a picture and multiplication sentence in your work.

$6 \times 4 = 24$      There are 24 desks in his classroom.

a.  What does the product in your multiplication sentence represent?

The product is 24 and it represents the total number of desks.

b.  Fill in the blanks below to complete a related division sentence.

_24_ ÷ 4 = _6_

c.  What does the quotient in part (b) represent?

The quotient is 6 and it represents the number of equal groups of desks.

EUREKA MATH™

2.

a. Draw an array that shows 9 rows of 2. Write a multiplication sentence to represent the array, and circle the factor that represents the number of rows.

$$\textcircled{9} \times 2 = 18$$

b. Draw another array that shows 2 rows of 9. Write a different multiplication sentence and circle the factor that represents the size of the row.

$$2 \times \textcircled{9} = 18$$

c. Explain the relationship between the two arrays using number sentences and words.

The arrays have the same totals, 18 and they have the same factors, 2 and 9. The factors switch places. In 9×2=18, the 9 is the number of rows, but in 2×9=18, the 9 is the size of the row. It's the commutative property!

3.  Ms. Park buys a tray of apples for a class party.  There are 5 rows of 4 red apples.  There is 1 row of 4 green apples.

    a.  The picture below shows Ms. Park's apples.  Fill in the blanks to complete the expressions.

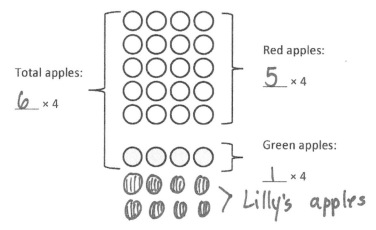

Total apples:

6 × 4

Red apples:

5 × 4

Green apples:

1 × 4

> Lilly's apples

    b.  Fill in the unknowns in the equation below to match the picture of the apples in part (a).  Use the break apart and distribute strategy to find the total number of apples Ms. Park bought.

$$\underline{6} \times 4 = \underline{5} \times 4 + \underline{1} \times 4$$

6 × 4 = 20 + 4

6 × 4 = 24

Ms. Park bought __24__ apples.

    c.  Lilly brings 8 green apples for the class party.  Show Lilly's green apples on the picture in part (a).  Then, fill in the unknowns in the equation below to match the new picture.  Solve to find the total number of apples.

$$\underline{8} \times 4 = \underline{5} \times 4 + \underline{3} \times 4$$

8 × 4 = 20 + 12

8 × 4 = 32

There are __32__ apples in all.

Module 1:    Properties of Multiplication and Division and Solving Problems with Units 2–5 and 10

©2015 Great Minds. eureka-math.org
G3-M1-TE-B1-1.3.1-01.2016

EUREKA
MATH

4. Mr. Myer's class plays a game. The class earns 5 points each time they answer a question correctly. The class earns 50 points playing the game on Monday.

     a. How many questions did the class answer correctly? Show a picture and division sentence in your work.

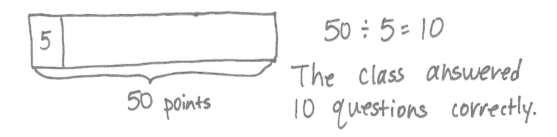

$$50 \div 5 = 10$$

The class answered 10 questions correctly.

     b. Mr. Myer uses the equation 5 × _____ = 50 to find how many questions the class answered correctly. Is his method correct? Why or why not?

Yes, his method is correct. I solved using division, but he is solving using multiplication. The blank shows he is looking for a factor. 5 × 10 = 50, so he gets the same answer as 50 ÷ 5 = 10. Both show the class answered 10 questions correctly.

     c. The class answered 7 questions correctly Tuesday. What is the total number of points the class earned on both days?

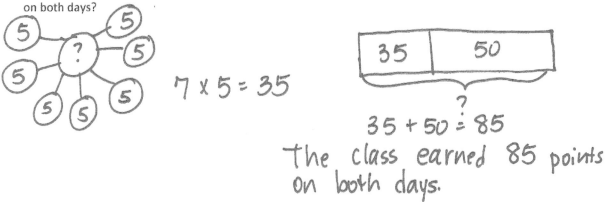

$$7 \times 5 = 35$$

$$35 + 50 = 85$$

The class earned 85 points on both days.

EUREKA
MATH™

Module 1:   Properties of Multiplication and Division and Solving Problems with Units 2–5 and 10

285

©2015 Great Minds. eureka-math.org
G3-M1-TE-B1-1.3.1-01.2016

5. Complete as many problems as you can in 100 seconds. Your teacher will time you and tell you when to stop.

$4 \times 1 = \underline{4}$   $3 \div 1 = \underline{3}$   $10 \times \underline{2} = 20$   $2 \times 3 = \underline{6}$   $10 \div 5 = \underline{2}$

$4 \div 2 = \underline{2}$   $2 \times \underline{2} = 4$   $15 \div 5 = \underline{3}$   $10 \times 3 = \underline{30}$   $4 \times \underline{3} = 12$

$3 \times 3 = \underline{9}$   $5 \times \underline{3} = 15$   $16 \div 4 = \underline{4}$   $2 \times \underline{4} = 8$   $10 \times 4 = \underline{40}$

$2 \times 4 = \underline{8}$   $12 \div 4 = \underline{3}$   $4 \times \underline{5} = 20$   $5 \times 5 = \underline{25}$   $50 \div 10 = \underline{5}$

$15 \div 3 = \underline{5}$   $2 \times \underline{5} = 10$   $24 \div 4 = \underline{6}$   $10 \times 6 = \underline{60}$   $5 \times \underline{6} = 30$

$2 \times 6 = \underline{12}$   $4 \times \underline{6} = 24$   $35 \div 5 = \underline{7}$   $3 \times \underline{7} = 21$   $10 \times 7 = \underline{70}$

$4 \times 7 = \underline{28}$   $14 \div 2 = \underline{7}$   $3 \times \underline{8} = 24$   $5 \times 8 = \underline{40}$   $80 \div 10 = \underline{8}$

$32 \div 4 = \underline{8}$   $10 \times \underline{8} = 80$   $27 \div 3 = \underline{9}$   $2 \times 9 = \underline{18}$   $5 \times \underline{9} = 45$

**Module 1:** Properties of Multiplication and Division and Solving Problems with Units 2–5 and 10

EUREKA MATH

# Answer Key

# Eureka Math Grade 3 Module 1

Special thanks go to the Gordon A. Cain Center and to the Department of Mathematics at Louisiana State University for their support in the development of *Eureka Math*.

For a free *Eureka Math* Teacher Resource Pack, Parent Tip Sheets, and more please visit www.Eureka.tools

Answer Key

# GRADE 3 • MODULE 1

Properties of Multiplication and Division and Solving
Problems with Units of 2–5 and 10

# Lesson 1

## Problem Set

1.    a.   15; 15; 15
        b.   15; 15; 15
        c.   24; 4, 24; 6, 24
        d.   4, 4, 4, 4, 4, 24; 4, 24; 4, 24
2.    No; explanations will vary.
3.    2 equal groups of 3 apples
4.    Chocolates circled to show 3 groups of 4; $4 + 4 + 4 = 12$; $3 \times 4 = 12$ or $4 \times 3 = 12$

## Exit Ticket

1.    2, 2, 2, 8; 2, 8
2.    Picture showing $3 + 3 + 3 = 9$ drawn; $3 \times 3 = 9$

## Homework

1.    a.   20; 20; 20
        b.   20; 20; 20
        c.   18; 3, 18; 6, 18
        d.   3, 3, 3, 3, 3, 18; 3, 18; 3, 18
2.    Yes; explanations will vary.
3.    Picture showing $4 \times 2 = 8$ drawn
4.    Pencils circled to show 3 groups of 6; $6 + 6 + 6 = 18$; $3 \times 6 = 18$ or $6 \times 3 = 18$

   **Module 1:**    Properties of Multiplication and Division and Solving Problems with Units 2–5 and 10

EUREKA MATH™

# Lesson 2

## Sprint

### Side A

| | | | | | | | |
|---|---|---|---|---|---|---|---|
| 1. | 2 | 12. | 16 | 23. | 6 | 34. | 88 |
| 2. | 4 | 13. | 14 | 24. | 8 | 35. | 66 |
| 3. | 6 | 14. | 12 | 25. | 10 | 36. | 44 |
| 4. | 8 | 15. | 10 | 26. | 12 | 37. | 22 |
| 5. | 10 | 16. | 8 | 27. | 14 | 38. | 0 |
| 6. | 12 | 17. | 6 | 28. | 16 | 39. | 22 |
| 7. | 14 | 18. | 4 | 29. | 18 | 40. | 44 |
| 8. | 16 | 19. | 2 | 30. | 20 | 41. | 66 |
| 9. | 18 | 20. | 0 | 31. | 22 | 42. | 88 |
| 10. | 20 | 21. | 2 | 32. | 44 | 43. | 666 |
| 11. | 18 | 22. | 4 | 33. | 66 | 44. | 444 |

### Side B

| | | | | | | | |
|---|---|---|---|---|---|---|---|
| 1. | 2 | 12. | 16 | 23. | 6 | 34. | 88 |
| 2. | 4 | 13. | 14 | 24. | 8 | 35. | 66 |
| 3. | 6 | 14. | 12 | 25. | 10 | 36. | 44 |
| 4. | 8 | 15. | 10 | 26. | 12 | 37. | 22 |
| 5. | 10 | 16. | 8 | 27. | 14 | 38. | 0 |
| 6. | 12 | 17. | 6 | 28. | 16 | 39. | 22 |
| 7. | 14 | 18. | 4 | 29. | 18 | 40. | 44 |
| 8. | 16 | 19. | 2 | 30. | 20 | 41. | 66 |
| 9. | 18 | 20. | 0 | 31. | 22 | 42. | 88 |
| 10. | 20 | 21. | 2 | 32. | 44 | 43. | 444 |
| 11. | 18 | 22. | 4 | 33. | 66 | 44. | 666 |

EUREKA
MATH™

Module 1:  Properties of Multiplication and Division and Solving Problems with
Units 2–5 and 10

289

©2015 Great Minds. eureka-math.org
G3-M1-TE-B1-1.3.1-01.2016

## Problem Set

1.  a.  4
    b.  2
2.  a.  3
    b.  6
3.  a.  8
    b.  $2 \times 4$
4.  a.  4
    b.  $5 \times 4$

5.  a.  2 rows of 5 drawn
    b.  Answers will vary.
6.  4 rows of 3 drawn; $4 \times 3 = 12$
7.  5 rows of 3 drawn; $5 \times 3 = 15$

## Exit Ticket

1.  a.  3
    b.  $4 \times 3 = 12$
2.  3 rows of 6 drawn; $3 \times 6 = 18$

## Homework

1.  a.  3
    b.  2
2.  a.  4
    b.  3
3.  a.  15
    b.  $5 \times 3$
4.  a.  4
    b.  $6 \times 4$

5.  a.  3 rows of 4 drawn
    b.  Answers will vary.
6.  5 rows of 4 drawn; $5 \times 4 = 20$
7.  Answers will vary.

**Module 1:**    Properties of Multiplication and Division and Solving Problems with Units 2–5 and 10

**EUREKA MATH™**

# Lesson 3

## Sprint

**Side A**

| | | | |
|---|---|---|---|
| 1. 4 | 12. 20 | 23. 14 | 34. 12 |
| 2. 4 | 13. 8 | 24. 14 | 35. 20 |
| 3. 10 | 14. 8 | 25. 18 | 36. 20 |
| 4. 10 | 15. 6 | 26. 18 | 37. 18 |
| 5. 6 | 16. 6 | 27. 16 | 38. 18 |
| 6. 6 | 17. 12 | 28. 16 | 39. 24 |
| 7. 8 | 18. 12 | 29. 9 | 40. 24 |
| 8. 8 | 19. 10 | 30. 9 | 41. 21 |
| 9. 15 | 20. 10 | 31. 12 | 42. 21 |
| 10. 15 | 21. 25 | 32. 12 | 43. 27 |
| 11. 20 | 22. 25 | 33. 12 | 44. 27 |

**Side B**

| | | | |
|---|---|---|---|
| 1. 10 | 12. 8 | 23. 16 | 34. 9 |
| 2. 10 | 13. 6 | 24. 16 | 35. 20 |
| 3. 4 | 14. 6 | 25. 14 | 36. 20 |
| 4. 4 | 15. 12 | 26. 14 | 37. 21 |
| 5. 15 | 16. 12 | 27. 18 | 38. 21 |
| 6. 15 | 17. 8 | 28. 18 | 39. 27 |
| 7. 20 | 18. 8 | 29. 12 | 40. 27 |
| 8. 20 | 19. 25 | 30. 12 | 41. 18 |
| 9. 6 | 20. 25 | 31. 12 | 42. 18 |
| 10. 6 | 21. 10 | 32. 12 | 43. 24 |
| 11. 8 | 22. 10 | 33. 9 | 44. 24 |

EUREKA
MATH™

**Module 1:**   Properties of Multiplication and Division and Solving Problems with
Units 2–5 and 10

**291**

©2015 Great Minds. eureka-math.org
G3-M1-TE-B1-1.3.1-01.2016

## Problem Set

1.  a.  4; 5
    b.  20
    c.  20
2.  3
    a.  6; 3
    b.  3, 18
    c.  18
3.  3
    a.  3; 4
    b.  3, 12
    c.  12

4.  2
    a.  5; 2
    b.  5, 2, 10
    c.  10
5.  a.  $4 \times 3 = 12$
    b.  Number bond showing 4 units of 3 equals 12 drawn
6.  Array showing 2 rows of 3 or 3 rows of 2 drawn; number bond drawn depending on the array, showing 2 units of 3 equals 6 or 3 units of 2 equals 6

## Exit Ticket

Array showing 5 rows of 3 squares drawn; number bond showing 5 units of 3 equals 15 drawn

## Homework

1.  a.  5; 5
    b.  25
    c.  25
2.  4
    a.  6; 4
    b.  4, 24
    c.  24
3.  4
    a.  4; 4
    b.  4, 16
    c.  16

4.  3
    a.  6; 3
    b.  6, 3, 18
    c.  18
5.  Array showing 4 rows of 2 or 2 rows of 4 drawn; number bond drawn depending on the array, showing 4 units of 2 equals 8 or 2 units of 4 equals 8

Module 1:      Properties of Multiplication and Division and Solving Problems with Units 2–5 and 10

©2015 Great Minds. eureka-math.org
G3-M1-TE-B1-1.3.1-01.2016

**EUREKA MATH™**

## Lesson 4

### Sprint

#### Side A

| | | | | | | | |
|---|---|---|---|---|---|---|---|
| 1. | 15 | 12. | 8 | 23. | 12 | 34. | 18 |
| 2. | 15 | 13. | 10 | 24. | 12 | 35. | 18 |
| 3. | 15 | 14. | 10 | 25. | 12 | 36. | 18 |
| 4. | 6 | 15. | 10 | 26. | 9 | 37. | 12 |
| 5. | 6 | 16. | 6 | 27. | 9 | 38. | 12 |
| 6. | 6 | 17. | 6 | 28. | 15 | 39. | 12 |
| 7. | 10 | 18. | 6 | 29. | 15 | 40. | 16 |
| 8. | 10 | 19. | 20 | 30. | 15 | 41. | 16 |
| 9. | 10 | 20. | 20 | 31. | 14 | 42. | 16 |
| 10. | 8 | 21. | 20 | 32. | 14 | 43. | 28 |
| 11. | 8 | 22. | 4 | 33. | 14 | 44. | 28 |

#### Side B

| | | | | | | | |
|---|---|---|---|---|---|---|---|
| 1. | 6 | 12. | 10 | 23. | 12 | 34. | 16 |
| 2. | 6 | 13. | 6 | 24. | 12 | 35. | 16 |
| 3. | 6 | 14. | 6 | 25. | 12 | 36. | 16 |
| 4. | 15 | 15. | 6 | 26. | 16 | 37. | 14 |
| 5. | 15 | 16. | 10 | 27. | 16 | 38. | 14 |
| 6. | 15 | 17. | 10 | 28. | 20 | 39. | 14 |
| 7. | 8 | 18. | 10 | 29. | 20 | 40. | 18 |
| 8. | 8 | 19. | 20 | 30. | 20 | 41. | 18 |
| 9. | 8 | 20. | 20 | 31. | 12 | 42. | 18 |
| 10. | 10 | 21. | 20 | 32. | 12 | 43. | 24 |
| 11. | 10 | 22. | 4 | 33. | 12 | 44. | 24 |

## Problem Set

1.  7
2.  7
3.  3; 10
4.  12, 2; 6; 6
5.  5; 5
6.  3
7.  6; 6
8.  Four apples drawn in each basket; 4; 5, 4
9.  3; 15, 5, 3

## Exit Ticket

1.  Four glue sticks drawn in each group; 4; 4, 4
2.  Picture showing 15 ÷ 3 drawn; 5

## Homework

1.  6
2.  7
3.  5; 5
4.  9, 3; 3; 3
5.  3; 3
6.  4
7.  7; 7
8.  Five pencils drawn on each table; 5; 4, 5
9.  4; 20, 5, 4

EUREKA
MATH™

# Lesson 5

## Problem Set

1.    2

2.    Four groups of 2 shown; 4; 4

3.    Two groups of 5 shown; 2

4.    4 groups of 3 shown; 4; 4

5.    Three groups of 3 circled

    a.   $9 \div 3 = 3$

    b.   Number bond showing 3 units of 3 equals 9 drawn

6.    a.   Count-by fours from 4 to 16 written and drawn

    b.   $16 \div 4 = 4$

## Exit Ticket

1.    Two groups of 6 shown; 2

2.    Count-by fives from 5 to 20 written and drawn

## Homework

1.    Answer given; 2

2.    Three groups of 3 shown; 3; 3

3.    Four groups of 3 shown; 4

4.    Three groups of 5 shown; 3; 3

5.    Two groups of 6 circled

    a.   $12 \div 6 = 2$

    b.   Number bond showing 2 units of 6 equals 12 drawn

6.    a.   Count-by fours from 4 to 24 written and drawn

    b.   $24 \div 4 = 6$

# Lesson 6

## Problem Set

1. Five groups of 3 circled; 5; 5; 5

2. Five groups of 3 drawn and circled; 3; 3; 3

3. Array of 5 rows of 3 drawn

    a. 5; 5; the number of groups

    b. 3; 3; the size of each group

4. 3; 3; the number of groups

5. 3; 3; answers will vary

6. Array of 4 rows of 3 drawn

## Exit Ticket

Array of 2 rows of 6 drawn; 2; 2; the number of groups

## Homework

1. Three groups of 4 circled; 3; 3; 3

2. Three groups of 4 drawn and circled; 4; 4; 4

3. Array of 3 rows of 4 drawn

    a. 3; 3; the number of groups

    b. 4; 4; the size of each group

4. 6; 6; the size of each group

5. 3; 3; answers will vary

6. Array of 3 rows of 5 drawn

**Module 1:** Properties of Multiplication and Division and Solving Problems with Units 2–5 and 10

©2015 Great Minds. eureka-math.org
G3-M1-TE-B1-1.3.1-01.2016

# Lesson 7

## Problem Set

1.  a.  Array of 6 rows of 2 drawn

    b.  6, 2, 12

2.  a.  Array of 2 rows of 6 drawn

    b.  2, 6, 12

3.  a.  Same array in Problem 1 turned on its side in Problem 2

    b.  The meaning of the factors switched; 2 represents size of each group, and 6 represents number of

        groups in Problem 1; 2 represents number of groups, and 6 represents size of each group in

        Problem 2

4.  a.  Answer provided

    b.  $2 \times 6 = 12$

    c.  $7 \times 2 = 14$

    d.  $2 \times 7 = 14$

    e.  $9 \times 2 = 18$

    f.  $2 \times 9 = 18$

    g.  $11 \times 2 = 22$

    h.  $2 \times 12 = 24$

5.  $4 \times 2 = 8$; $2 \times 4 = 8$

6.  Agree; array of 7 rows of 2 and array of 2 rows of 7 drawn

7.  5; 2; 10; 9

8.  a.  Array of 2 rows of 6 drawn

    b.  $2 \times 6 = 12$

    c.  $6 \times 2 = 12$

## Exit Ticket

Agree; array of 2 rows of 5 and array of 5 rows of 2 drawn; skip-counts by fives or twos, depending on the
array, written to show a total of 10 each

©2015 Great Minds. eureka-math.org
G3-M1-TE-B1-1.3.1-01.2016

## Homework

1. a. Array of 7 rows of 2 drawn

   b. 7, 2, 14

2. a. Array of 2 rows of 7 drawn

   b. 2, 7, 14

3. a. Same array in Problem 1 turned on its side in Problem 2

   b. The meaning of the factors switched;  2 represents size of each group, and 7 represents number of groups in Problem 1; 2 represents number of groups, and 7 represents size of each group in Problem 2

4. a. Answer provided.

   b. $3 \times 2 = 6$

   c. $2 \times 3 = 6$

   d. $2 \times 4 = 8$

   e. $4 \times 2 = 8$

   f. $5 \times 2 = 10$

   g. $2 \times 5 = 10$

   h. $6 \times 2 = 12$

   i. $2 \times 6 = 12$

5. $6 \times 2 = 12$; $2 \times 6 = 12$

6. Agree; array of 2 rows of 8 and array of 8 rows of 2 drawn

7. 2; 7; 2; 10

8. a. Array of 2 rows of 7 drawn

   b. $2 \times 7 = 14$

   c. $7 \times 2 = 14$

Module 1:     Properties of Multiplication and Division and Solving Problems with Units 2–5 and 10.

©2015 Great Minds. eureka-math.org
G3-M1-TE-B1-1.3.1-01.2016

EUREKA
MATH

## Lesson 8

### Problem Set

1.  Array of 5 rows of 3 drawn

2.  Array of 3 rows of 5 drawn

3.  5; 3;  3; 5

4.  a.  Answer provided

    b.  $3 \times 2 = 6$

    c.  $3 \times 4 = 12$

    d.  $4 \times 3 = 12$

    e.  $3 \times 7 = 21$

    f.  $7 \times 3 = 21$

    g.  $3 \times 9 = 27$

    h.  $9 \times 3 = 27$

    i.  $10 \times 3 = 30$

5.  a.  15, matched with Part (e), 15

    b.  27, matched with Part (f), 3

    c.  24, matched with Part (d), 24

6.  a.  Array of 7 rows of 3 drawn

    b.  $7 \times 3 = 21$; Isaac picks 21 tangerines in 7 days.

    c.  3 rows of 3 x's added to array in Part (a)

    d.  $10 \times 3 = 30$

7.  a.  3, $2, 6

    b.  6, $2, 12

### Exit Ticket

a.  Array of 3 rows of 4 drawn

b.  $3 \times 4 = 12$

c.  Rows of array labeled 4, 8, 12

d.  $4 \times 3 = 12$

EUREKA MATH

**Module 1:**   Properties of Multiplication and Division and Solving Problems with Units 2–5 and 10.

299

©2015 Great Minds. eureka-math.org
G3-M1-TE-B1-1.3.1-01.2016

## Homework

1. Array of 6 rows of 3 drawn
2. Array of 3 rows of 6 drawn
3. 6; 3; 3; 6
4. a. Answer provided

    b. $3 \times 5 = 15$

    c. $6 \times 3 = 18$

    d. $3 \times 6 = 18$

    e. $7 \times 3 = 21$

    f. $3 \times 7 = 21$

    g. $8 \times 3 = 24$

    h. $3 \times 9 = 27$

    i. $10 \times 3 = 30$

5. a. 18, matched with Part (e), 18

    b. 15, matched with Part (f), 3

    c. 27, matched with Part (d), 27

6. a. Array of 8 rows of 3 circles drawn

    b. $8 \times 3 = 24$. Fernando uses 24 pictures.

    c. 2 rows of 3 x's added to array in Part (a)

    d. $10 \times 3 = 30$

7. a. 4, 3 cents, 12

    b. 7, 3 cents, 21

**EUREKA MATH**™

## Lesson 9

### Pattern Sheet

| | | | |
|---|---|---|---|
| 2 | 4 | 6 | 8 |
| 10 | 2 | 4 | 2 |
| 6 | 2 | 8 | 2 |
| 10 | 2 | 4 | 6 |
| 4 | 8 | 4 | 10 |
| 4 | 2 | 4 | 6 |
| 2 | 6 | 4 | 6 |
| 8 | 6 | 10 | 6 |
| 8 | 2 | 8 | 4 |
| 8 | 6 | 8 | 10 |
| 8 | 10 | 2 | 10 |
| 4 | 10 | 6 | 10 |
| 8 | 4 | 8 | 6 |
| 10 | 6 | 4 | 8 |
| 6 | 10 | 4 | 8 |

### Problem Set

1.  a.  25

    b.  3, 5

    c.  5, 25

2.  14; 10; 4; 14; 7

3.  18; 20; 2; 2; 18

4.  a.  Array of 4 rows of 3 x's drawn

    b.  12

5.  2 rows of 3 circles added to array in Problem 4(a)

    a.  2, 6

    b.  12, 6

    c.  6, 3

## Exit Ticket

1. 10, 2, 20

2. a. 10, 2, 8

   b. 4

   c. 8, 16

## Homework

1. a. 20

   b. 2, 5

   c. 5, 20

2. 14; 12; 2; 14; 7

3. 27; 30; 3; 3; 9

4. a. Array of 5 rows of 4 x's drawn

   b. 20

5. 2 rows of 4 circles added to array in Problem 4

   a. 2, 8

   b. 20, 8

   c. 7

**Module 1:**    Properties of Multiplication and Division and Solving Problems with
Units 2–5 and 10.

EUREKA
MATH

# Lesson 10

## Pattern Sheet

| 2 | 4 | 6 | 8 |
|----|----|----|----|
| 10 | 12 | 14 | 16 |
| 18 | 20 | 10 | 12 |
| 10 | 14 | 10 | 16 |
| 10 | 18 | 10 | 20 |
| 12 | 10 | 12 | 14 |
| 12 | 16 | 12 | 18 |
| 12 | 14 | 12 | 14 |
| 16 | 14 | 18 | 14 |
| 16 | 12 | 16 | 14 |
| 16 | 18 | 18 | 12 |
| 18 | 14 | 18 | 16 |
| 18 | 16 | 12 | 18 |
| 14 | 18 | 12 | 16 |
| 18 | 14 | 12 | 16 |

## Problem Set

1. 21; 6; 6; 6, 21

2. 24; 4, 12; 4, 12; 12, 12; 8, 24

3. a. Array of 2 rows of 3 shown in upper album, 2; array of 3 rows of 3 shown in lower album, 3

   b. $5 \times 3$ broken into two smaller facts: $2 \times 3 = 6$ and $3 \times 3 = 9$; answers of two smaller facts added: $6 + 9$; $5 \times 3 = 6 + 9 = 15$

## Exit Ticket

1. 18; 12; 6; 12, 6; 12, 6; 6, 18

2. 21; 5, 15; 2, 6; 15, 6; 15, 6; 7, 21

**Module 1:** Properties of Multiplication and Division and Solving Problems with Units 2–5 and 10.

©2015 Great Minds. eureka-math.org
G3-M1-TE-B1-1.3.1-01.2016

303

## Homework

1. 18; 6; 6, 18; **18**

2. 16; 4, 8; 4, 8; **8, 8; 8, 16**

3.   a.  Array of **5** rows of 3 shown on top shelf, 5; array of **1** row of 3 shown on bottom shelf, 1

   b.  6 × 3 broken into two smaller facts:  5 × 3 = 15 and 1 × 3 = 3; answers of two smaller facts added:
       15 + 3; 6 × 3 = 15 + 3 = 18

**Module 1:**    Properties of Multiplication and Division and Solving Problems with
Units 2–5 and 10.

©2015 Great Minds. eureka-math.org
G3-M1-TE-B1-1.3.1-01.2016

**EUREKA
MATH**

# Lesson 11

## Pattern Sheet

| | | | |
|---|---|---|---|
| 3 | 6 | 9 | 12 |
| 15 | 3 | 6 | 3 |
| 9 | 3 | 12 | 3 |
| 15 | 3 | 6 | 9 |
| 6 | 12 | 6 | 15 |
| 6 | 3 | 6 | 9 |
| 3 | 9 | 6 | 9 |
| 12 | 9 | 15 | 9 |
| 12 | 3 | 12 | 6 |
| 12 | 9 | 12 | 15 |
| 12 | 15 | 3 | 15 |
| 6 | 15 | 9 | 15 |
| 12 | 6 | 12 | 9 |
| 15 | 9 | 6 | 12 |
| 9 | 15 | 6 | 12 |

## Problem Set

1.  a.  Array drawn showing 2 columns of 6; 12, 6

    b.  2 oranges drawn in each unit; unit labeled 2 oranges; whole labeled 12 oranges and/or ? bags

2.  3; array drawn showing 6 columns of 3; tape diagram drawn showing 6 groups of 3 is 18

3.  2; array drawn showing 7 columns of 2; tape diagram drawn showing 7 groups of 2 is 14

4.  3; array drawn showing 8 columns of 3; tape diagram drawn showing 8 groups of 3 is 24

5.  8

## Exit Ticket

9; array and tape diagram drawn showing 9 groups of 2 is 18

Module 1:    Properties of Multiplication and Division and Solving Problems with
             Units 2–5 and 10.

305

©2015 Great Minds. eureka-math.org
G3-M1-TE-B1-1.3.1-01.2016

**Homework**

1. a. Array drawn showing 2 rows of 5; 10, 5

   b. 2 pears drawn in each unit; unit labeled 2 pears; whole labeled 10 pears and/or ? baskets

2. 5; array drawn showing 3 columns of 5; tape diagram drawn showing 3 groups of 5 is 15

3. 8; array drawn showing 2 columns of 8; tape diagram drawn showing 2 groups of 8 is 16

4. 6; array drawn showing 3 columns of 6; tape diagram drawn showing 3 groups of 6 is 18

5. 7

**Module 1:** Properties of Multiplication and Division and Solving Problems with Units 2–5 and 10.

©2015 Great Minds. eureka-math.org
G3-M1-TE-B1-1.3.1-01.2016

EUREKA MATH™

# Lesson 12

## Pattern Sheet

| | | | |
|---|---|---|---|
| 3 | 6 | 9 | 12 |
| 15 | 18 | 21 | 24 |
| 27 | 30 | 15 | 18 |
| 15 | 21 | 15 | 24 |
| 15 | 27 | 15 | 30 |
| 18 | 15 | 18 | 21 |
| 18 | 24 | 18 | 27 |
| 18 | 21 | 18 | 21 |
| 24 | 21 | 27 | 21 |
| 24 | 18 | 24 | 21 |
| 24 | 27 | 27 | 18 |
| 27 | 21 | 27 | 24 |
| 27 | 24 | 18 | 27 |
| 21 | 27 | 18 | 24 |
| 27 | 21 | 18 | 24 |

## Problem Set

1. 4 groups of 2 birds circled; 4; 4

2. 2 fish drawn in each bowl; 2; 2; 2

3. First rabbit matched to 5

   Second rabbit matched to 8

   Third rabbit matched to 9

   Fourth rabbit matched to 7

   Fifth rabbit matched to 6

4. 7; labels will vary.

5. 6

6. $9

## Exit Ticket

7; tape diagram drawn and labeled to represent the problem

## Homework

1. 5 groups of 2 people circled; 5; 5

2. 2 frogs drawn in each group; labels will vary; 2; 2; 2

3. First frog matched to 5

   Second frog matched to 8

   Third frog matched to 9

   Fourth frog matched to 7

4. 8; labels will vary.

5. 7

6. $8

EUREKA
MATH

# Lesson 13

## Sprint

### Side A

| | | | | | | | |
|---|---|---|---|---|---|---|---|
| 1. | 4 | 12. | 14 | 23. | 10 | 34. | 8 |
| 2. | 6 | 13. | 16 | 24. | 2 | 35. | 7 |
| 3. | 8 | 14. | 18 | 25. | 3 | 36. | 9 |
| 4. | 10 | 15. | 20 | 26. | 10 | 37. | 6 |
| 5. | 2 | 16. | 8 | 27. | 5 | 38. | 8 |
| 6. | 2 | 17. | 7 | 28. | 2 | 39. | 22 |
| 7. | 3 | 18. | 9 | 29. | 2 | 40. | 11 |
| 8. | 5 | 19. | 6 | 30. | 3 | 41. | 24 |
| 9. | 2 | 20. | 10 | 31. | 6 | 42. | 12 |
| 10. | 4 | 21. | 5 | 32. | 7 | 43. | 28 |
| 11. | 12 | 22. | 6 | 33. | 9 | 44. | 14 |

### Side B

| | | | | | | | |
|---|---|---|---|---|---|---|---|
| 1. | 2 | 12. | 12 | 23. | 2 | 34. | 7 |
| 2. | 4 | 13. | 14 | 24. | 10 | 35. | 8 |
| 3. | 6 | 14. | 16 | 25. | 3 | 36. | 9 |
| 4. | 8 | 15. | 18 | 26. | 2 | 37. | 6 |
| 5. | 10 | 16. | 7 | 27. | 2 | 38. | 7 |
| 6. | 3 | 17. | 6 | 28. | 10 | 39. | 22 |
| 7. | 2 | 18. | 8 | 29. | 5 | 40. | 11 |
| 8. | 4 | 19. | 10 | 30. | 3 | 41. | 24 |
| 9. | 2 | 20. | 9 | 31. | 6 | 42. | 12 |
| 10. | 5 | 21. | 6 | 32. | 8 | 43. | 26 |
| 11. | 20 | 22. | 5 | 33. | 9 | 44. | 13 |

EUREKA
MATH™

Module 1:    Properties of Multiplication and Division and Solving Problems with
Units 2–5 and 10.

309

## Problem Set

1. Top row:  1; 2; 9; 12, 12; 15, 15

   Bottom row:  18, 18; 21, 21; 24, 24; 27, 27; 30, 30

2. a. 4 groups of 3 circled; skip-count written as 3, 6, 9, 12

   b. Tape diagram drawn and labeled to represent problem; 12, 4; 4

3. 5; tape diagram drawn and labeled to represent problem

4. 10

5. 8

## Exit Ticket

1. 7; tape diagram drawn and labeled to represent problem

2. 8

## Homework

1. 2; 3, 3; 21, 21; 27, 27

2. a. 5 groups of 3 circled; skip-count written as 3, 6, 9, 12, 15

   b. Tape diagram drawn and labeled to represent problem; 15, 5; 5

3. 6

4. 8

5. 9

Properties of Multiplication and Division and Solving Problems with Units 2–5 and 10.

EUREKA
MATH™

# Lesson 14

## Sprint

### Side A

| | | | | | | | |
|---|---|---|---|---|---|---|---|
| 1. | 6 | 12. | 21 | 23. | 10 | 34. | 8 |
| 2. | 9 | 13. | 24 | 24. | 2 | 35. | 7 |
| 3. | 12 | 14. | 27 | 25. | 3 | 36. | 9 |
| 4. | 15 | 15. | 30 | 26. | 10 | 37. | 6 |
| 5. | 3 | 16. | 8 | 27. | 5 | 38. | 8 |
| 6. | 2 | 17. | 7 | 28. | 3 | 39. | 33 |
| 7. | 3 | 18. | 9 | 29. | 2 | 40. | 11 |
| 8. | 5 | 19. | 6 | 30. | 3 | 41. | 36 |
| 9. | 3 | 20. | 10 | 31. | 6 | 42. | 12 |
| 10. | 4 | 21. | 5 | 32. | 7 | 43. | 39 |
| 11. | 18 | 22. | 4 | 33. | 9 | 44. | 13 |

### Side B

| | | | | | | | |
|---|---|---|---|---|---|---|---|
| 1. | 3 | 12. | 18 | 23. | 2 | 34. | 7 |
| 2. | 6 | 13. | 21 | 24. | 10 | 35. | 8 |
| 3. | 9 | 14. | 24 | 25. | 3 | 36. | 9 |
| 4. | 12 | 15. | 27 | 26. | 2 | 37. | 6 |
| 5. | 15 | 16. | 7 | 27. | 3 | 38. | 7 |
| 6. | 3 | 17. | 6 | 28. | 10 | 39. | 33 |
| 7. | 2 | 18. | 8 | 29. | 5 | 40. | 11 |
| 8. | 4 | 19. | 10 | 30. | 3 | 41. | 36 |
| 9. | 3 | 20. | 9 | 31. | 6 | 42. | 12 |
| 10. | 5 | 21. | 4 | 32. | 8 | 43. | 39 |
| 11. | 30 | 22. | 5 | 33. | 9 | 44. | 13 |

EUREKA MATH™

**Module 1:** Properties of Multiplication and Division and Solving Problems with Units 2–5 and 10.

311

©2015 Great Minds. eureka-math.org
G3-M1-TE-B1-1.3.1-01.2016

## Problem Set

1.  12, 16, 20, 24, 28, 32, 36, 40

    Answer provided; 8 matched to 2 × 4; 12 matched to 3 × 4; 16 matched to 4 × 4; 20 matched to 5 × 4;

    24 matched to 6 × 4; 28 matched to 7 × 4; 32 matched to 8 × 4; 36 matched to 9 × 4;

    40 matched to 10 × 4

2.  Tape diagram drawn and labeled to represent problem; 28

3.  Tape diagram drawn and labeled to show 24 beads used

4.  20

## Exit Ticket

24; tape diagram drawn and labeled to represent problem

## Homework

1.  8, 12, 16, 20, 24, 28, 32, 36, 40

    Answer provided; 8 matched to 2 × 4; 12 matched to 3 × 4; 16 matched to 4 × 4; 20 matched to 5 × 4;

    24 matched to 6 × 4; 28 matched to 7 × 4; 32 matched to 8 × 4; 36 matched to 9 × 4;

    40 matched to 10 × 4

2.  Array of 5 rows of 4 drawn; skip-count shown as 4, 8, 12, 16, 20; 20

3.  24; tape diagram drawn and labeled to represent problem

4.  32

**Module 1:**    Properties of Multiplication and Division and Solving Problems with
                                 Units 2–5 and 10.

©2015 Great Minds. eureka-math.org
G3-M1-TE-B1-1.3.1-01.2016

## Lesson 15

### Pattern Sheet

| | | | |
|---|---|---|---|
| 4 | 8 | 12 | 16 |
| 20 | 4 | 8 | 4 |
| 12 | 4 | 16 | 4 |
| 20 | 4 | 8 | 12 |
| 8 | 16 | 8 | 20 |
| 8 | 4 | 8 | 12 |
| 4 | 12 | 8 | 12 |
| 16 | 12 | 20 | 12 |
| 16 | 4 | 16 | 8 |
| 16 | 12 | 16 | 20 |
| 16 | 20 | 4 | 20 |
| 8 | 20 | 12 | 20 |
| 16 | 8 | 16 | 12 |
| 20 | 12 | 8 | 16 |
| 12 | 20 | 8 | 16 |

### Problem Set

1.  a.  Top: 8; 8

    Bottom: 8; 8

    b.  Top: 4, 12; 3, 12

    Bottom: 3, 12; 3, 12

    Array showing 3 rows of 4 or 4 rows of 3 drawn

    c.  Top: 4, 28; 7, 4

    Bottom: 7, 28; 4, 7

    Array showing 7 rows of 4 or 4 rows of 7 drawn

2.  Two tape diagrams drawn and labeled to model $4 \times 6 = 6 \times 4$

3.  Tape diagram drawn and labeled to represent 32 petals

4.  32

Module 1:   Properties of Multiplication and Division and Solving Problems with Units 2–5 and 10.

©2015 Great Minds. eureka-math.org
G3-M1-TE-B1-1.3.1-01.2016

**Exit Ticket**

Two tape diagrams drawn and labeled to show 4 × 3 = 3 × 4; both total 12

**Homework**

1.  a.  Top:  12; 12

    Bottom:  12; 12

    b.  Top:  9, 36; 9, 36

    Bottom:  4, 36; 9, 36

    Array showing 9 rows of 4 or 4 rows of 9 drawn

    c.  Top:  4, 24; 6, 24

    Bottom:  6, 24; 6, 24

    Array showing 6 rows of 4 or 4 rows of 6 drawn

2.  Tape diagram drawn and labeled to represent 28 balloons

3.  28

Module 1:     Properties of Multiplication and Division and Solving Problems with
Units 2–5 and 10.

**EUREKA MATH**™

# Lesson 16

## Pattern Sheet

| | | | |
|---|---|---|---|
| 4 | 8 | 12 | 16 |
| 20 | 24 | 28 | 32 |
| 36 | 40 | 24 | 28 |
| 24 | 32 | 24 | 36 |
| 24 | 40 | 24 | 28 |
| 24 | 28 | 32 | 28 |
| 36 | 28 | 40 | 28 |
| 32 | 24 | 32 | 28 |
| 32 | 36 | 32 | 40 |
| 32 | 36 | 24 | 36 |
| 28 | 36 | 32 | 36 |
| 40 | 36 | 40 | 24 |
| 40 | 28 | 40 | 32 |
| 40 | 36 | 40 | 24 |
| 32 | 40 | 28 | 36 |

## Problem Set

1.  a.   24; 4; 4, 24

    b.   28; 20; 8; 20, 8

    c.   32; 20; 3, 12; 3, 20, 12, 32

    d.   36; 20; 4, 16; 4, 20, 16, 36

2.   First cloud matched to 8 × 4; second cloud matched to 6 × 4; third cloud matched to 9 × 4; fourth cloud matched to 7 × 4

3.   10 fours broken into two smaller facts:  5 fours and 5 fours, or 5 fours doubled; sum of two smaller facts found to answer larger fact

## Exit Ticket

8; 20, 8, 28; 7 fours broken into two smaller facts:  5 fours and 2 fours;  sum of two smaller facts found to answer larger fact

## Homework

1.  a.   24; 1, 4; 1, 4, 24

    b.   32; 20; 3, 12; 3, 20, 12, 32

2.   First sun matched to 24; second sun matched to 28; third sun matched to 32;

     fourth sun matched to 36

3.   20; 16; 9 fours broken into two smaller facts:  5 fours and 4 fours; sum of two smaller facts found to answer larger fact

**316**            **Module 1:**      Properties of Multiplication and Division and Solving Problems with
                            Units 2–5 and 10.

                    ©2015 Great Minds. eureka-math.org
                    G3-M1-TE-B1-1.3.1-01.2016

**EUREKA
MATH**™

# Lesson 17

## Sprint

### Side A

| | | | | | | | |
|---|---|---|---|---|---|---|---|
| 1. | 8 | 12. | 28 | 23. | 10 | 34. | 8 |
| 2. | 12 | 13. | 32 | 24. | 2 | 35. | 7 |
| 3. | 16 | 14. | 36 | 25. | 3 | 36. | 9 |
| 4. | 20 | 15. | 40 | 26. | 10 | 37. | 6 |
| 5. | 4 | 16. | 8 | 27. | 5 | 38. | 8 |
| 6. | 2 | 17. | 7 | 28. | 4 | 39. | 44 |
| 7. | 3 | 18. | 9 | 29. | 2 | 40. | 11 |
| 8. | 5 | 19. | 6 | 30. | 3 | 41. | 3 |
| 9. | 4 | 20. | 10 | 31. | 4 | 42. | 12 |
| 10. | 4 | 21. | 5 | 32. | 7 | 43. | 56 |
| 11. | 24 | 22. | 6 | 33. | 9 | 44. | 14 |

### Side B

| | | | | | | | |
|---|---|---|---|---|---|---|---|
| 1. | 4 | 12. | 24 | 23. | 2 | 34. | 7 |
| 2. | 8 | 13. | 28 | 24. | 10 | 35. | 8 |
| 3. | 12 | 14. | 32 | 25. | 3 | 36. | 9 |
| 4. | 16 | 15. | 36 | 26. | 2 | 37. | 6 |
| 5. | 20 | 16. | 7 | 27. | 4 | 38. | 7 |
| 6. | 3 | 17. | 6 | 28. | 10 | 39. | 44 |
| 7. | 2 | 18. | 8 | 29. | 5 | 40. | 11 |
| 8. | 4 | 19. | 10 | 30. | 3 | 41. | 48 |
| 9. | 4 | 20. | 9 | 31. | 3 | 42. | 12 |
| 10. | 5 | 21. | 4 | 32. | 6 | 43. | 52 |
| 11. | 40 | 22. | 5 | 33. | 9 | 44. | 13 |

EUREKA MATH

Module 1:    Properties of Multiplication and Division and Solving Problems with Units 2–5 and 10.

317

## Problem Set

1.  Answer provided

    8; 8

    3; 3

    4; 4

    5, 4; 4, 5

    6, 4; 4, 6

    7, 28; 28, 7

    8, 32; 32, 8

    9, 4, 36; 36, 4, 9

    10, 4, 40; 40, 4, 10

2.  Tape diagram drawn and labeled showing 9 boxes packed

3.  8

4.  $14

## Exit Ticket

1.  4; number bond drawn showing 4 units of 4 equals 16

2.  14; tape diagram drawn and labeled to represent the problem

## Homework

1.  4; 4

    8; 8

    3; 3

    4; 4

    5, 4; 4, 5

    6, 4; 4, 6

    7, 28; 28, 7

    8, 32; 32, 8

    9, 4, 36; 36, 4, 9

    10, 4, 40; 40, 4, 10

2.  8; tape diagram drawn and labeled to represent the problem

3.  6

4.  12

**Module 1:**   Properties of Multiplication and Division and Solving Problems with Units 2–5 and 10.

©2015 Great Minds. eureka-math.org
G3-M1-TE-B1-1.3.1-01.2016

EUREKA MATH™

# Lesson 18

## Sprint

### Side A

| | | | |
|---|---|---|---|
| 1. 5 | 12. 40 | 23. 15 | 34. 60 |
| 2. 10 | 13. 35 | 24. 20 | 35. 55 |
| 3. 15 | 14. 30 | 25. 25 | 36. 50 |
| 4. 20 | 15. 25 | 26. 30 | 37. 65 |
| 5. 25 | 16. 20 | 27. 35 | 38. 70 |
| 6. 30 | 17. 15 | 28. 40 | 39. 65 |
| 7. 35 | 18. 10 | 29. 45 | 40. 60 |
| 8. 40 | 19. 5 | 30. 50 | 41. 150 |
| 9. 45 | 20. 0 | 31. 50 | 42. 200 |
| 10. 50 | 21. 5 | 32. 100 | 43. 150 |
| 11. 45 | 22. 10 | 33. 55 | 44. 100 |

### Side B

| | | | |
|---|---|---|---|
| 1. 5 | 12. 40 | 23. 15 | 34. 60 |
| 2. 10 | 13. 35 | 24. 20 | 35. 55 |
| 3. 15 | 14. 30 | 25. 25 | 36. 50 |
| 4. 20 | 15. 25 | 26. 30 | 37. 65 |
| 5. 25 | 16. 20 | 27. 35 | 38. 70 |
| 6. 30 | 17. 15 | 28. 40 | 39. 65 |
| 7. 35 | 18. 10 | 29. 45 | 40. 60 |
| 8. 40 | 19. 5 | 30. 50 | 41. 150 |
| 9. 45 | 20. 0 | 31. 50 | 42. 200 |
| 10. 50 | 21. 5 | 32. 100 | 43. 150 |
| 11. 45 | 22. 10 | 33. 55 | 44. 100 |

**Module 1:**     Properties of Multiplication and Division and Solving Problems with Units 2–5 and 10.                    **319**

©2015 Great Minds. eureka-math.org
G3-M1-TE-B1-1.3.1-01.2016

## Problem Set

1. 80; 3 tens; 3 tens; 3; 30, 80; 80

2. 28; 2 fours; 2 fours; 2; 8, 28; 28

3. 90; 4 × 10; 4 tens; 4; 50, 40, 90; 90

4. 100; 5 × 10, 5 × 10; 5 tens, 5 tens; 5, 5; 50, 50, 100; 100

5. 70; number bond showing (5 × 10) + (2 × 10) equals 7 × 10 drawn

6. 24

7. 120

## Exit Ticket

6 × 4; 1 × 4; 6, 4, 24

## Homework

1. First apple matched to third bucket; second apple matched to first bucket; third apple matched to fourth bucket; fourth apple matched to second bucket

2. 36; 5 × 4, 4 × 4; 5, 4; 20, 16, 36; 36

3. 40; number bond showing (5 × 4) + (5 × 4) equals 10 × 4 drawn

4. Answers will vary.

5. 70

     **Module 1:**    Properties of Multiplication and Division and Solving Problems with Units 2–5 and 10.

EUREKA MATH™

# Lesson 19

## Problem Set

1.  a.  12; 10; 2; 2

    b.  5; 1; 1, 5

    c.  7; 5; 8, 2; 8, 5, 2, 7

    d.  8; 20, 5; 12, 3; 20, 12, 5, 3, 8

2.  First bucket matched to fourth ball; second bucket matched to first ball; third bucket matched to second ball; fourth bucket matched to third ball

3.  24 ÷ 2 broken into two smaller facts: 12 ÷ 2 and 12 ÷ 2; sum of two smaller facts found to answer larger fact

## Exit Ticket

11; 10; 2, 1; 2; 10, 1, 11

## Homework

1.  a.  6; 3; 3

    b.  7; 2; 2, 7

    c.  6; 5, 1; 4, 5, 1, 6

    d.  9; 5, 4; 20, 16, 5, 4, 9

2.  First white board matched to fourth clipboard; second white board matched to first clipboard; third white board matched to third clipboard; fourth white board matched to second clipboard

3.  35 ÷ 5 broken into two smaller facts:  20 ÷ 5 and 15 ÷ 5; sum of two smaller facts found to answer larger fact

# Lesson 20

## Sprint

### Side A

| | | | | | | | |
|---|---|---|---|---|---|---|---|
| 1. | 10 | 12. | 30 | 23. | 40 | 34. | 15 |
| 2. | 15 | 13. | 25 | 24. | 20 | 35. | 40 |
| 3. | 20 | 14. | 20 | 25. | 45 | 36. | 20 |
| 4. | 25 | 15. | 15 | 26. | 20 | 37. | 45 |
| 5. | 30 | 16. | 10 | 27. | 45 | 38. | 25 |
| 6. | 35 | 17. | 5 | 28. | 15 | 39. | 50 |
| 7. | 40 | 18. | 5 | 29. | 40 | 40. | 60 |
| 8. | 45 | 19. | 30 | 30. | 10 | 41. | 55 |
| 9. | 50 | 20. | 10 | 31. | 35 | 42. | 60 |
| 10. | 40 | 21. | 35 | 32. | 5 | 43. | 65 |
| 11. | 35 | 22. | 15 | 33. | 30 | 44. | 70 |

### Side B

| | | | | | | | |
|---|---|---|---|---|---|---|---|
| 1. | 15 | 12. | 25 | 23. | 20 | 34. | 20 |
| 2. | 20 | 13. | 20 | 24. | 40 | 35. | 45 |
| 3. | 25 | 14. | 15 | 25. | 25 | 36. | 25 |
| 4. | 30 | 15. | 10 | 26. | 20 | 37. | 50 |
| 5. | 35 | 16. | 5 | 27. | 45 | 38. | 15 |
| 6. | 40 | 17. | 5 | 28. | 15 | 39. | 40 |
| 7. | 45 | 18. | 30 | 29. | 40 | 40. | 55 |
| 8. | 50 | 19. | 10 | 30. | 10 | 41. | 60 |
| 9. | 40 | 20. | 35 | 31. | 30 | 42. | 65 |
| 10. | 35 | 21. | 15 | 32. | 5 | 43. | 60 |
| 11. | 30 | 22. | 40 | 33. | 30 | 44. | 65 |

Module 1:     Properties of Multiplication and Division and Solving Problems with Units 2–5 and 10.

EUREKA
MATH

## Problem Set

1. Tape diagram labeled
   a. $24
   b. $28

2. Tape diagram labeled
   a. 4
   b. 12

3. 12

4. 5 blue and 3 red

5. 4

## Exit Ticket

1. Tape diagram labeled
   a. 4
   b. 16

2. 10

## Homework

1. Tape diagram labeled
   a. $12
   b. $9

2. Tape diagram labeled
   a. 6
   b. 24

3. 4 green and 5 purple

4. 9

5. 4

**Module 1:**  Properties of Multiplication and Division and Solving Problems with Units 2–5 and 10.

323

©2015 Great Minds. eureka-math.org
G3-M1-TE-B1-1.3.1-01.2016

# Lesson 21

## Pattern Sheet

| | | | |
|---|---|---|---|
| 5 | 10 | 15 | 20 |
| 25 | 5 | 10 | 5 |
| 15 | 5 | 20 | 5 |
| 25 | 5 | 10 | 15 |
| 10 | 20 | 10 | 25 |
| 10 | 5 | 10 | 15 |
| 5 | 15 | 10 | 15 |
| 20 | 15 | 25 | 15 |
| 20 | 5 | 20 | 10 |
| 20 | 15 | 20 | 25 |
| 20 | 25 | 5 | 25 |
| 10 | 25 | 15 | 25 |
| 20 | 10 | 20 | 15 |
| 25 | 15 | 10 | 20 |
| 15 | 25 | 10 | 20 |

## Problem Set

1. Tape diagram labeled; 4 × 6 = 24; 24 + 4 = 28; $28

2. Tape diagrams labeled; 22

3. Tape diagram drawn and labeled to represent problem; 12

4.   a. 7

    b. 5

## Exit Ticket

Tape diagram drawn and labeled to represent problem; 18

    **Module 1:**     Properties of Multiplication and Division and Solving Problems with Units 2–5 and 10.

**EUREKA MATH**™

## Homework

1. Tape diagram labeled; 4 × 8 = 32; 32 + 5 = 37; 37

2. Tape diagrams labeled; 23

3. Tape diagram drawn and labeled to represent problem; 12

4. 3

Module 1: Properties of Multiplication and Division and Solving Problems with Units 2–5 and 10.

©2015 Great Minds. eureka-math.org
G3-M1-TE-B1-1.3.1-01.2016

This page intentionally left blank

This page intentionally left blank

This page  intentionally left  blank